Commission of the European Communities

energy

Improved energy efficiency in the process industries

Proceedings of a European Seminar
Brussels, 23 and 24 October 1990

Edited by P. A. Pilavachi
Commission of the European Communities
Rue de la Loi, 200
B-1049 Brussels

Joule R&D programme:
Rational use of energy

Directorate General
Science, Research and Development
Joint Research Centre

1991 EUR 13541 EN-FR

Published by the
COMMISSION OF THE EUROPEAN COMMUNITIES
Directorate-General
Telecommunications, Information Industries and Innovation
L-2920 Luxembourg

Cataloguing data can be found at the end of this publication

Luxembourg: Office for Official Publications of the European Communities, 1991

ISBN 92-826-2550-8

Catalogue number: CD-NA-13541-2A-C

Printed in Belgium

SUMMARY

European Commission, in its continuing effort to conserve energy within the Community, the same time improving the environment in which its inhabitants live, sees improved energy efficiency in industrial processes as a major aim. In promoting energy efficient technologies in the process industries, through Non Nuclear Energy Programmes like JOULE, the Commission is influencing a sector which accounts for over 34% of the primary energy use in the Community, representing annually in excess of 350 mtoe (million tonnes of oil equivalent).

The current Non-Nuclear Energy R&D Programme, JOULE, covers the areas of: Rational Use of Energy, Energy from Fossil Sources, and Renewable Energies. Within the context of "Rational Use of Energy", the Commission has funded a number of important collaborative projects directed at achieving improved energy efficiency in the process industries.

Preliminary results from current projects carried out within the JOULE Programme were presented in a European Seminar on "Improved Energy Efficiency in the Process Industries" in October 1990, which also comprised a workshop.

Topics covered, relating to present R&D activities within JOULE, included the following:

Heat exchangers: enhanced evaporation, shell and tube heat exchangers including distribution of fluids, and fouling.

Low energy separation processes: adsorption, melt-crystallisation and supercritical extraction.

Chemical reactors: methanol synthesis and reactors with integral heat exchangers.

Other unit operations: evaporators, glass-melting furnaces, cement kilns and baking ovens, dryers and packed columns and replacements for R12 in refrigeration.

Energy and system process models: batch processes, simulation and control of transients and energy synthesis.

Development of advanced sensors.

The workshop was made up of 13 working groups, formed to discuss future R&D needs. This identified sectors of great significance, both in terms of potential energy savings and, increasingly important, with regard to their prospects for reducing the detrimental impact of the process industries on the environment. The following were covered:

Chemical reactors, heat exchanger intensification, process plant intensification, heat exchanger fouling, gas-adsorption, melt crystallisation, glass-making and ceramic furnaces, cement kilns and baking ovens, dryers, refrigeration (replacement of CFCs), energy and environmental process integration, advanced sensors for process control, catalytic combustion, efficient use of electricity.

The working groups came up with a number of recommendations for future R&D, many of which were detailed in terms of the content and the impact which such R&D might have on energy use and the environment.

The Seminar was attended by approximately 150 participants from industry, research laboratories and academic institutions.

Further information on the Seminar may be obtained by writing to Dr. P. A. Pilavachi, DG XII, Commission of the European Communities.

CONTENTS

INTRODUCTION

OPENING ADDRESS

Ph. BOURDEAU

Commission of the European Communities

Ladies and Gentlemen. On behalf of the Commission of the European Communities, I would like to welcome you to this Seminar on Improved Energy Efficiency in the Process Industries. This Seminar is organized in the framework of the Non-Nuclear Energy R&D Programme entitled JOULE.

The First Energy Crisis in 1973 was reflected in massive increases in the price of oil and other fuels. This was a major factor leading to the establishment of the Commission's Non-Nuclear Energy R&D Programmes. The First Programme started in 1975, with a planned duration of four years. A Second Energy Crisis strengthened the case for similar Programmes in 1979, 1985 and 1989. Recent events in the Gulf highlight our dependence on imported oil and the importance of minimizing that dependence, which confirms the needs for these Energy Programmes.

The Commission has consistently been aware of the importance of linking the aims of energy efficiency and environmental protection in the planning of these Programmes. This is reflected most strongly in the current JOULE Programme as you will hear from the reports to be presented today. We also strongly believe in the role of the Community's institutions to promote industrial competitiveness, and improved energy efficiency has an important role to play. These are particularly relevant to this meeting, which is concerned with technologies for industrial processes.

In presenting information on projects recently started in the current JOULE Programme, and by convening the Workshop tomorrow which will address critical areas of industrial process technology, including unit operations, the Commission hope to satisfy two requirements. Firstly, it will inform you, as leading European industrialists and academics, of current projects devoted to the Rational Use of Energy in Industry. Secondly, with your co-operation, it will ensure that the next Programme to be initiated in 1991 addresses those topics seen by you as critical to furthering its aims - energy saving, pollution control and industrial competitiveness.

I would like to wish you a successful and worthwhile meeting.

OVERVIEW

P. A. PILAVACHI

Commission of the European Communities

Ladies and gentlemen. I welcome you and I am pleased to see the great interest for this specialised Seminar on Improved Energy Efficiency in the Process Industries. Some participants are well known to us but we are pleased to see some new participants as well.

I would like to begin by describing briefly those parts of the JOULE Programme covered by today's papers on the Rational Use of Energy in Industry.

The objective of these projects is to develop techniques and technologies which enhance energy saving and pollution abatement in industry. Four areas are covered, these being:

1. Alternative or improved unit operations and reaction routes.
2. Energy and process system models.
3. Sensors, instrumentation and control.
4. Refrigeration.

I would like to remind you the procedures for the next two days, which we adopted with success in 1988.

Today we will hear presentations from the current JOULE contractors in the area of industrial process technologies. These will be discussed in six Sessions. In total, seventeen multi-national projects will be presented, most of which have now been underway for some months. As we are at a comparatively early stage in the JOULE Programme, hard data are less likely to be reported today - rather the contractors will discuss the background to their projects, the planned implementation and the perceived benefits of the work.

Tomorrow you are all invited to participate in Working Groups which will address a number of areas of technology which might be included in the next Non-Nuclear Energy R&D Programme, for which it is anticipated that a call for proposals will be published in 1991. With regard to energy efficiency in the process industries, it is probable that the generic technology areas will be similar to those in the current JOULE Programme. However, the trends which will appear at the end of this Seminar could be integrated by the Commission for the next call for proposals.

The range of topics which could be discussed is very wide. For example, in the current Programme, the Commission has put emphasis on process intensification, as applied to heat exchangers, and sees the extension of this technology to other unit operations and ultimately to whole plants, where the greatest benefits could arise. Another example is fouling of heat exchangers, in particular gas-side fouling, which is being covered in the present programme, although liquid-side fouling is not being dealt with in detail. Opportunities arise for further work on a variety of unit operations, including low energy routes, and in the field of refrigeration it may be necessary to consider other alternatives to CFCs, and their effect on system performance. Process integration techniques applied together to energy and the environment are a logical extension of current procedures. New topics, including catalytic combustion and electricity savings, have implications in these fields.

A total of 15 subjects areas have been provisionally selected for treatment by the Workin Groups. Chairmen have been invited to lead the Groups, and to present the conclusions tomorrow afternoon. It is hoped that several of the Working Groups will formulate potentially viable collaborative proposals for submission in 1991.

It should be noted that we regard the participation of industry in this meeting, and indeed in the next Programme, as being particularly important. Industry-led projects are attractive because we see their direct interest in the eventual exploitation of results, but in any event we request that industry participates as a collaborator in each project.

We have here many leaders in their field in Europe. It is to be hoped that, as far as possible, during the Workshop of tomorrow the discussion will be free and open, so that the optimum use can be made collectively of your knowledge and experience to maintain our Programme at the forefront of new energy efficient process technologies. While we cannot cover all the areas of interest to energy efficiency in industry, we are, we believe, able to target those of importance both now and, increasingly, in the future. With your help this will be confirmed in the next call for proposals.

The three experts who assist the Commission in monitoring the progress of these projects, Mr. Dumon, Prof. Reay and Prof. Peters, will act as Chairmen of these Sessions.

I would like to thank the European Federation of Chemical Engineering and the European Federations of the Chemical, Glass, Textile, Cement, Ceramics and Paper Industry for their contribution and participation.

I also thank you all for your participation, and wish you a successful Meeting, and a pleasant stay in Brussels.

PRESENT R&D ACTIVITIES

Improved Energy Efficiency in the Process Industries

23 October 1990

HEAT EXCHANGERS

Chairman: Prof. D. A. Reay

ENHANCED EVAPORATION HEAT TRANSFER SURFACES

Prof. M. Groll, Dipl.-Ing. S. Rösler
Institut für Kernenergetik und Energiesysteme (IKE)
Univ. Stuttgart, Stuttgart, Federal Republic of Germany

CONTRACT JOUE-0041-C

Participants

- Dr. C. Marvillet, CEA-GRETh, F
- Dr. J.E. Hesselgreaves
  National Engineering Lab.(NEL), UK
- Dr. P. Kew/Dr. K. Cornwell
  Engineering Technology Unit(ETU), Heriot-Watt Univ., UK
- Prof. S. Yanniotis/Dr. P. Valachis
  Centre for Renewable Energy Sources(CRES), GR
- Prof. N.C. Markatos
  National Technical Univ.of Athens(NTUA), GR
- Dr. C. Ramshaw
  ICI Chemicals & Polymers Ltd., R&D Dept., UK
- Dr. M.J. Gough/Dr. J.V. Rogers, CAL GAVIN Ltd., UK
- Dr. A. Bailly, CIAT, F
- Dr. M. Messant, TREFIMETAUX(TMX), F

SUMMARY

Different techniques to enhance evaporation heat transfer surfaces for heat exchangers in industrial applications shall be experimentally and theoretically investigated. Both static and dynamic techniques shall be involved, i.e. evaporation heat transfer from planar and tubular surfaces in a pool boiling and flow boiling mode, and evaporation heat transfer from rotating surfaces.

INTRODUCTION

This R&D work aims at providing scientific/technical knowledge and expertise for the design and manufacture of intensified heat exchangers utilizing enhanced surfaces for evaporation heat transfer. Thereby it is expected to make a significant contribution to the improvement of energy efficiency in the process industries, viz. reduction of energy consumption, reduction of environmental pollution, improvement of process operation.

Highly efficient heat transfer, e.g. for evaporation and condensation, requires excellent heat transfer surfaces. The many enhancement techniques can be divided into passive and active techniques. Among the passive techniques are treated or rough surfaces, extended surfaces, twisted inserts in tubes, surfaces tension devices, additives. Among the active techniques are centrifugal fields, vibrations, injection or suction, jet impingement.

This R&D work concentrates on passive techniques, employing specially treated (structured) surfaces and covered surfaces, in both planar and tubular geometry. As a special enhancement technique for planar surfaces narrow vertical channels shall be investigated. As one of the most promising active techniques the use of centrifugal fields, viz. rotating plates, shall be investigated.

The major work shall be carried out by R&D laboratories. The participation and the role of industry will be to act as advisors in their capacity as users of heat exchangers and as manufacturers of heat exchanger tubes and of heat exchangers. Industry will especially be associated to the technical realization of enhanced surfaces. This shall enable a cost-efficient industrial manufacture of the developed and investigated enhanced surfaces.

OBJECTIVES

The objectives of the R&D work are the development and investigation, both theoretical and experimental, of enhanced evaporation heat transfer surfaces. The range of applications is limited to low temperatures (≤ 120°C). The expected benefits comprise more compact devices due to reduced heat transfer area and equipment volume, reduced energy consumption due to a closer approach to ideal operation (smaller temperature differences), improvement of overall process operation and reduction of environmental pollution due to intensified heat exchanger equipment and more efficient process operation.

TASKS OF PARTICIPANTS

IKE will act as project coordinator. The following tasks will be handled by the project partners.

1 Evaporation Heat Transfer from Structured Surfaces

This work package will be carried out by **IKE** and **NEL** with the support of **TMX, CAL GAVIN** and **ICI**.

1.1 **IKE** will carry out experiments, including visual observations, with different structured surfaces. Suitable surfaces will also be prepared for **CRES**, to be used in their programme on rotating surfaces.

a) A test facility for testing planar samples will be made available for the present programme. The surface structures will comprise micro-cavities. Micro-cavity size and distribution shall be varied as major parameters influencing the evaporation heat transfer.

b) A test facility for testing of horizontal cylindrical tubes will be built. The test tubes will be provided with a helically-wrapped fine wire structure on their outside. Wire diameter and wire spacing are the two major parameters influencing the evaporation heat transfer; they shall be systematically varied.

Both test facilities will be operated at low temperatures (< 120°C) and low pressures (< 5 bar). The power input will be of the order of 1 to 10 kW. Fluids to be used are water and a suitable higher alcohol (iso-propanol or iso-butanol) or silicon fluid.

1.2 **NEL** will perform a modellization of the evaporation process from structured surfaces. The obtained theoretical results shall be compared with the experimental data.

1.3 **TMX** will act as an advisor in their capacity as tube manufacturer. Aspects of commercial fabrication of structured surfaces, the impact of possible fabrication constraints on the efficiency of structured surfaces shall be elaborated.

1.4 **CAL GAVIN** will act as an advisor in their capacity as tube manufacturer. The future cost-effective manufacture of tubes with structured surfaces shall be elaborated.

1.5 **ICI** will act as an advisor in their capacity as user of heat exchangers. The various aspects and the feedback of potential applications on the design of structured surfaces shall be elaborated.

2 Evaporation Heat Transfer from Covered Surfaces *

This work package will be carried out by **GRETh** and **NEL** with the support of **TMX, CAL GAVIN and CIAT.**

---

* The term "evaporation heat transfer from covered surfaces" describes the evaporation in a narrow gap between two surfaces, one of which is heated.

2.1 **GRETh** will carry out experimental investigations, including visual observations, with planar surfaces. In front of such a surface another surface will be arranged, so that a narrow gap is formed between the two plates. This gap width is one of the important optimization parameters for boiling from an enhanced surface of this type. Other parameters to be varied are the orientation of the two plates, from horizontal with heating at the bottom surface to horizontal with heating at the top surface, and the angle between the two plates. Moreover, metallic and non-metallic surfaces shall be used; the heated evaporative surface and the non-heated cover surface can be perforated or non-perforated, smooth or roughened.

An experimental facility will be built for that purpose. This facility will be operated at atmospheric pressure and low temperatures ($\leq$ 100°C). The power input will be about 1 to 2 kW. The fluids shall be water and a suitable higher alcohol or silicon fluid.

2.2 **NEL** will carry out experiments with horizontal covered tubes. Covered tube means that the heated tube is partly surrounded by a second tube thus generating a narrow annular gap. The surrounding tubes shall be made of different materials (metallic or non-metallic) having different thermal conductivities.

An existing test facility shall be employed for testing of single tubes in horizontal position using water and dimethyl silicone fluids at about atmospheric pressure. The power input will be about 1 kW.

NEL will develop a theoretical model for evaporation from covered plates and tubes.

2.3 **TMX** will act as advisor in their capacity as tube manufacturer. The future cost-effective manufacture of covered tube systems shall be elaborated.

2.4 **CAL GAVIN** will act as an advisor in their capacity as manufacturer of tubes and special heat exchanger surfaces and arrangements. Aspects of cost of manufacture of covered surface systems shall be elaborated.

2.5 **CIAT** will act as an advisor in their capacity as heat exchanger manufacturer. The requirements and constraints arising from cost-effective heat exchanger manufacture and their impact on the design of covered tube systems shall be elaborated.

3 Evaporation Heat Transfer from Vertical Narrow Channels

This work package will be carried out by **ETU**. It will be concerned with the experimental and theoretical aspects of boiling heat transfer in compact heat exchangers with channels of novel geometry and/or special surface channels.

Experiments will be carried out using planar surfaces, into which narrow channels (typical dimensions 1 mm) have been machined. At least for initial studies a Printed Circuit Heat Exchanger shall be used. The vertically oriented channels shall be smooth in a first phase; in a second phase they shall be roughened or treated in some way so as to help initiate the boiling process at lower temperature differences.

An experimental facility shall be built, allowing flow visualization studies. The power input will be of the order of 5 kW. A closed-loop boiling-condensing cycle employing water or suitable non-chlorofluoro-carbons as working fluid will be used; operation will be at about atmospheric pressure.

The boiling heat transfer from vertical narrow channels shall be theoretically modelled. The theoretical results shall be compared with the experimentally obtained data.

4 Evaporation Heat Transfer form Rotating Smooth and Structured Surfaces

This work package will be carried out by **CRES** and **NTUA** with the support of **ICI**.

4.1 **CRES** will develop an experimental unit employing a rotating surface as heat transfer surface. The rotational speed of the rotating disc will vary in the range of 100 to 1000 rpm. The unit is planned for operation as liquid/liquid heat exchanger, liquid/steam heat exchanger, evaporator and condenser. In the frame of the present project only evaporation and condensation heat transfer from different surfaces shall be investigated. The surfaces shall comprise a smooth surface as a reference case and enhanced (structured) surfaces. The effect of the fluid flow rate on the film thickness and thus the heat transfer coefficient shall be studied. The fluids will be water and steam. The power input will be about 5 kW.

Visualization shall allow insight into the physical phenomena. The experimentally obtained heat transfer data shall be compared with those from static heat exchangers and with the theoretical results of **NTUA**.

4.2 **NTUA** will model the heat transfer both from enhanced static surfaces and from rotating surfaces. Three-dimensional or two-dimensional with swirl analyses will be performed according to the findings of the experimental programmes of the other partners. The PHOENICS computational flow software shall be used for the theoretical investigations.

4.3 **ICI** will act as an advisor in their capacity as user of heat exchangers and provide support concerning the aspects of practical application of rotating heat exchanger surfaces.

PRELIMINARY RESULTS

Work on the different tasks has been initiated by the partners. Development of test rigs and preparatory work for modellization are in progress.

Preliminary results are not yet available.

FUTURE R & D

There is a need for R&D in the high temperature range of evaporation heat transfer, e.g. heat transfer from/to hot gases employing metallic and non-metallic tubes , evaporation/condensation heat transfer utilizing liquid metals as heat transfer fluids.

Moreover an extended testing on a prototype size basis of promising heat transfer surfaces from the present lab scale investigations is recommended. Problems of extended lifetime, operational behaviour under practical load conditions, degradation, and fouling require special attention.

References

/1/ Bergles, A.E., Nirmalan, V. Junkhan, G.H., Webb, R.L.: Bibliography on Augmentation of Convective Heat and Mass Transfer - Part II, HTI-31, ISU-FRI-Ames-84222, DE-84018484, Iowa State University, Ames, 1983

/2/ Bergles, A.E.: Heat Transfer Augmentation, Lecture held at NATO-ASI on Two-Phase Flow Heat Exchangers, Povoa de Varzim, Portugal, 1987

/3/ Newson, I.H.: Heat Transfer Characteristics of Horizontal Tube Multiple Effect Evaporation - Possible Enhanced Tube Profiles, Proc. 6th Int. Symposium Fresh Water from the Sea, Vol.2. pp.113-124, 1978

/4/ Gorenflo, D.: Zum Wärmeübergang bei Blasenverdampfung an Rippenrohren, Diss. Techn. Hochschule Karlsruhe, 1966

/5/ Webb, R.L.: The Evaluation of Enhanced Surface Geometries for Nucleate Boiling, Heat Transfer Engineering, Vol.2, No.3-4, 1981

/6/ Webb, R.L.: Heat Transfer Surface Having a High Boiling Heat Transfer Coefficient, U.S. Patent 3 906 861, 1972

/7/ Nishikawa, K., Ito, T.: Augmentation of Nucleate Boiling Heat Transfer by Prepared Surface, Heat Transfer in Energy Problems, Ed. Hzushina-Yang, 1982

/8/ Gottzmann, C.F., O'Neill, P.S.: High Efficiency Heat Exchangers, Chemical Engineering Progress, Vol.60, No.7, 1973

/9/ Marvillet, C., Messant, M.: Tubes d'échange de chaleur à hautes performances pour échangeurs de pompe à chaleur et groupe de réfrigération, Colloque "Progrès récents dans les échangeurs de chaleur", Grenoble, 1988

/10/ Guo,X.,Cai,Z.,Lin,L.: Boiling Heat Transfer on Porous Surfaces with Teflon Coating in Cavities, Proc. 1988 Internat. Conf. on Heat Transfer in Energy Conservation, pp.126-129, Shengyang, China, 1988

/11/ Gray, V.H.: The Rotating Heat Pipe - A Wickless, Hollow Shaft for Transferring High Heat Fluxes, ASME 69-HT-19, ASME New York, 1969

/12/ Roetzel, W.: A New Rotary Plate Evaporator, Wärme- und Stoffübertragung, Vol.10, No.2, pp.61-70, 1977

/13/ Tleimat, B.W.: Performance of a Rotating Flat-Disc Wiped Film Evaporator, ASME 71-HT-37, ASME New York, 1971

/14/ Wood, R.M. and Watts, B.E.: The Flow, Heat and Mass Transfer Characteristics of Liquid Films on Rotating Discs, Trans.IChE, Vol.51, p.315, 1973

/15/ Cross, W.T. and Ramshaw, C.: Centrifugal Heat Pump, US Patent 4 553 408, 1985

/16/ Ramshaw, C.: Separation Processes: The Opportunities for Exploiting Centrifugal Fields, Report of the UK Science & Engineering Research Council, 1986

/17/ Reay, D.A.: Impact of New Technologies on Future Heat Exchanger Design, Heat Recovery Systems & CHP, Vol.8, No.4, 1988

IMPROVING THE PERFORMANCE OF SHELL AND TUBE HEAT EXCHANGERS

Dr J E Hesselgreaves
National Engineering Laboratory (NEL), UK

Contract JOUE-0016-C

PARTICIPANTS

Dr B Stergiopoulos, Centre for Renewable Energy Sources (CRES), GR
Mr F Lauro, Centre d'Etudes Nucleaires de Grenoble (GRETh), F
Dr P D Hills, ICI plc, UK
Mr B Bishop, COVRAD Heat Transfer, UK

SUMMARY

Experimental investigations, backed up by Computational Fluid Dynamics (CFD) analysis, are being made of recent developments in tube support methods for shell and tube heat exchangers such as rod and grid baffles. Concepts for improved 'baffle' systems giving higher shell-side heat transfer performance with acceptable pressure drop are also being explored by systematic tests, both in an ideal longitudinal flow facility and in full-size heat exchangers. To enable good matching of shell-side and tube-side performance, in-tube enhancement devices will also be tested including novel types as appropriate. The overall performance with tube and shell-side enhancements will be evaluated on the basis of overall exchanger shape and size compared with a conventionally baffled exchanger with similar tube diameter and pitch.

1 INTRODUCTION

This paper describes a collaborative research programme aimed at enabling shell and tube heat exchangers to meet increasing demands for energy efficiency by performing with lower temperature differences.

The heat exchanger market for EEC countries has been estimated to approach 1.6 billion ECU/1/ in the early 1990s and about half of this market is of the shell and tube type. Whilst this proportion will reduce steadily with the progressive exploitation of more compact types, the shell and tube type will remain for many years the dominant type in industry. The potential for saving energy is thus considerable.

Whilst energy as a resource is of fluctuating market importance, the international concern over the greenhouse effect will maintain a steady demand for energy efficiency in order to reduce CO_2 emissions. It is pertinent, therefore, to explore ways of making shell and tube exchangers more effective, so to reduce operating temperature differences within size and cost constraints.

The common segmentally-baffled exchanger has several sources of inherent inefficiency: these are the various leakage paths which reduce the effective driving temperature difference and the sharp turn-arounds at the baffle edges which cause flow separations with consequent parasitic pressure drop. The exchanger types to be investigated in this project are the longitudinal flow types, which avoid many of the limitations and thus offer the prospect of increased performance. Investigations and correlations have been made of two of these types in recent years, namely those of the rod and grid baffle/2,3/. Both types give simultaneous tube support and heat-transfer enhancement over pure (baffle-free) longitudinal flow. The heat-transfer enhancement arises both from the increased turbulence generated downstream of each baffle. However, the turbulence for both types is largely parasitic, being more effective at increasing pressure drop than heat transfer. This arises from the bluff-body separated flows forming the wakes of the baffles. Baffle systems which avoid such separated flows have the potential for creating the flow mixing required without excess pressure drop and it is the investigation of such systems which forms the core of this project.

2 OBJECTIVES

The overall objective is to improve the technology of longitudinal flow tube support in order to obtain better heat transfer and pressure drop characteristics than is possible with either rod, grid or segmentally-baffled systems.

The benefits of the new longitudinal baffles will be to enable closer overall temperature differences to be obtained within economical size constraints. Although the investigations are being conducted with single phase shell-side flow, the results should be applicable in principle to multiphase flows and thus the results should be replicable over most of the current applications of shell and tube heat exchangers.

3 TASKS OF PARTICIPANTS

3.1 Literature and Applications Review

Comparative information will be collected on the performance of segmental, disc and doughnut, rod and grid baffle arrangements and also on available augmentation techniques for shell-side and tube-side flows. Industrial applications will be reviewed.

(NEL, GRETh, CRES, ICI and COVRAD)

3.2 Numerical (CFD) Studies of Rod, Grid and Alternative Baffle Systems (using code TRIO-VF)

3.2.1 Local calculations, using CFD code TRIO-VF, of flow in 'ideal' shell-side passage with rod, grid and alternative baffle arrangements. Derivation of Nusselt numbers and skin friction coefficients for comparison with experimental data.

(CRES)

3.2.2 Global calculations of flow and heat transfer in real heat exchangers with rod, grid and alternative baffle arrangements, using longitudinal and transverse Nusselt number and skin friction coefficients with the CFD code TRIO-VF.

(GRETh)

The above numerical work will be phased as appropriate to make the two-way links with the experimental programme.

3.2.3 Comparisons of flows and overall performance will be made with experimental investigations (Sections 3.3.2 and 3.3.4).

(GRETh and NEL)

3.3 Experimental Programme

3.3.1 Heat transfer and pressure drop of rod and grid baffle systems

Heat-transfer and pressure-drop measurements will be performed on two variants of configurations of rod baffles at four spacings, to confirm and amplify existing data and to produce similar data for different forms of grid baffles (varying thickness, width and spacing). Rod baffle experiments will be confined to square tube pitch layouts, while triangular pitch will be used for grid baffle tests.

Local (longitudinal) values of Nusselt number and friction factor will be derived, for comparison with numerical results.

(NEL)

3.3.2 Performance of rod and grid baffled exchangers

Comparative experiments with rod and grid baffled exchangers with selected similar baffle geometries to the above will be performed at GRETh.

(GRETh and COVRAD)

3.3.3 Alternative tube supports/enhancement devices - detailed performance

An exploratory examination will be made of novel 'baffle' designs which allow longitudinal flow (countorflow) whilst retaining adequate tube support and providing necessary heat-transfer augmentation over unbaffled flow. These new designs will include longitudinal tape type inserts for which patent applications are being prepared. It is hoped to improve on the overall performance of rod and grid baffle types. This exploratory work will be performed in the longitudinal channel facility at NEL, simulating both triangular and square tube pitch arrangements.

(NEL)

3.3.4 Performance of exchangers with alternative systems

A full-size heat exchanger will be used with oil and air for selective tests on the most promising arrangements (three or four versions), in order to ascertain the effects on performance of variable Prandtl number.

(NEL, GRETh and COVRAD)

GRETh will also undertake an experiment to measure the pressure drop of a bundle in adiabatic conditions with the above baffle arrangements in crossflow. This will provide transverse friction factor data for the numerical estimation of the performance of complete heat exchangers with these baffle systems.

In order to establish a comprehensive validation of the TRIO-VF code, it is necessary to show that the flow fields predicted by the code correspond to reality. This will be achieved by a flow visualisation experiment with a glass heat exchanger.

(GRETh)

3.3.5 Studies of tube-side enhancements

The main emphasis of this work will be on the use of removable inserts in plain tubes. Published data on commercially available types will be collected and reviewed, and recommended correlations given.

Testing will be conducted in those areas indicated by the survey described in Section 3.1, for which an acknowledged paucity of data exists, and on any inserts identified as having particular promise, for laminar, transitional or turbulent flows. A total of about 20 tests is anticipated, using three or four insert types (including novel types). These tests will be conducted at NEL or at an academic institution.

(NEL)

4 PRELIMINARY RESULTS

4.1 CFD Modelling in Pure Longitudinal Flow (CRES)

A preliminary assessment of available turbulence models for predicting complex flows with heat transfer has been carried out. The assessment covers three different approaches for resolving the turbulent fluxes. These can be summarised as the

a two-equation models,

b second order closure models, and

c large eddy simulation models.

From the above, the first two approaches have been used by engineers and scientists for predicting 'practical' types of flows, while the third is still in a developing stage.

The most popular model for resolving the turbulence is the ($k-\epsilon$). This solves two transport equations for the kinetic energy of turbulence, k, and the dissipation rate ϵ. The ($k-\epsilon$) model is the one which is used in most available codes such as FLUENT, PHOENICS and TRIO-VF.

The second order closure models solve transport equations for the Reynolds stresses. To the best of our knowledge this model, in its basic form, is only implemented in FLUENT AND FLOW3D. However, many other researchers have used Reynolds stress models for specific applications.

It is well known that the standard form of the ($k-\epsilon$) model has many shortcomings when applied to flows with streamline curvature and also to flows with strong pressure gradients (separated flows). Such flows are encountered in many kinds of heat exchangers with rod, baffle and tapes. Furthermore, the standard form of the k and ϵ equations is usually applicable to high Reynolds number regions.

The drawbacks of the model in separating flows have been removed by introducing a curvature 'Richardson number' parameter. When the standard form of the equation is used in separating flows, skin friction coefficients which are too large are produced. In turn, this produces heat-transfer coefficients which are six times larger to those measured. It has to be stressed here that all the commercially available codes use the standard form of (k-ε).

These limitations of the (k-ε) model together with the necessary modifications needed to accurately predict the flows in heat exchangers will be further examined. Furthermore, the suitability of a Reynolds stress model and its advantages over the (k-ε) model for heat exchangers with tapes will also be assessed.

4.2 CFD Modelling - Three-dimensional Flows in Heat Exchangers (GRETh)

In the nuclear reactor field, numerical models based on Navier-Stokes equations have been widely used for the computation of single-phase thermal-hydraulics problems. This is true in particular for multi-dimensional heat exchanger design of liquid metal fast breeder reactors. The model is able to predict the flow field and temperature field on both shell-and-tube sides, in steady-state or transient regimes/4/. The model for shell-side flow has been validated by comparison with velocity measurements in a hydraulic test section.

For industrial non-nuclear heat exchangers, the software makes use of all the benefits of the above model development. Nevertheless, particular adaptations are needed for a realistic modelling of the specific geometries of this type of exchanger.

a The arrangement of tube bundles is of the square or triangular type, rather than disposed in concentric layers as in nuclear internal heat exchangers. As a consequence, the bundle is more compact. New constitutive laws (friction factor and heat transfer at the tube wall) are also needed for the closure of the model, according to the flow configuration and the geometry of the tubes.

b The entry of shell-side flow is made through nozzles, directly connected to the shell. The velocity of the fluid (of several meters per second in the inlet nozzle) creates a jet entrance effect, impinging on the first tube rows. This requires special attention and further tests when modelling.

In order to compare the efficiencies of several baffle types, the following points were studied:

i modelling of shell and tube, triangular arrangement, heat exchanger with TRIO and run of the code in a pure counterflow situation without any longitudinal obstacle,

ii runs of CETUC (software of thermal design of heat exchanger/5/ based on the Bell-Delaware method/6/) for classical segmentally baffled exchangers,

iii uses of existing correlations for prediction of the thermal and hydraulic performance of rod baffle exchangers/7/.

These comparisons were performed on a unique geometry to ensure a comparison based on equal surface area. The main geometric data are - tube diameter 19.05 mm o.d., 15.75 mm i.d. - number of tubes 218, length 2.4 m - pitch to diameter ratio 1.25 - shell inlet diameter 0.4 m.

The mass flow rate of water on both sides is taken to have turbulent regimes.

The main results are summarised on Figs 1 and 2:

*Pressure drop versus mass flowrate for shell side, for a and b calculations, showing two limiting situations - on one side a pure longitudinal flow without any arrangement and on the other side a classical segmentally baffled heat exchanger (Fig. 1).

*An idea of efficiency of different arrangements by plotting the ratio of global heat exchange coefficient over shell-side pressure drop versus mass flowrate; this illustrates the promising performance of longitudinal rod baffle compared with classical baffles (Fig. 2).

4.3 Experimental Programme - Ideal Longitudinal Facility (NEL)

4.3.1 Flow with no baffles

Friction factor and Nusselt number have been measured over a Reynolds number range of 4000-80 000 for equilateral triangle tube layouts with tube pitch to diameter ratios from 1.25, 1.33, 1.50 and 1.73. These results will act as base data for heat-transfer augmentation and friction factor increase for the cases with grid baffles and alternative baffles. The results are shown in Figs 3 and 4.

Both friction factor and Nusselt number are based on hydraulic diameter of the actual wetted surface, and the conventional Colburn correlation for circular tubes is shown for comparison. The results indicate a strong dependence of channel shape on Nusselt number, a factor also observed by other workers. The Nusselt number increases steadily with pitch to diameter (P/D) ratio throughout the range of Reynolds number. The change is not surprising when referred to the cross-sections of channel geometries, which start from a strongly cusped near-triangle section at P/D = 1.25 and approach a regular hexagon at P/D = 1.73. Of interest is the fact that a plot of heat-transfer coefficient against mass velocity (which does not invoke a reference length such as hydraulic diameter) shows a close approach to correlation at high Re (Fig. 4). This is to be expected since the channel boundary layers are progressively less influenced by shape as Re increases.

4.3.2 Flow with twisted tapes

Because a set of twisted tapes was available, this form of tube support was tested first, with equilateral triangular tube pitch.

Results for tube pitch to diameter ratios of 1.25 and 1.73 are shown in Fig. 5, for twist ratios (TR = length of full turn/diameter of tape) of 5 to 15. The best correlation lines for Colburn heat transfer j factor and Fanning friction f factor of baffle-free flow are also shown for comparison.

For a pitch to diameter ratio of 1.25, a maximum heat transfer enhancement of about 1.7 is observed, corresponding to a friction factor penalty factor of about 3.6. The heat-transfer enhancement is very similar to that encountered in rod-baffled exchangers/2/ but the friction penalty is of the order of one-tenth of a typical rod-baffled value. For the larger pitch to diameter ratio of 1.73 the heat-transfer enhancement is strongly Reynolds number dependent but approaches 2 at the lower Re values. The friction factor penalty is between 5 and 7. A rod-baffled exchanger would not be practicable for this geometry.

It is clear from these results that the unseparated longitudinal flow from this form of tube support has definite advantages over the rod baffle arrangement and would result in smaller and/or more effective exchangers in applications where rod-baffled exchangers are currently used. Further analysis and interpretation are continuing.

5 FUTURE RESEARCH AND DEVELOPMENT

From the Japanese results of Ohashi and Hashizumi/8/ it is clear that shell-side flows with tapes and low-fin tubes are worth close investigation. In addition, compound augmentation on the tube side, involving fins or shaped surface with inserts, could well repay attention.

Current CFD codes do not predict separations well, although most heat exchangers have substantial separated flow regimes. Modifications to turbulence models have, however, been made to improve the prediction of low Reynolds number regions and flow separations, and it is very desirable that such modifications are built into codes such as FLUENT or TRIO. Without such improvements the ability to predict real heat exchanger performance will always be poor.

Many industrial processes involve the boiling and/or condensing of multicomponent fluids. Whilst progress has been made in the understanding and prediction of these processes in heat exchangers with conventional plain tubes, little is correspondingly known about such processes with enhanced tubes.

REFERENCES

/1/ The European market for heat exchangers. Report E1021/1. Frost and Sullivan, London, 1988.

/2/ HESSELGREAVES, J. E. A mechanistic model for heat transfer and pressure drop in rod-baffled heat exchangers. Second UK National Heat Transfer Conference, Glasgow, 1988.

/3/ TABOREK, J. Longitudinal flow in tube bundles with grid baffles. AIChE Symposium Series, No 269 Vol. 85, Philadelphia 1989.

/4/ GRAND, D., MENANT, B., VILLAND, M. and MERCIER, P. Numerical modelling of thermal-hydraulics in heat exchangers of LMFER. IARH Meeting, Lausanne, 1987.

/5/ RATEL, G., MERCIER, P. Dimensionnement des échangeurs à tubes et calandre. Revue générale de Thermique, n. 313, 1988.

/6/ BELL, K. J. Final report of the cooperative research program on shell and tube heat exchangers. University of Delaware, 1963.

/7/ GENTRY, C. C. and SMALL, W. M. RODBaffle exchanger thermal-hydraulic predictive models over expanded baffle-spacing and Reynolds number ranges. AIChE Symposium Series, Heat Transfer, Vol. 80, n. 245, Denver 1985.

/8/ OHASHI, Y. and HASHIZUME, K. Heat transfer and pressure drop of water flowing in the shell side of shell-tube heat exchanger with no baffles. HTFS Research Symposium, 1989.

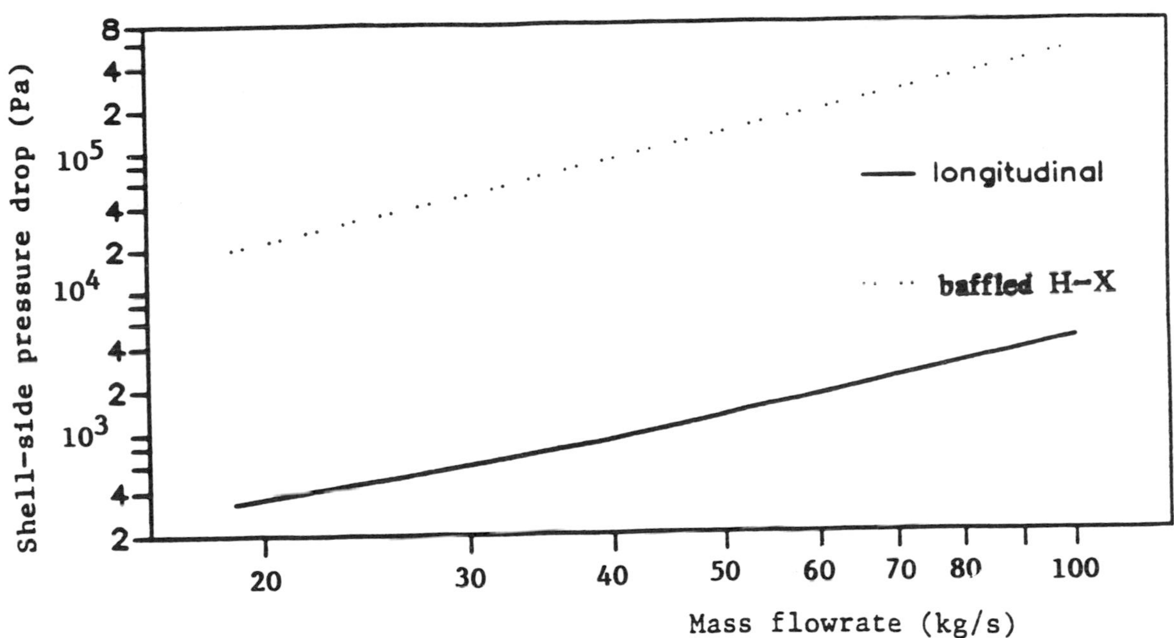

Fig 1 Shell-side pressure drop in tubular heat exchanger by CFD codes CETUC and TRIO-VF

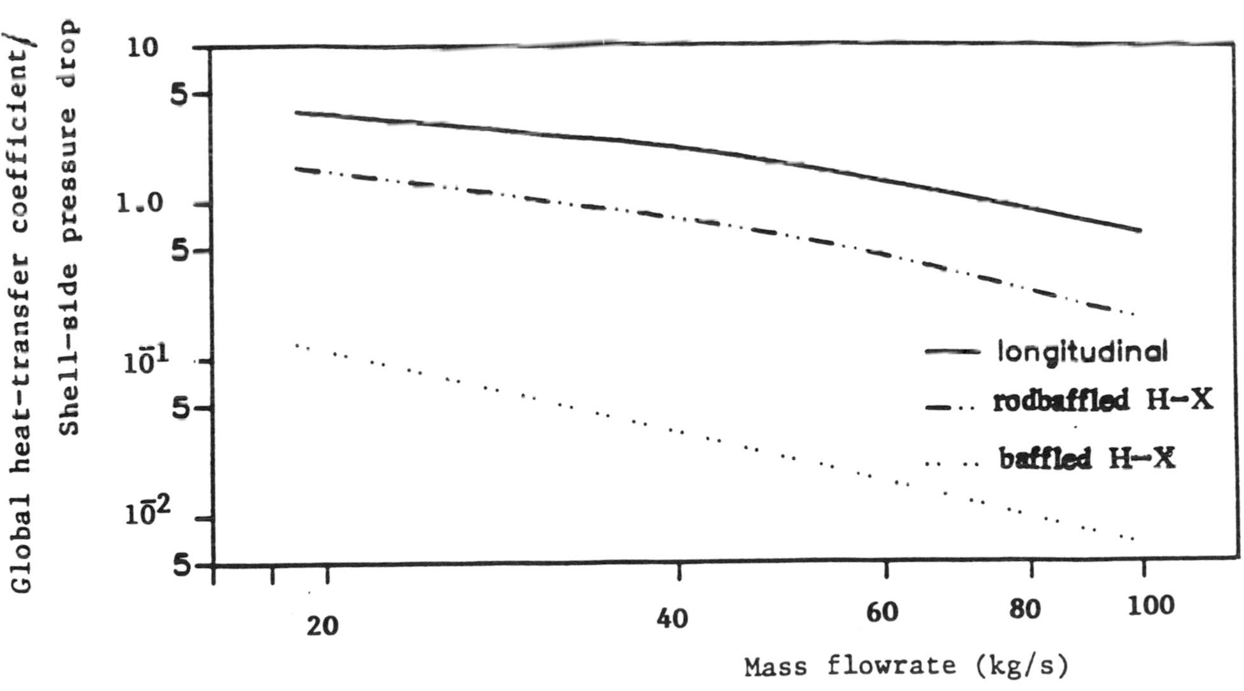

Fig 2 Hydraulic performance of tubular heat exchangers

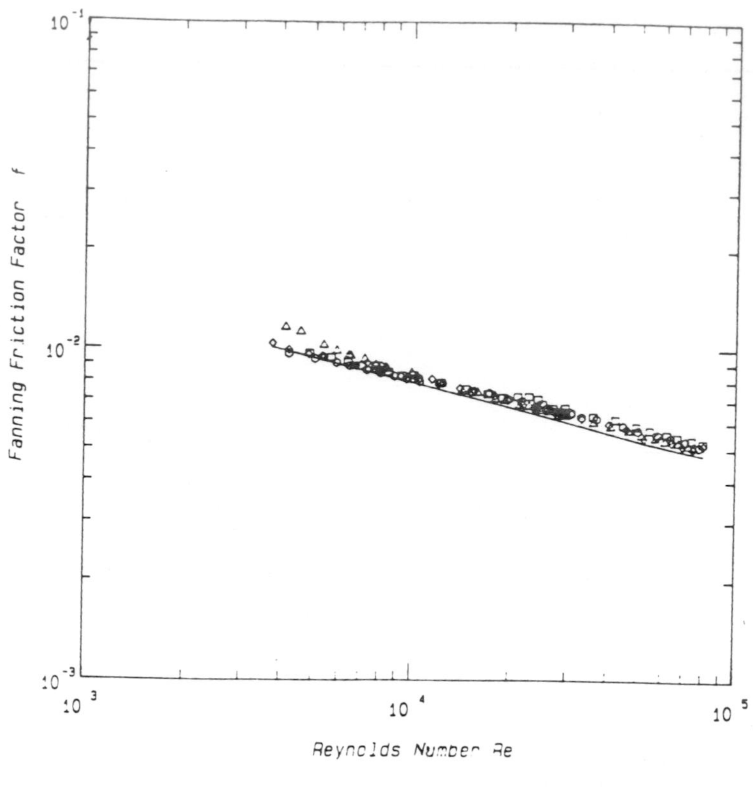

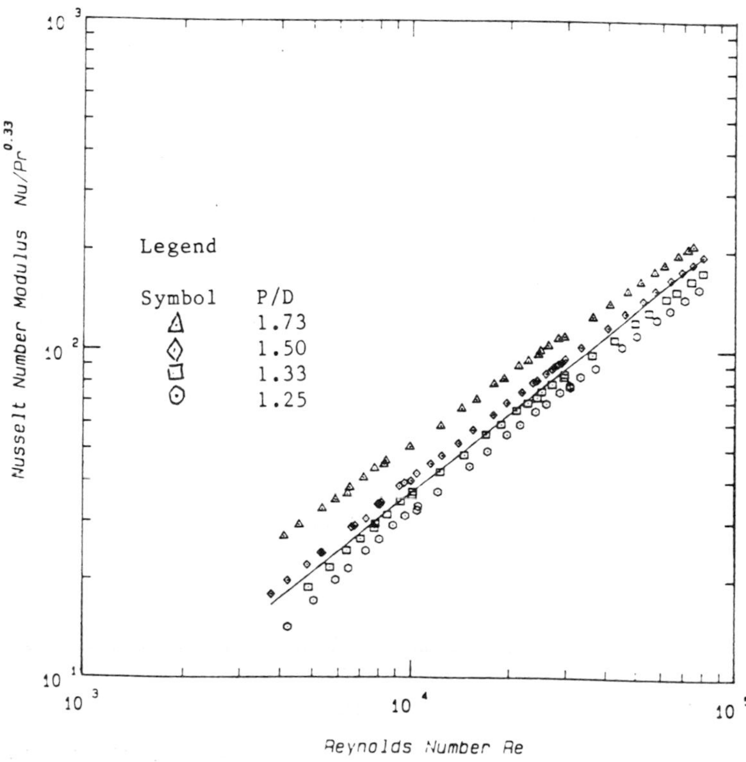

Fig 3 Heat transfer and friction factor for baffle-free flow

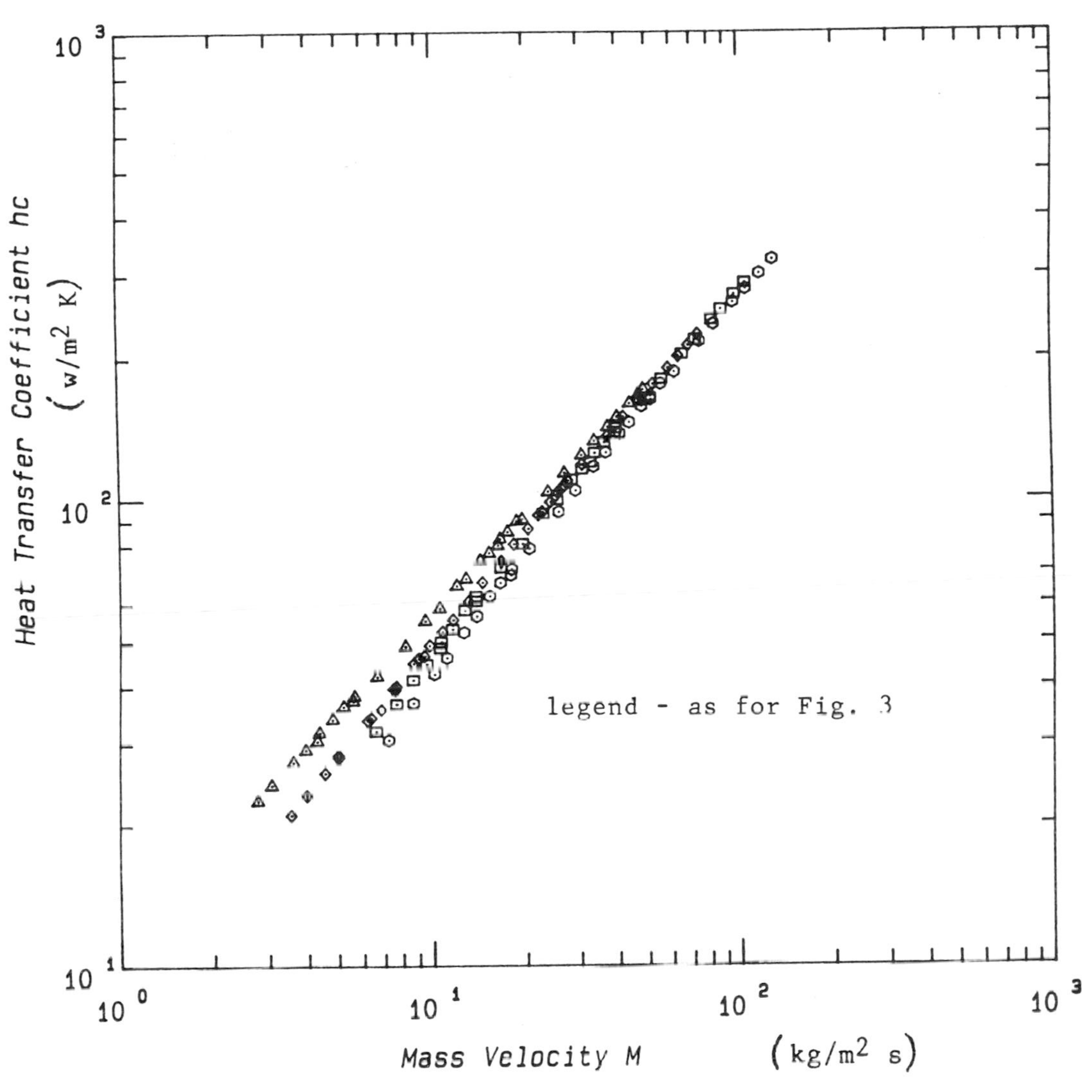

Fig 4 Basic heat transfer for baffle-free flow

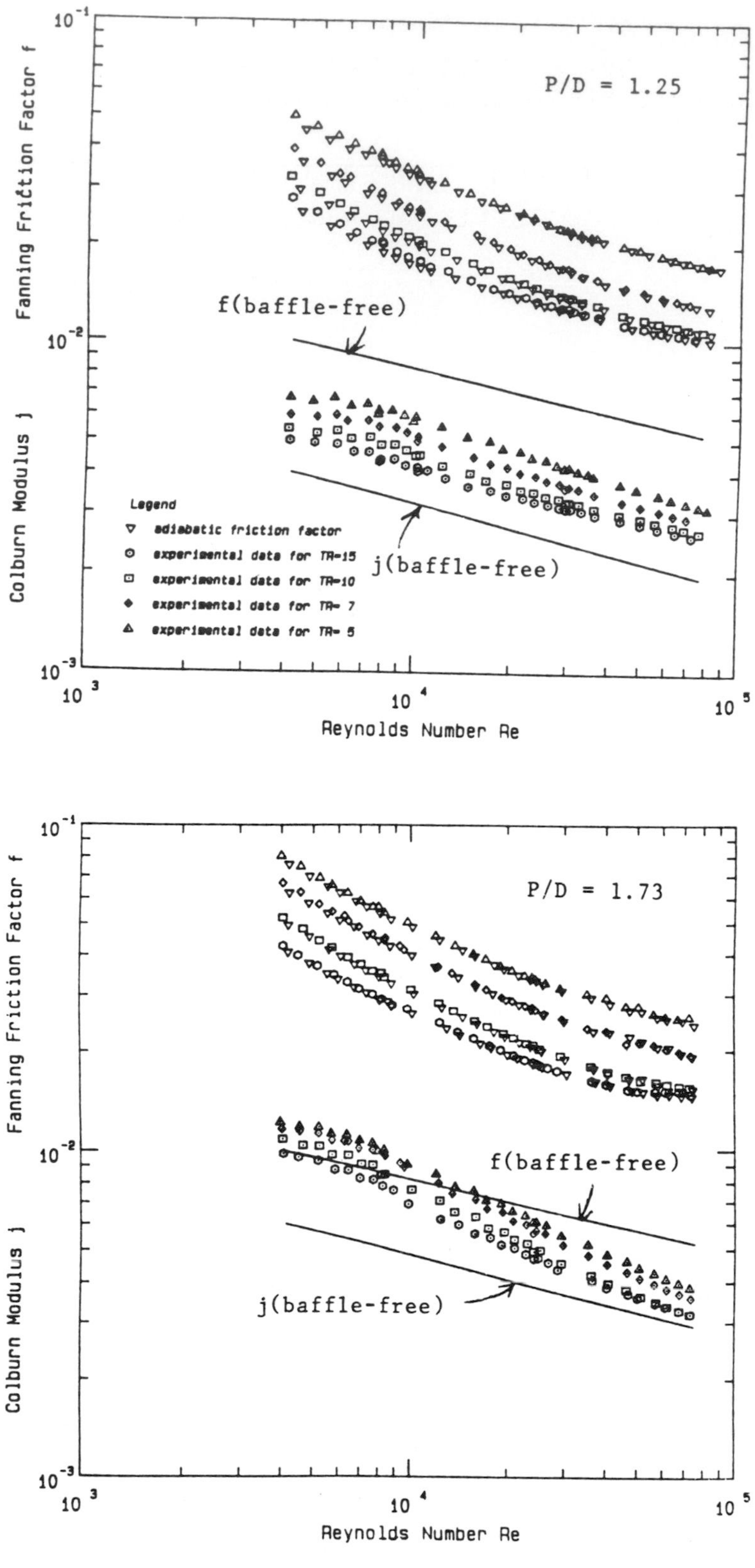

Fig 5 Heat transfer and friction factor with tapes

ETUDE DE LA DISTRIBUTION, COTE TUBES, DU MELANGE LIQUIDE-VAPEUR DANS UN ECHANGEUR DE CHALEUR TUBE-CALANDRE

F. LAURO
GRETh. CEN. GRENOBLE France

Contrat JOUE-0039-FR

PARTICIPANTS

M. J. GARCIN	GRETh (FRANCE)
Dr K. CORNWELL	HERIOT WATT UNIVERSITY (H.W.U.) (U.K.)
Dr A. REIS	CENERTEC (PORTUGAL)
M. A. BAILLY	CIAT (FRANCE)

RESUME

Le programme de recherche consiste en une étude expérimentale et une étude de modélisation à partir du code de calcul TRIO qui simule, par un modèle à deux fluides, un écoulement diphasique.

Une simulation d'échangeur thermique avec un mélange air-eau sera faite afin de valider le code TRIO. Un échangeur évaporateur sera spécialement réalisé pour une expérimentation en condition industrielle. Cet échangeur sera installé sur une machine frigorifique de 250 kW fonctionnant avec le fluide R 22. Au cours de ces essais en condition industrielle, des capteurs spéciaux équiperont un certain nombre de tubes pour mesurer d'une part, le taux de vide (valeur locale du rapport volume air sur volume total) et, si possible, le débit massique du mélange liquide-vapeur à l'intérieur de ces tubes.

1. INTRODUCTION

L'efficacité d'un échangeur avec changement de phase est fortement affectée par la mauvaise distribution du mélange liquide-vapeur, soit à l'entrée de l'échangeur, soit au passage d'une passe à l'autre. C'est le cas des évaporateurs et condenseurs à tubes et calandre avec changement de phase à l'intérieur des tubes. Pour ce type d'application, on est amené, pour des raisons d'optimisation, à prévoir plusieurs passes pour le circuit interne aux tubes et il est nécessaire de réaliser, dans les meilleures conditions possibles, la redistribution du mélange au passage d'une passe à l'autre. Les passes comportent souvent un nombre de tubes différent ce qui rend impossible la conception d'une distribution "tube à tube".

Dans certaines applications (évaporateurs frigorifiques par exemple), le liquide à évaporer entre avec une fraction du débit total sous forme de vapeur et il est important, là aussi, de réaliser une bonne distribution du mélange (en débit massique et en titre de vapeur) à l'entrée de l'évaporateur.

Le problème de la distribution du mélange liquide-vapeur à l'intérieur d'un échangeur (à plaques ou tubulaire) n'a pas fait l'objet jusqu'à aujourd'hui de beaucoup d'études [1] [2] [3] [4].

Une étude a été menée au GRETh en 1986/88 pour un échangeur à plaques en simulation eau-air [5] . La figure 1 donne un exemple de résultat de cette étude pour une pression de 20 bar, un débit massique de 100 kg/m2.s et un titre massique de 40 % (rapport du débit d'air au débit total). La Fig.1a donne la répartition des débits d'air et débit d'eau dans les canaux de sortie.
La Fig 1b donne les courbes iso-taux de vide dans le plan médian de la boîte de retour entre passes.

2. OBJECTIF

L'objectif du programme de recherche est d'obtenir les critères nécessaires à la réalisation d'une bonne distribution du mélange liquide-vapeur à l'entrée d'un échangeur et entre passes. Les résultats de la recherche seront concrétisés par un bon dessin du dispositif d'entrée et des boîtes de retour entre passes, ce qui permettra d'augmenter notablement l'efficacité des évaporateurs et des condenseurs.

3. REPARTITION DES TACHES ENTRE LES PARTICIPANTS

Le programme comprendra trois études expérimentales complémentaires réalisées sur trois installations implantées sur trois sites différents. Le fluide frigorigène utilisé serale R 22 autorisé par la règlementation de la Communauté Européenne.

Parallèlement à ces trois études expérimentales, un travail de modélisation de l'écoulement d'un fluide à deux phase séparées (liquide et vapeur) sera réalisé avec validation sur les expériences. Le point de départ de cette modélisation sera le logiciel de Grenoble dénommé TRIO.

3.1. Etudes expérimentales

3.1.1. Etudes expérimentales au GRETh

Pour réaliser cette étude expérimentale le GRETh utilisera la boucle d'essais BEATRICE (Fig. 2). Cette boucle est conçue pour fonctionner jusqu'à une pression de 20 bar. Elle permet d'obtenir un débit de mélange eau-air donné et de le répartir, suivant une loi de répartition choisie, entre les différents canaux (ou tubes) d'une passe amont d'une maquette d'échangeur. Des dispositifs appropriés permettent de mesurer à la sortie de la maquette d'échangeur les débits d'air et d'eau reçus par chacun des canaux (ou tubes) de la passe aval. Ces essais se font en condition adiabatique.

Les mesures de débits d'air et d'eau à la sortie de la passe aval se font selon une séquence complètement automatisée. Le mélange sortant d'un canal donné de la maquette d'échangeur est dévié, à l'aide de vannes trois voies, vers les systèmes de séparation des phases. Ensuite, les débits d'eau et d'air sont mesurés par des débitmètres.
Afin de ne pas perturber les pressions qui régnent à la sortie des tubes de la passe aval de la maquette d'échangeur, par la mise en ligne des systèmes de séparation et de mesure, une vanne de régulation ajuste automatiquement la perte de pression du canal en cours de mesure pour la rendre égale à celle mesurée avant la déviation. Cette procédure de régulation permet de conserver constant, pendant toute la séquence de mesure, l'ensemble des pressions que l'on a affiché en sortie des canaux de la passe aval de la maquette.
Une maquette d'échangeur tubulaire sera montée sur la boucle BEATRICE et permettra de simuler l'écoulement du mélange diphasique entre les différentes passes d'un échangeur évaporateur. La Fig. 3 montre le principe utilisé pour cette similitude.
La procédure simplifiée d'un test peut être décrite de la manière suivante : on injecte dans chaque tube de la passe numéro n un mélange homogène d'eau et air (même débit massique et même titre) et on mesure pour chaque tube en sortie de la passe n + 1, les débits d'eau et d'air reçus. Ces mesures sont faites en imposant une pression représentative d'un fonctionnement réel d'un échangeur à l'entrée de chaque tube de la passe n + 1 (conditions aux limites).
La même procédure est utilisée pour simuler le passage aux différentes passes de l'échangeur (jusqu'à n = 4). Voir Fig. 3.
Une visualisation de l'écoulement diphasique pourra être réalisée au travers de la plaque de fond transparente de la boîte de retour.

3.1.2. Etude expérimentale à H.W.U.

L'étude à H.W.U. consistera principalement à adapter et tester sur l'appareil frigorifique CIAT l'évaporateur expérimental défini par l'cnsemble des partenaires et réalisé par CENTAURO. H.W.U. équipera cet évaporateur d'un maximum d'instrumentation de mesure, et en particulier de la sonde étudiée par CENERTEC pour la mesure du débit diphasique total par tube.
Plusieurs répartitions de l'ensemble des tubes dans les différentes passes de l'évaporateur pourront être étudiées grâce à la conception spéciale de celui-ci. Les performances globales de l'évaporateur seront relevées pour toutes les configurations géométriques de l'évaporateur et pour une large gamme de conditions de fonctionnement compatible avec les caractéristiques de l'appareil CIAT. Le circuit de l'appareil frigorifique fonctionnera avec R 22 fluide frigorigène autorisé par la règlementation de la Communauté Européenne.
La Figure 4 représente le schéma d'ensemble de cet appareil.
Les mesures effectuées à H.W.U. seront comparées aux essais effectués au GRETh en similitude eau/air.

3.1.3. Etude expérimentale à CENERTEC

La sonde, mise au point par H.W.U., mesure le taux de vide du mélange diphasique à l'intérieur d'un tube. Cette indication est précieuse pour avoir un aperçu de la bonne ou mauvaise répartition du mélange diphasique entre les tubes à l'entrée d'une passe.

Cette indication serait encore plus précieuse si on pouvait l'accompagner d'une mesure du débit massique dans ce même tube. Ce résultat pourrait être obtenu grâce à une sonde qui pourrait à la fois mesurer le débit massique total et le taux de vide.

CENERTEC est chargé d'essayer de mettre au point une telle sonde. Pour mettre au point celle-ci CENERTEC, réalisera un circuit d'essai (Fig.5).

Cette sonde devra pouvoir se monter dans les tubes de l'évaporateur testé à HWU sans réusinage de celui-ci.

3.2. Participations des deux partenaires industriels

3.2.1. CIAT étudiera et réalisera un appareil frigorifique qui sera confié pour la durée de l'étude à H.W.U. La puissance de cet appareil est d'environ 250 kW (voir schéma sur Figure 4).

CIAT équipera son appareil des prises, pour mesures, nécessaires à H.W.U. pour déterminer les performances globales de l'évaporateur.

3.2.2. CENTAURO réalisera l'évaporateur spécial qui sera monté sur l'appareil frigorifique CIAT. Cet évaporateur devra permettre, de façon aisée, de modifier le nombre de passes ainsi que la répartition des tubes par passe.

3.3. Modélisation

Le GRETh utilisera pour cette modélisation le modèle de calcul TRIO VF (Volumes Finis) mis au point à Grenoble. Une version MC (Multi-composants) de ce modèle écrit en 3D sera, si possible, validée à partir des expériences réalisées sur le circuit BEATRICE.

Voir la Figure 6 qui explicite, sous forme schématique, la participation de chaque partenaire au projet de recherche.

4. RESULTATS PRELIMINAIRES

A la date d'aujourd'hui aucun résultat expérimental n'a été obtenu puisque les dispositifs expérimentaux ne sont pas encore opérationnels.

- La maquette pour similitude eau/air est en cours de réalisation et sera montée sur le circuit BEATRICE.

- La spécification de l'évaporateur spécial est faite et CENTAURO est en train de faire les plans pour réalisation.

- CIAT va lancer, sous peu, la réalisation de l'appareil frigorifique.

- CENERTEC est en cours de définition de son circuit pour étudier la nouvelle sonde de mesure simultanée : taux de vide/débit massique.

5. REFERENCES

[1] M. LEDINEGG
Instability of flow during natural and forced convection.
Die Warme 61, 8, AEC-tr-1861 (1938)

[2] A.P. BIRD et al.,
An investigation into excursive flow instability in a pair of horizontal parallel condensing channels.
The 24th ASME/AIChE National Heat Transfr Conference, Pittsburgh, Pennsylvania USA (1987)

[3]A.C. MUELLER and J.P. CHIOU
Review of various types of flow maldistribution in heat exchangers.
Heat Transfert Engineering, Vol. 9 N° 2 (1988)

[4] J.B. KITTO Jr. and J.M. ROBERTSON
Effets of maldistribution of flow on heat transfer equipment performance.
Heat Transfert Engineering, Vol. 10, N° 1 (1989).

[5] L.F. MENDES DE MOURA
Etude de la distribution d'un écoulement diphasique entre passes d'un échangeur à plaques.
Thèse INPG GRENOBLE, 1988

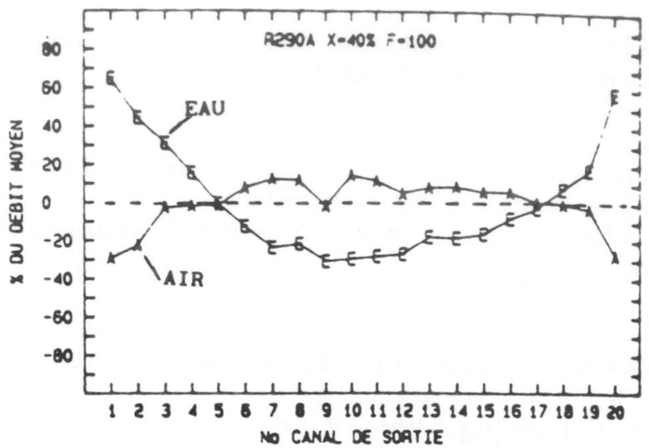

Fig. 1a

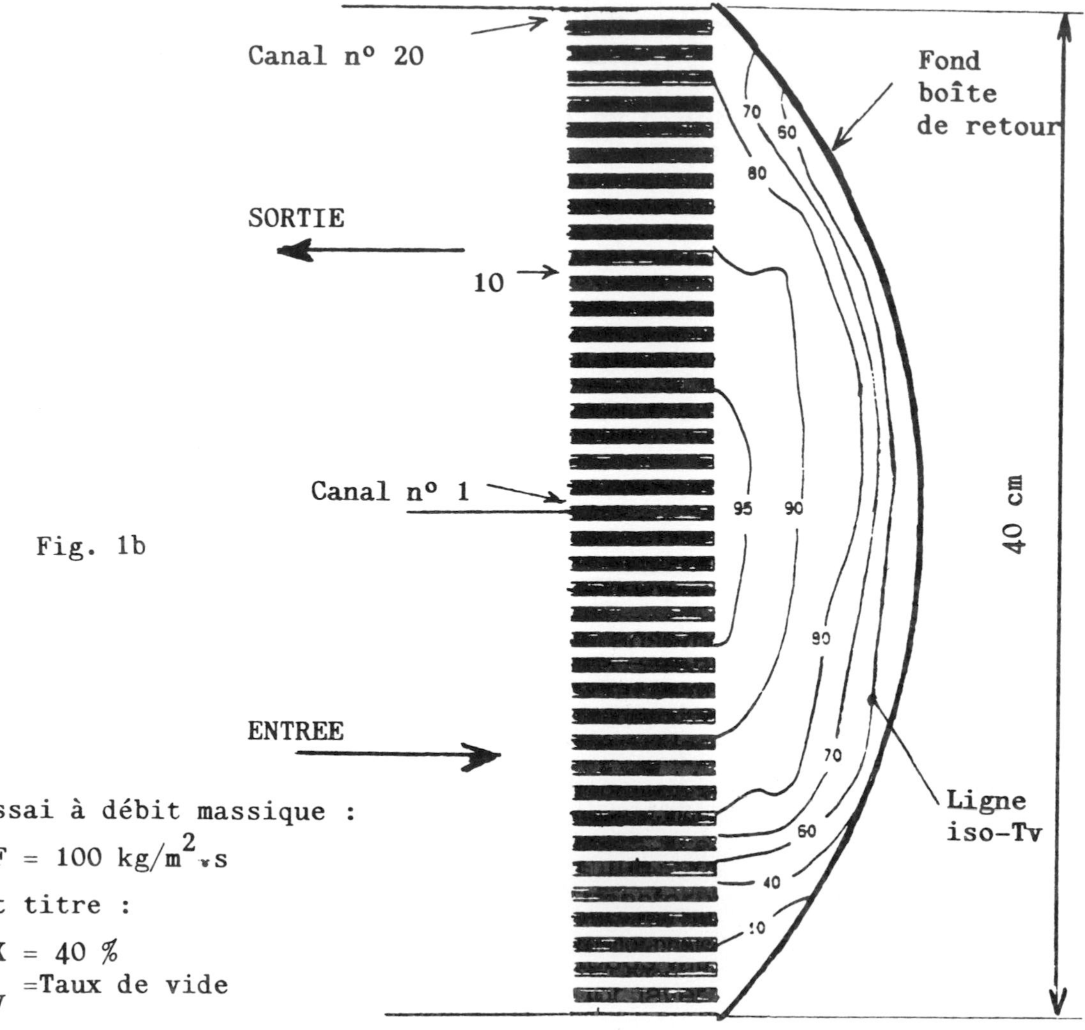

Fig. 1b

Essai à débit massique :

$F = 100\ kg/m^2 \cdot s$

et titre :

$X = 40\ \%$

T_v =Taux de vide

Figure 1
Distribution d'un mélange eau-air à 20 bar à la sortie des 20 canaux d'un échangeur à plaques, le mélange étant régulièrement répartie dans les 20 canaux d'entrée

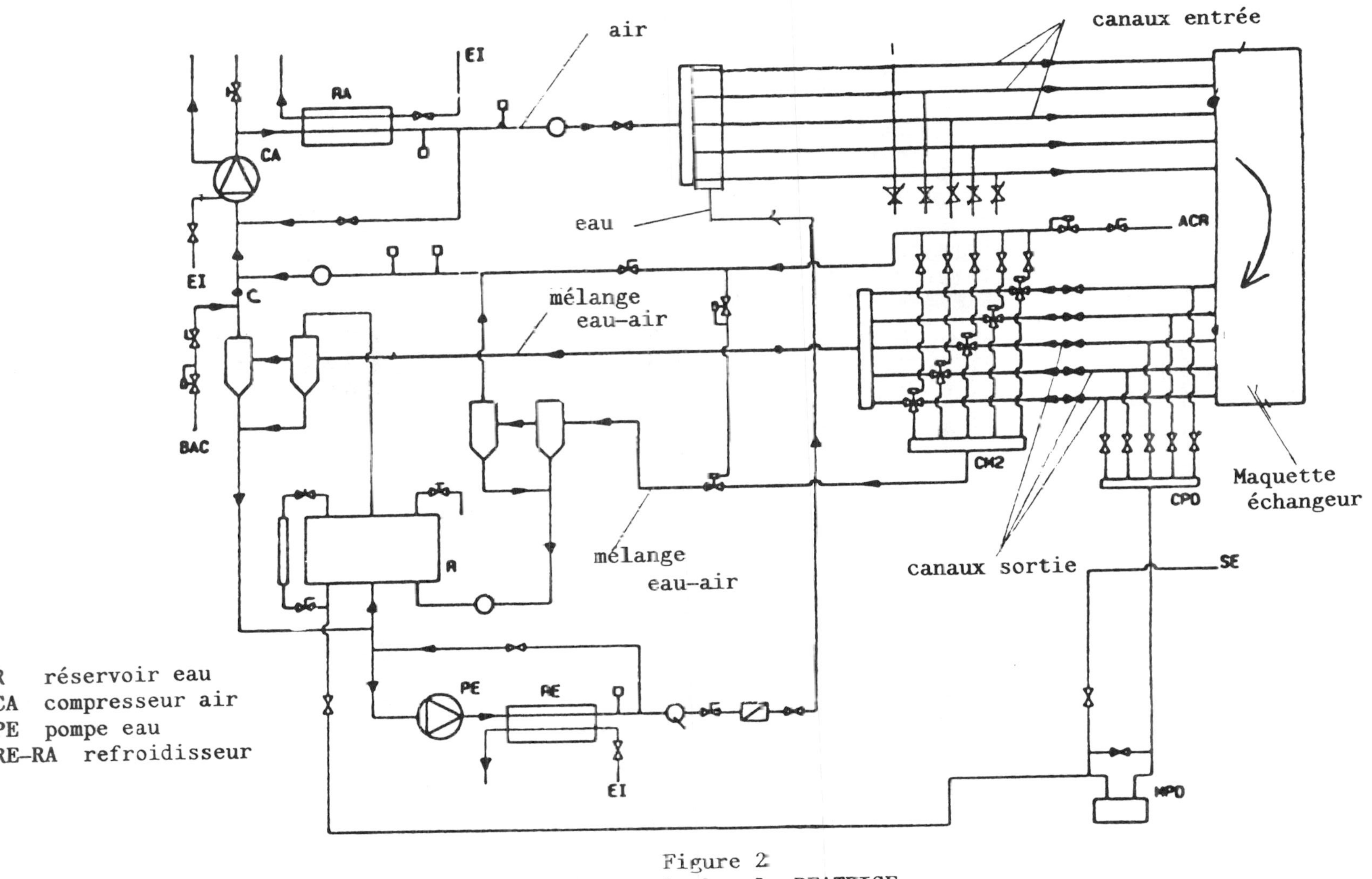

R réservoir eau
CA compresseur air
PE pompe eau
RE–RA refroidisseur

Figure 2
Schéma de la boucle BEATRICE

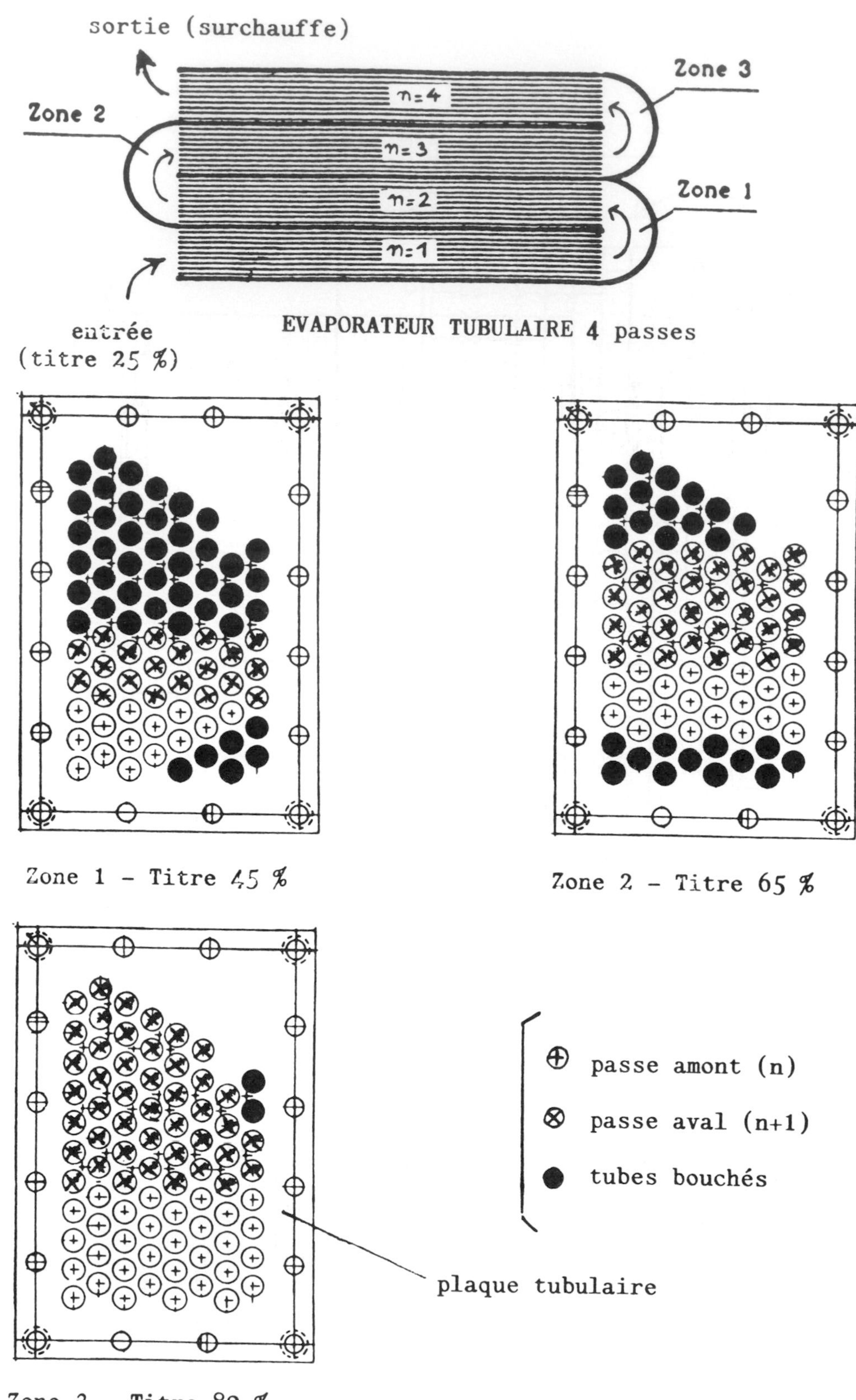

Figure 3
Principe de simulation des trois zones de retour
sur la maquette d'échangeur par bouchages successifs de tubes

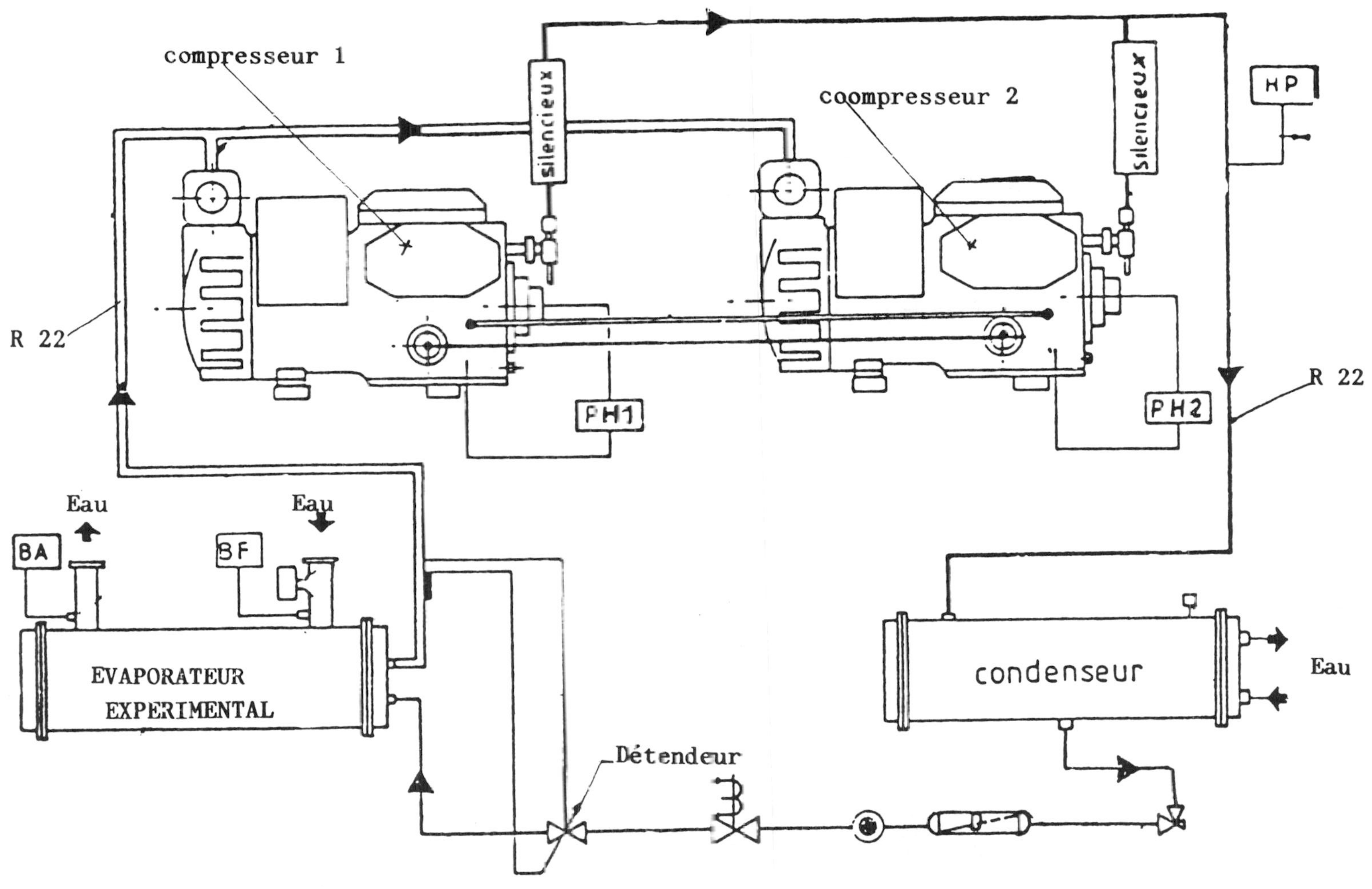

Figure 4
Machine frigorifique CIAT

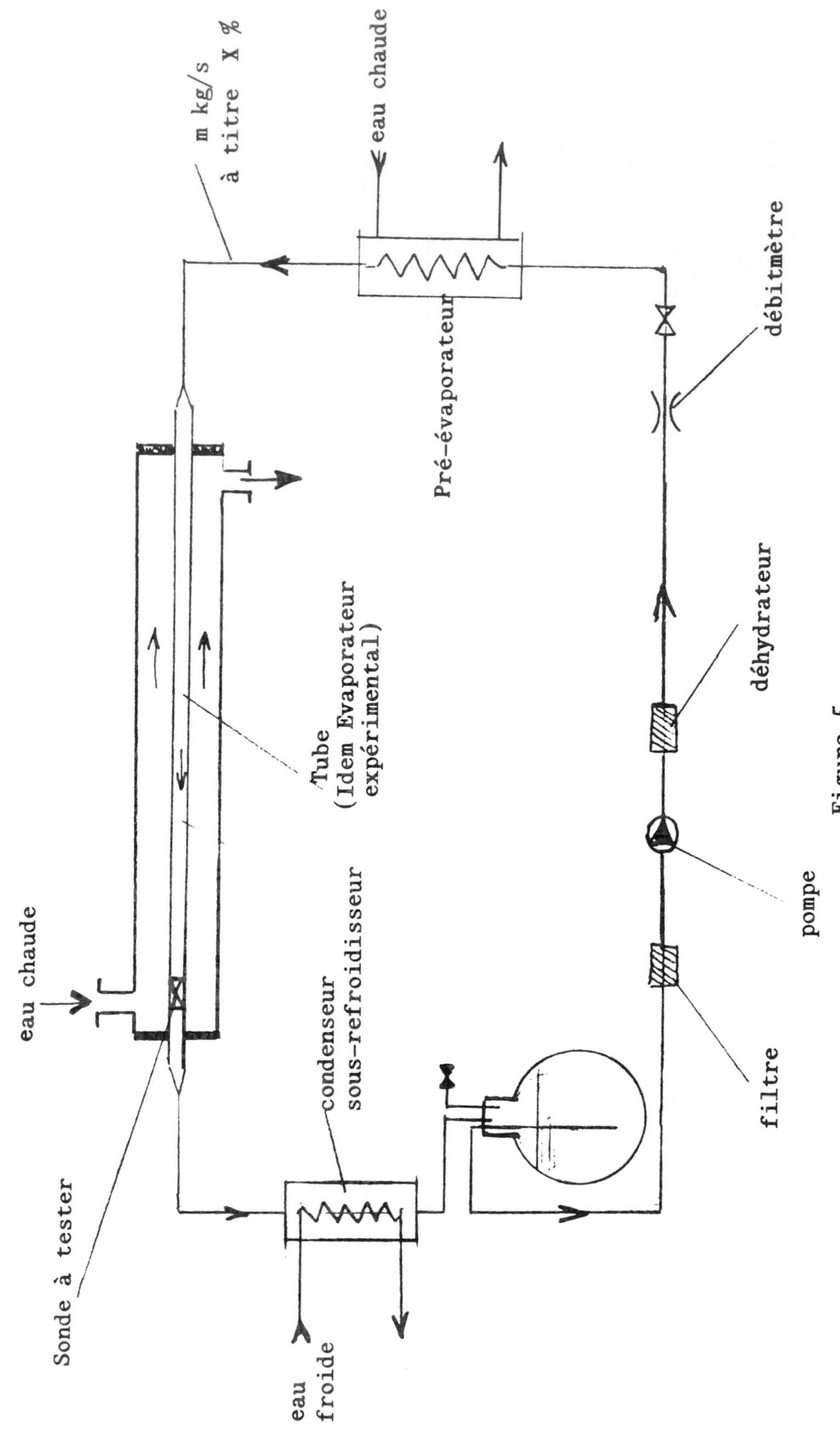

Figure 5

Circuit d'essai pour mise au point sonde tubulaire

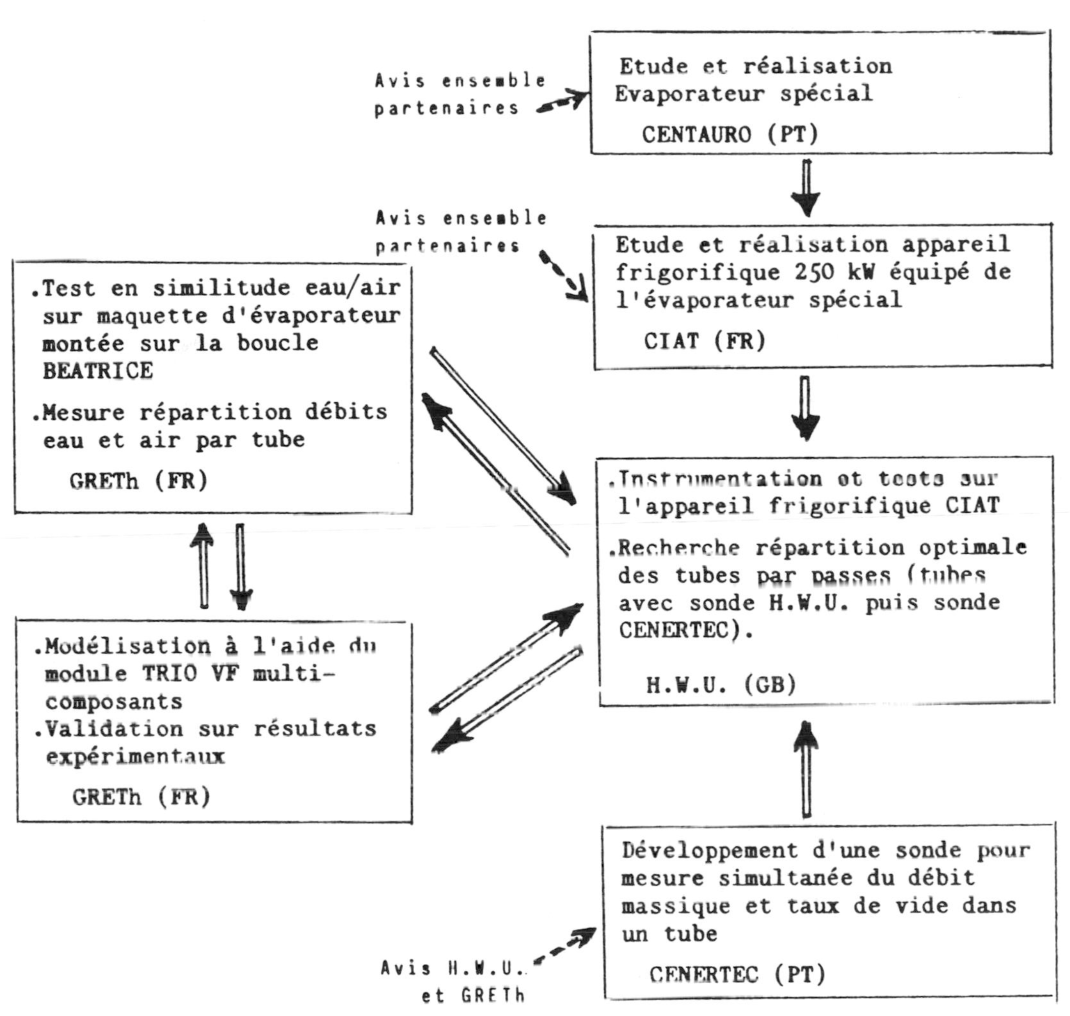

Figure 6

Plan du travail

GENERIC STUDIES FOR INDUSTRIAL HEAT EXCHANGER FOULING

Dr J D Isdale
National Engineering Laboratory (NEL)
United Kingdom

Contract JOUE - 0040 - C

PARTICIPANTS

Mr R Vidil
Commissariat a l'Energie Atomique (GRETh)
France

Mr J-P Durand
Constructions Industrielles de la Mediterranee (CNIM)
France

Prof A J Karabelas
Chemical Process Engineering Research Institute (CPERI)
Greece

Ir L W Koot
TNO Division of Technology for Society (TNO)
The Netherlands

Mr M Vouche
Hamon-Sobelco SA (H-S)
Belgium

SUMMARY

The main core of the work requires the development and construction of mathematical models which may be used to predict gas-side exchanger fouling for a range of environments. This involves the identification, assessment and implementation (through computer programs) of a set of equations which describe the transport of material from exhaust gas streams to the exchanger surfaces. In addition to this theoretical equation framework, correlations will be developed which will provide information on the retention of that material by the exchanger surface. The latter will be developed using experimental data obtained from both site tests in the environments concerned, and from laboratory tests designed to quantify specific effects such as the influence of surface temperature and geometry. The value of this gas-side method for potential application to liquid-side problems will also be assessed, and recommendations provided.

In addition, a practical fouling monitor for non-specialist use will be developed. This requires the selection of a practical method which will be robust and reliable and, were possible, integrate the results of the analytical and experimental work.

The project therefore contains a wide range of theoretical, experimental and development work from a multi-disciplinary team.

1 INTRODUCTION

This project is about tackling the problem of prediction of fouling on heat exchanger surfaces, with the aim of providing types of solution which will be generic over a wide range of industrial processes. The background to the project is based on a strong economic need for work of this type, combined with an examination of the complexity which has hindered the resolution of the problem.

1.1 The Economics of Fouling

The cost of fouling of heat exchanger surfaces is extremely difficult to estimate on a national, international or even a local scale. This is partly because published values are comparatively few, and partly because fouling is often regarded as inevitable and the costs integrated within other operational and capital expenditure. It is, however, accepted that the total annual cost for developed countries may be measured in thousands of millions of pounds(1). Even if these estimates were to be limited to gas-side fouling (as distinct from liquid-side) the costs are clearly substantial for the European Community as a whole, and even a small improvement could make a significant contribution to industrial competitiveness and economic efficiency. For less developed countries the consequences are also significant. The cost of installation and operation of plant facilities is elevated to compensate in part for fouling, and confidence in fouling predictions is low. As a result even new developments based on existing technologies are inhibited, particularly for alternative or unfamiliar fuels, and industrial, economic and therefore social progress further delayed. For similar reasons the development of new technologies, such as compact exchangers, is also inhibited.

The concept of fouling being inevitable arises mainly from the technical difficulty of the topic, outlined in the following section, and from the consequent treatment of fouling problems on an isolated individual basis. While some fouling problems may be inevitable, it is clear that industry would benefit economically from a more generic approach leading to the definition of standard methods of measurement, prediction and hence control. In the worst cases these might not eliminate fouling but they would make a significant impact on efficiency through the optimisation of plant design and operation.

The direct costs of fouling arise from additional capital, fuel and maintenance, as well as through production losses. The normal design reaction to prospective fouling is to install extra heat-transfer surface, perhaps in the form of a standby exchanger, and anti-fouling devices such as sootblowers. These measures call directly on capital for both installation and materials, and they may necessitate an increase in plant size so incurring extra building and construction costs. Additional fuel costs arise not only from the reduced heat transfer but also from circuit losses caused by increased pressure drop, and from secondary energy required to compensate for plant inefficiency. Deposit removal is the most obvious maintenance cost, to which must be added that of sootblower operation and any additives used.

Less direct and less quantifiable costs arise from the inhibition of progress mentioned above, and from safety aspects in cases where inadequate provision for fouling has been made.

1.2 The Fouling Problem

The study of fouling of heat exchanger surfaces is a specialised subject which depends on a combination of physical and chemical processes. While it is closely linked with the design and performance of the exchangers themselves, it requires the application of significant multi-disciplinary knowledge and techniques additional to those needed for the study of heat transfer.

Examination of the published literature and data on fouling shows that research to date can be divided into two distinct categories. The first and largest of these is based on theoretical studies of fouling and its mechanisms. Publications on these topics are numerous and generally of a very high standard, and they are often supported by small-scale laboratory experiments for the particular system being studied. The second category is at the other end of the spectrum, and is concerned with the study of fouling of specific heat exchangers in a selected environment, usually a pilot or full-scale operating plant. Again these studies are usually thorough and well executed, since it is widely recognised that the development of methods to predict or control fouling is a vital need for improved energy efficiency and better understanding and control of environmental emissions.

However, it is also true that nearly all of the work in both of the above categories has a very limited range of application to the solution of industrial problems. The theoretical studies invariably provide solutions which are necessarily quite complex, even for simplified fouling situations, and they are, of course, only tested and can only be tested using the simplified laboratory system studied. In addition, for particulate fouling, they have not yet provided access to the calculation of particle sticking probabilities for other than the simplest case.

The studies of pilot or larger scale plant on the other hand, clearly provide results of direct value to the particular installation. However, the complexity of the combined physical and chemical contributions to the net fouling process allows large and unpredictable variations in behaviour to occur, even for quite small changes in configuration or environment. This type of study is therefore also of limited value, and the results from one test cannot be directly transferred to another with sufficient confidence.

It is therefore very difficult to provide a generic core for future work using either of these methods, and it is essential to define a new approach which will. For maximum benefit it is clearly important that any new approach should be of such a form that it can incorporate as much as possible of the knowledge and data provided by the earlier work.

The reasons for this lack of real progress on prediction of fouling are obviously technical, and they arise both from the complexity of individual factors, and from the complexity of the interactions between those factors. The factor most familiar to heat exchanger engineers arises from the aerodynamic conditions which may vary markedly throughout an individual exchanger or even between nominally identical installations. Since each fouling mechanism is influenced by the local conditions of velocity (including direction), for example, it follows that, even if only one mechanism is active, absolute knowledge of velocity is required throughout the configuration to predict the fouling which will occur. Even if the exact influence of velocity on the active mechanism is known, such detailed velocity data are not normally available and this factor on its own limits understanding of observed fouling and inhibits progress.

A similar argument, however, could also be applied to local temperatures (for temperature dependent or temperature gradient driven mechanisms), to local particulate concentrations and size distributions, to the concentration of active chemical species such as SO_2, or to several other parameters.

Though each of the factors noted in itself presents difficulties, they may in addition, influence each other. The most obvious effect here is probably that of velocity on particulate concentration and size distribution. For low velocities or sharp changes of direction, particles in the larger size ranges may be removed by gravitational settling or impaction mechanisms in one stage of the exchanger, leaving a modified concentration and distribution for mechanisms active in later stages.

Again, similar arguments may be applied to interactions between other parameters such as chemical reactions, or between individual fouling mechanisms.

Because of these difficulties, current industrial design practice relies on the only two options available: published values of thermal fouling resistance or experiential information for the type of installation being considered. While tabulated fouling resistances are available(2), these are necessarily simplified with respect to both the environments and the effects of variables such as velocity or temperature. Variations of fouling with time are invariably ignored, so that it is not possible to optimise the provision or frequency of operation of removal devices such as sootblowers. In addition, the accuracy of the published values is often doubtful and the source unknown(3). The use of experiential information is also subject to a high risk and considerable uncertainty for the reasons outlined above. It follows that currently available methods to predict fouling are inconsistent with the rational development of efficient systems, from both the thermal and operational points of view.

It is therefore clear that any development which aims to be generic, must recognise the potential influence of the complexities and provide a framework which will allow them to be incorporated progressively in a quantified way. It is also clear that future methods of prediction must be capable of interfacing with advances in computational fluid dynamics and other techniques which will provide access to the necessary variables. In addition, it should be possible to interface with thermal design programs, such as those for process integration, of which fouling predictions will be an essential part.

Validated fouling models will be invaluable tools for design and operation of plant. However, there is also a need for a reliable device for use by plant operators, which provides operational fouling information in a usable form. This will necessitate the development of reliable and cost effective fouling monitors, as such devices are not commercially available. A variety of optical, acoustical and electrical techniques can potentially be used for this purpose.

Clearly no single project can attempt to satisfy all of the needs of the fouling field. Indeed, for some complex environments the theoretical framework available is inadequate(4), and it is but correct to conclude(5) that some degree of empiricism will always be necessary. Nevertheless, unless some generic approach based on analysis and accurate monitoring is made to the fouling problem, it is likely that industry will continue to pay the penalty of high costs and inefficiency resulting from heat exchanger fouling. The projects selected for this work therefore aim to provide a suitable basis for present and future developments in fouling measurement and prediction.

1.3 Project

The combination of projects assembled for this work provides a unique opportunity to examine in detail the relationships between industrial exhausts and better controlled laboratory experiments. This will provide the basis for generic work on exchanger fouling through a greater insight on fouling mechanisms and behaviour, which may be applied to both theoretical and practical problems. Existing probe techniques will be used to generate much of the data required but development work will be carried out to provide an on-line monitor to enable site operators direct access to some form of fouling measurement. To provide interpretable information these devices need to be combined with valid fouling models, and the programme therefore includes the concurrent development of a fouling monitoring device for this purpose.

The project will also contribute to improved energy efficiency and to better control of environmental factors. Successful completion will provide models which demonstrate an alternative approach, which can potentially be applied to a wide range of fouling situations and will be capable of further development.

Several environments covering a very wide range of conditions will be used to develop and test the models and the newly developed monitoring equipment. These include incinerator exhausts, the simpler diesel system, a cast steel furnace, an environment yet to be chosen from the petrochemical industry, and laboratory fouling rigs. Both the mathematical fouling model and the fouling monitoring device will therefore find ready application in a wide range of industries.

Integration of the results requires the close co-operation of all the partners involved, and careful scheduling of the programme of tasks. The inclusion of additional environments would also be of benefit to the study, since the scope of the concept is not limited to those listed.

Earlier work(6,7) has included specific studies of a diesel exhaust, a paint stoving line, incinerator exhausts and, more recently, pulverised and grate fired coal combustion. These studies have shown that the basic method, which depends on a combination of the equation framework with experimental data from real exhaust environments, may be applied successfully to both simple and complex environments. Both the type of data required and the probe techniques for obtaining it have therefore already been developed and proved(8,9,10).

For the more complex fouling environments such as incinerator and steel furnace exhausts, the influence of chemical effects may be large(7,11) and chemical analysis of deposits is required for model development. The purpose of these analyses is to help determine the proportions of particles arriving by impactive and non-impactive mechanisms, to provide information on the influence of non-particulate mechanisms and to help identify significant chemical species.

2 OBJECTIVES

The aim of this study is to provide better methods to measure and predict gas-side fouling in a generic way. The two main technical objectives are to construct predictive mathematical models for a range of environments, and to provide practical fouling monitors for non-specialist use. A third objective is to provide an assessment of the methodology, and recommendations for its potential application to liquid-side problems.

The complete project will provide a wide range of valuable results. These will include: measurements of mass accumulation rates and other data for diesel, refuse incinerator and cast steel furnace environments; laboratory measurements of fin temperature distribution and fouling due to larger particles; analyses of the data and analytic models for the environments; applications programs for the implementation of the models; recommendations on the method for liquid-side applications; and a practical monitor. These are expected to have a wide range of applications in several industrial sectors.

3 TASKS OF PARTICIPANTS

The main technical content of the project may be divided into three phases, Model Development, Experimental Tests and Validation. Each of these involves a number of separate tasks, which interact with one or more tasks in different phases as shown in Fig. 1.

3.1 Parameter Selection

This phase will define the exchanger surface geometries, configurations and the range of parameters such as temperature, velocity and concentration, which will be required in other parts of the project. Any 'in-house' data or information which can be released by the partners will also be provided. (NEL, GRETh, CNIM, H-S, TNO)

3.2 Model Development

3.2.1 Development of an integrated fouling model

The first main objective will be achieved by extending current analytic modelling and experimental techniques, and integrating these with data from both laboratory and plant measurements. The modelling work will provide an equation framework (the models) capable of describing and predicting fouling for the environments considered. The main steps in this phase are critical for the whole project and these are: the identification and assessment of a suitable suite of equations; development of FORTRAN 77 analysis programs; calculation of equation parameters such as particle sticking probability, from the experimental data; development of suitable functions to describe these; and finally the incorporation of any adjustments found necessary by the validation studies. Sticking probability, the fraction of impacting particles retained by a surface,

cannot at present be determined by calculation, and is the key unknown in most fouling processes. Data produced by Experimental Tests 3.1 to 3.5 will be required to complete the calculation of sticking probabilities.
(NEL)

3.2.2 Applications software development

This work will provide programs aimed at convenient application of the results, rather than analysis only. The program will be refined continuously, in parallel with the development of the model, starting as soon as the equation framework has been defined. A trial version will be provided early in the project, to allow preparations for the validation work to begin. Further development will continue to incorporate more advanced sticking probability parameters as these are developed, and these will be provided to the appropriate partners involved with the validation tests as they become available. Any final adjustments indicated by the results of the validation tests will be incorporated at the end of the project.
(NEL)

3.2.3 Preparation of a pilot monitor

The second main objective will be achieved by the concurrent development of plant monitoring equipment. This device will be designed to provide some indication of the progress of fouling within a plant. Translation of the reading indicated by the monitor, to the fouling of the actual heat exchanger, may be achieved using the applications program, developed in Section 3.2.2, combined with knowledge of the plant heat exchanger.

The first phase of this work is the identification of the most suitable sensoring principle and the production of a prototype design. This phase will include formulation of selection criteria, and selection of the most suitable method based on these criteria. The work will also require close collaboration with the analytical model development, to ensure that compatible methods are used. Methods considered will include techniques based on acoustical, electrical or optical detection of fouling deposits.
(TNO with consultation from NEL and GRETh)

3.3 Experimental Tests

The experimental work required includes measurements both under laboratory and full-scale operating conditions.

3.3.1 Determination of fin temperature distribution for the selected geometry

Laboratory tests will be carried out to determine the temperature distribution on exchanger fins of the selected geometry. The work will be carried out using the CARA experimental rig, which is a facility designed to carry out infra-red measurements of temperature on heat exchanger surfaces. CARA will be specially modified for these tests. Two tube configurations of ten rows will be used, one with the tubes aligned and the second staggered. The tube to be measured will be placed in three different positions within the tube array and its temperature controlled at selected levels. The other tubes in the array will operate at gas stream temperature. The temperature distribution will be determined by directly observing the tube under tests through fluorite windows which are transparent to infra-red radiation, and the local gas velocities will be calculated using TRIO, a numerical fluid dynamics program. The results will thus provide a unique and accurate determination of the temperature distribution for the particular fin configuration selected for this work. (GRETh)

3.3.2 Diesel exhaust tests

The work will be carried out using DELFINE, an experimental facility for the study of fouling in diesel exhaust environments. The rig will be specially modified for these tests. Two exchangers will be set up in series to allow the simultaneous study of the influence of network geometry. In this case, each exchanger is made up of 12 rows of tubes, with nine cooled tubes which are instrumented and which may be placed in different positions in the network.

For each set of conditions the rig will be used to measure the change of heat-transfer coefficient and pressure drop with time as the deposition progresses, with the fin geometry selected. The study will therefore include an examination of the effects of tube layout (aligned and staggered), tube position (1st, 5th and 10th rows), gas velocity (5 to 20 m/s), temperature of exhaust (300 to 700°C), surface temperature (80 to 200°C), and particle concentration. Supplementary analyses of the particle size distribution and concentration in the exhaust will also be carried out, as well as analyses of the deposit. (GRETh)

3.3.3 Larger particle tests

Deposition will be observed on an exchanger installed in the GAZPAR facility. This facility uses an ultrasonic aerosol generator to produce monodisperse particles for injection into a heated stream of air, so providing a simulated exhaust environment. For the proposed experiments the exchangers will consist of a row of nine tubes, with two adjacent columns of uncooled half-section tubes to simulate a complete array. Measurements of the change of heat-transfer coefficient and pressure drop with time will be carried out as the deposition proceeds.

The investigation will include studies of the effect of particle size (0.5 to 3 microns), gas velocity (5 to 20 m/s), gas stream temperature (100 to 250°C), and surface temperature (20 to 100°C). Measurements will also be made of the mass and volume of the final deposits, and the particle size will be monitored using a cascade impactor. (GRETh)

3.3.4 Refuse incinerator tests

Measurements of mass accumulation rates and other relevant parameters will also be undertaken on full-scale operating plant for incorporation in the model. These will be made using a mobile laboratory, the Industrial Fouling Analysis Unit (IFAU), to service the NEL mass accumulation probe and other measurements in an incinerator in Toulon (with CNIM). The tests will be carried out to examine the influence of gas temperature, to obtain the influence of gas velocity at a given temperature, and to determine the influence of time and operating conditions on the deposition. (CNIM and NEL)

Extensive chemical analyses of the deposits and the gas streams will be carried out to provide input information for model interpretation. A variety of advanced chemical analytical methods will be used. (CNIM)

3.3.5 Cast steel furnace tests

The same test programme as given in Section 3.3.4 will be carried out in gas streams of a cast steel furnace at a Renault plant in Le Mans, France. (H-S and NEL)

Corresponding chemical analyses of gas stream and deposits will also be provided. (H-S)

3.3.6 Experimental monitor tests

This second phase of monitor development will include the construction and preliminary testing of the monitor under laboratory conditions. The steps required will include component tests and installation, initial manufacture of the sensor and its operational system, and assembly and initial testing. Any further modifications indicated by these tests will be incorporated along with any found to be needed from further developments from the modelling work. (TNO with consultation from NEL and GRETh)

3.4 Validation of the Model

3.4.1 Validation for diesel system

The models will be validated by carrying out calculations of deposition rates for various environments and comparing these with both the experimental data and any suitable values available in the literature. This will allow an assessment of the accuracy of both the prediction procedure and the complete methodology. As indicated above, the calculations will be carried out using the applications software developed in Section 3.2.2. For the diesel system, this will include an examination of calculated and observed deposition for the fin configuration and temperature distribution determined under Section 3.3.1, and the results from Section 3.3.2. (GRETh and NEL)

3.4.2 Validation for larger particles

An assessment similar to that given in Section 3.4.1 will be carried out for larger particles using the results from Section 3.3.3. (GRETh and NEL)

3.4.3 Validation for refuse incineration

An assessment similar to that given in Section 3.4.1 will be carried out for the incinerator environment. In this case the calculations will be carried out for conditions and geometries applicable to incinerator exchanger surfaces where fins are not used due to heavy fouling. Again the calculations will be made using the applications software from Section 3.2.2 but with the results from Section 3.3.4. (CNIM, GRETh and NEL)

3.4.4 Validation for cast steel furnace

An assessment, similar to that given in Section 3.4.3, will be carried out for the cast steel furnace environment, using corresponding results from Section 3.3.5. (H-S, GRETh and NEL)

3.4.5 Practical monitor tests

The final phase is aimed at the testing of the practical monitor developed in Section 3.3.6, under industrial conditions in the petroleum industry. Interaction between this phase and the modelling work will be maintained here also to ensure that the monitors are usable in as wide a range of environments as possible. The work will include selection and preparation of the site trials, experimental tests and analysis of the results. The tests will be repeated as necessary until satisfactory performance is attained. (TNO)

3.5 Method Assessment

Although the project is aimed principally at gas-side fouling, an additional study will be undertaken to investigate the potential of the gas-side methodology for liquid-side fouling problems. This will include provision of recommendations on the suitability of this approach for liquid-side problems such as cooling water systems.

This will require comprehensive study of the methods used to obtain data, the value and meaning of the data themselves, the methods used to develop appropriate equations and correlations, and the complete analytical and experimental framework. While it is unlikely that the specific experimental techniques used for the gas-side work will be directly useful for liquid side, it may be possible to identify modifications or alternative techniques which would be of value. Close collaboration and extensive exchange of information with appropriate partners will be essential, to gain the necessary insight to modelling and the use of laboratory and site experimental measurements.

The result will be recommendations on the viability or otherwise of the approach for liquid-side studies, and an identification of any additional techniques which may be needed. (CPERI)

4 PRELIMINARY RESULTS

While the projects have only recently started, some progress has already been made with the scheduled activities prior to the formal production of results.

Both the exchanger fin geometry for the experimental tests, and a fouling parameter list for the monitor development, have been identified and reports are being prepared. The latter report includes an assessment of the options available for the monitor, which will influence the choice of the physical detection method. The relative viability of optical and other methods, perhaps in combination, is at present being considered.

The equation framework on which the fouling model will initially be based has also been identified, and this has enabled the modular structure of the applications program to be designed. Construction of the analysis program and the applications program is in hand.

Rig modifications, based on the selected fin geometries, for the experimental tests have also been designed and are at present being constructed.

Suitable measurement locations for the site test work at Toulon have been identified during a visit to the plant by the Site Operations Manager. Construction of the essential access ports (shown in Fig. 2) is in progress, and arrangements have been made for the provision of facilities. Preliminary locations for the site measurements at Le Mans have been selected and will be finalised well in advance of the tests.

The literature survey for the method assessment work is in progress.

5 FUTURE R&D

Since this work is still at an early stage in its development, there is potentially a very wide range of activities which could be undertaken, while still in the precompetitive stage. For gas-side fouling these include:

* Production of 'valid' data for a wide range of processes. In this context valid data are those which would allow direct interpretation using the analyses developed as part of the current work. The aim would be to construct a translated data bank of sticking probability functions, to allow prediction in important fouling environments such as glass production, coal, oil or others chosen to meet environmental or energy efficiency criteria.

* Integration of fouling models with process integration programs. To obtain the maximum benefit from the present project it will be essential, at some stage, to combine fouling models with current or new methods for thermal process integration.

* Integration of combustion modelling with the above fouling and process integration work. The aim here would clearly be to provide a tool to carry out optimisation of thermal energy system for both energy and environmental criteria simultaneously. This would allow, for example, the direct calculation of the economic consequences of emissions legislation on specific energy system design and operation.

* Modifications and improvements to the existing methodology, including the development of practically oriented theoretical methods.

* Further development of the initial applications program, produced by this project, indicated by the needs of potential users.

For liquid-side fouling, future projects will depend to an extent on the results of the current method assessment study. However, for completeness all of the above items should in fact include provision for such effects. While a similar generic modelling approach to fouling prediction has not yet been defined (and may not be possible) for liquid-side effects, it will at least be possible to provide some of the basic data which will be essential for the development of future standards. At worst, it might only be feasible to utilise these data directly on a site by site basis for specific applications. It is more likely, however, that a simplified modelling approach could be used initially, to provide the predictive facility essential for more widespread utilisation. The main problem for liquid-side fouling lies in the identification (and sometimes measurement) of the controlling parameters. For example, the presence of trace quantities of impurities can alter the habit and growth of crystalline deposits, and so produce large differences in fouling rates. In a similar way, trace quantities of some chemical species can have a profound effect on the formation of biological films, and are often used to inhibit film formation.

Potential liquid-side projects therefore include:

* Production of 'valid' data for a wide range of processes. In this case the most useful data would be direct site measurements of thermal fouling resistance, and the corresponding controlling parameters.

* Development of a methodology based on predictive models.

Most of the above require a significant degree of direct industrial collaboration to provide access to real industrial streams which cannot be reproduced in the laboratory. An invaluable addition to these basic research activities would therefore be the provision of a forum for research workers and interested industrialists. This would not only help the dissemination and application of the results but also aid in the direction of the work towards the more important industrial processes. In addition, it would encourage the direct involvement of the industries concerned. This could be achieved by the formation of a European Fouling (or Clean Energy Systems) Group, with the aim of stimulating the generation and application of new ideas.

6 REFERENCES

1 Pritchard, A. M. The economics of fouling. In Fouling Science and Technology, pp 31-45, Volume 145 NATO ASI Series, Applied Sciences. Melo, L., Bott, T. R. and Bernardo, C. A. (eds). Kluwer Academic Publishers, 1988.

2 Tubular Exchanger Manufacturers Association (TEMA), Thermal Standards, Standards of Tubular Exchanger Manufacturers Association, 6th edition, New York, 1978.

3 Chenoweth, J. M. General design of heat exchangers for fouling conditions. In Fouling Science and Technology, pp 477-494, Volume 145 NATO ASI Series, Applied Sciences. Melo, L., Bott, T. R. and Bernardo, C. A. (eds). Kluwer Academic Publishers, 1988.

4 Isdale, J. D. Debate on gas-side fouling. In Fouling Science and Technology, pp 731-733, Volume 145 NATO ASI Series, Applied Sciences. Melo, L., Bott, T. R. and Bernardo, C. A. (eds). Kluwer Academic Publishers, 1988.

5 Bott, T. R. Gas-side fouling. In Fouling Science and Technology, pp 191-203, Volume 145 NATO ASI Series, Applied Sciences. Melo, L., Bott, T. R. and Bernardo, C. A. (eds). Kluwer Academic Publishers, 1988.

6 Isdale, J. D., Gas side fouling in heat exchanger plant. Report for Department of Energy, 1984. National Engineering Laboratory Report ENER20/24, 1984.

7 Glen, N. F. and Howarth, J. H. Modelling refuse incineration fouling. 2nd UK National Conference on Heat Transfer, University of Strathclyde, pp 401-420, Sept 1988, I.Mech.E.

8 Isdale, J. D., Scott, A. C., Cartwright, G. and Glen, N. F. The use of a portable probe to study fouling in exhaust gas streams. First UK National Conference on Heat Transfer, Leeds, 1984. I.Chem.E. Symposium Series No 86, Volume 1, pp 415-434. Pergamon, 1984.

9 Ewart, W. R. Obtaining valid fouling data from industrial gas streams. 2nd UK National Conference on Heat Transfer, University of Strathclyde, pp 421-432, Sept 1988, I.Mech.E.

10 Tsados, A. Gas-side fouling monitoring equipment. In Fouling Science and Technology, Volume 145 NATO ASI Series, Applied Sciences. Melo, L., Bott, T. R. and Bernardo, C. A. (eds). Kluwer Academic Publishers, 1988.

11 Howarth, J. H. and Bott, T. R. High temperature fouling: the nature of deposits. In Fouling Science and Technology, Volume 145 NATO ASI Series, Applied Sciences. Melo, L., Bott, T. R. and Bernardo, C. A. (eds). Kluwer Academic Publishers, 1988.

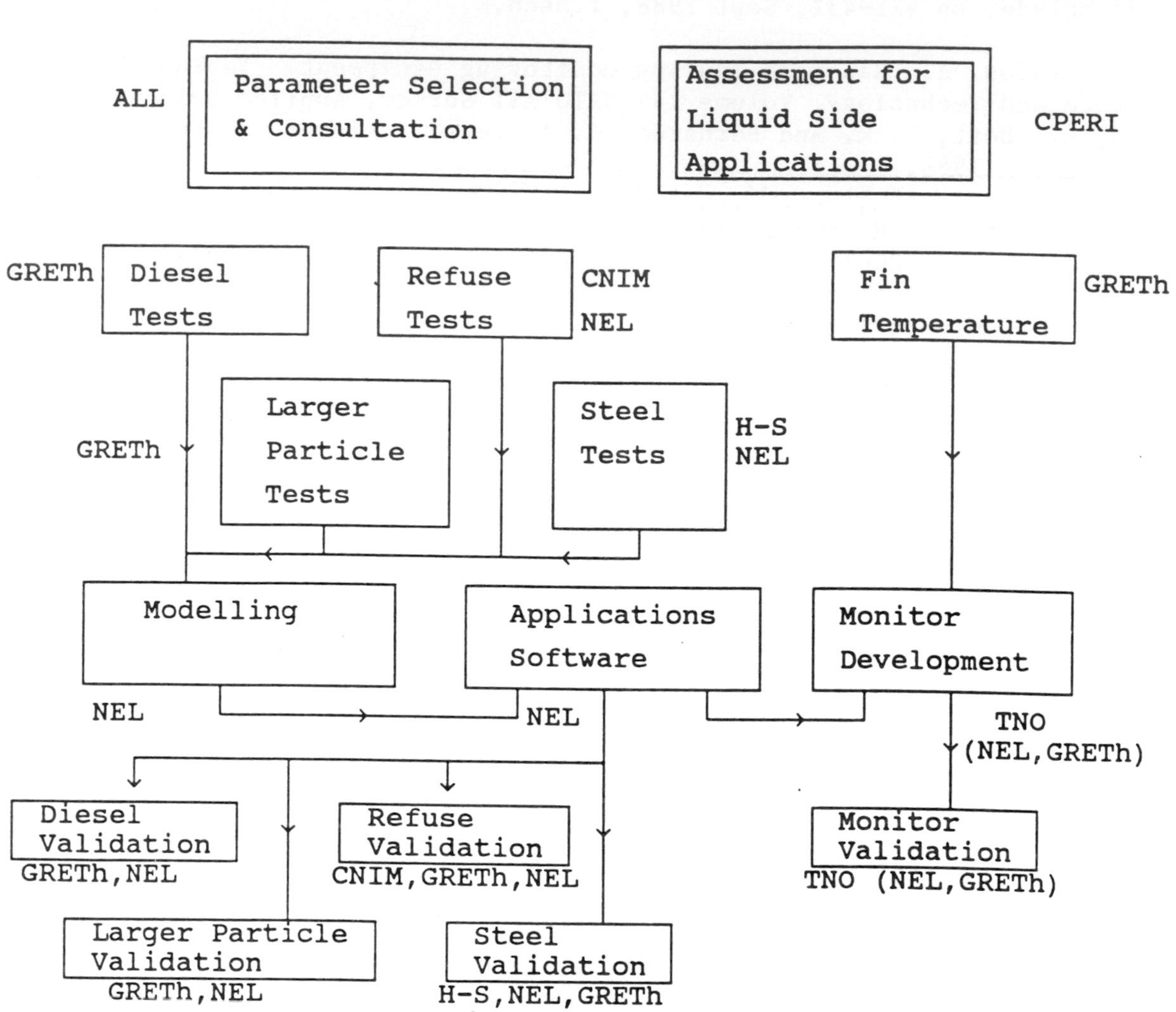

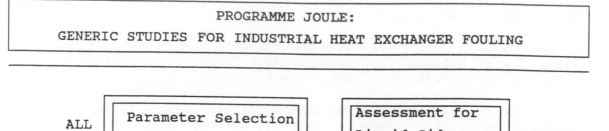

Fig 1 Project structure

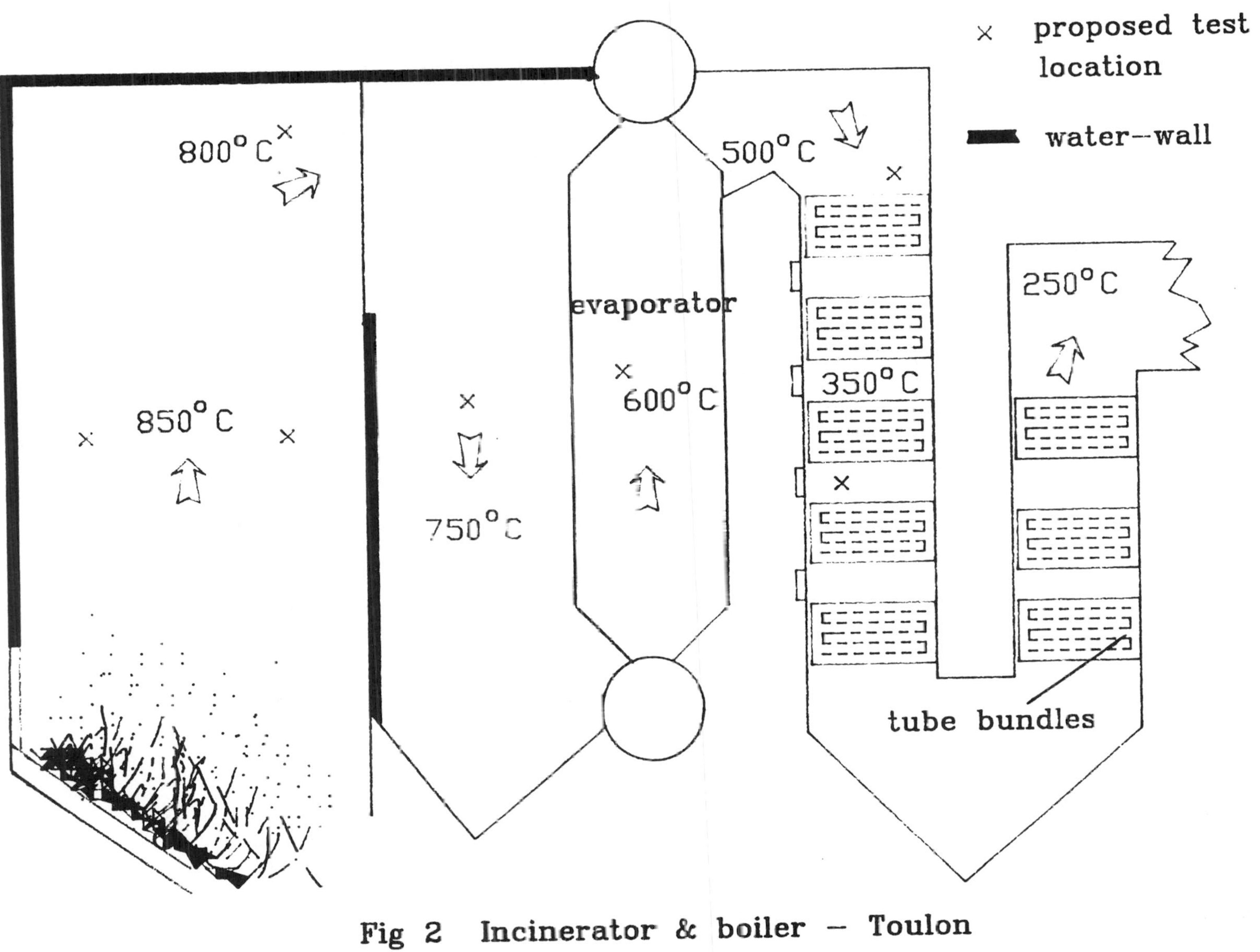

Fig 2 Incinerator & boiler – Toulon

LOW ENERGY SEPARATION PROCESSES

Chairman: Prof. D. A. Reay

THE METHODOLOGY OF GAS ADSORPTION PROCESS DESIGN

Project Coordinator: Dr. E K Macdonald
AEA Industrial Technology
Harwell Laboratory, (UK)

Contract JOUE-0052-C (JR)

1 PARTICIPANTS

Universities

Dr. B Crittenden	Bath (UK)
Prof. D Tondeur	CNRS - ENSIC, Nancy (F)
Prof. F Meunier	CNRS - LIMSI, Orsay (F)
Prof. A Mersmann	München (D)
Prof. G Calleja	Madrid (E)
Prof. A Rodrigues	Oporto (P)

Research Laboratories

Dr. N Jorgensen	AEA Industrial Technology, Harwell (UK)
Dr. A Deschamps	Institut Français Du Petrole (F)
Dr. E Garcin	Rhône-Poulenc Recherches (F)

Industrial Sponsors

Mr. G Salzgeber	L'Air Liquide (F)
Mr. K Wieringa	Shell- KSLA (Nl)
Mr. S Tennyson	British Petroleum (UK)
Mr. R Fielding	Domnick Hunter Filters (UK)

2 SUMMARY

This project addresses the strategic R&D needs of the European process industries in the field of low energy separation processes, specifically the topic of gas adsorption. The energy requirement of separation processes in the chemical and allied industries can account for as much as 40% of total manufacturing costs, therefore any reduction in the energy consumption of separation stages has a major impact on the overall cost of final products. This programme of work on gas phase adsorption consists of a coordinated series of research projects aimed at improving the energy efficiency of methods used to separate and recover gaseous products, or to eliminate pollutants before gases are discharged to the atmosphere. The projects are essentially pre-competitive, fundamental research, the results of which could have applications in a wide range of process industries.

The work falls into two categories; the development of improved methods for obtaining reliable basic data, and the development of improved methods to aid process design. The projects concerning basic data will investigate the equilibria and kinetics of single-phase and multi-component systems, to develop new techniques for measuring these properties, and to provide better information for process design models. The work on process design is aimed at a better understanding of discrete steps in the adsorption cycle, and includes studies of pressure swing systems and non-isothermal systems. The data generated by the first set of projects will provide valuable input for these models. The process design studies will also include experiments to validate models, both under controlled laboratory conditions and at pilot plant scale.

3 INTRODUCTION

This paper outlines the work that is to be undertaken by the various research groups, and shows how the projects link together to form a coherent, coordinated programme of work. In this introduction, the use of adsorption processes and the benefits to industry are outlined briefly, as a justification for the project.

3.1 Technical Background

The ability of porous solids to adsorb large volumes of gases, vapours and liquids has long been recognized. Early applications were generally limited to purification processes, for example, the drying of gases and liquids, the removal of hydrogen sulphide and mercaptans from natural gas and the removal of organic pollutants from water. More recently, adsorption processes have become well established for the selective bulk separation of components in a mixture. Classic examples include the use of molecular sieves for air separation and for the separation of normal paraffins from iso paraffins. The main advantage of adsorption in comparison with other separation techniques is that moderate to high recoveries of the adsorbed component can be achieved whilst achieving a non-adsorbed stream of very high purity.

Adsorptive separation processes may be divided broadly into two classes:

(1) cyclic batch systems in which the adsorbent bed is alternately saturated and regenerated in a cyclic manner, and

(2) continuous flow systems in which generally there is continuous countercurrent contact between feed and adsorbent.

For any adsorptive separation process to be technically and economically viable, the adsorbent must have high selectivity and high capacity, whilst having good strength and good kinetic properties. Also, the adsorbent must be easily regenerated and must not suffer deactivation. Additionally, the process must be capable of being integrated into the surrounding process environment. The raw materials and methods for producing adsorbents must ultimately be inexpensive.

3.1.1 Selectivity

Selectivity, which is particularly important to this study, may depend on:

(a) differences in adsorption equilibria between components in a mixture, and

(b) differences in adsorption and/or desorption kinetics between components in a mixture.

Both aspects may be important in particular adsorbate-adsorbent systems.

Equilibrium separation factors depend upon the nature of the adsorbent surface, whether it be polar, non-polar, hydrophilic, hydrophobic, etc., and on process conditions such as temperature, pressure and composition.

Kinetic separations are generally, but not exclusively, possible only with molecular sieve adsorbents such as zeolites and carbon sieves. The kinetic selectivity is largely determined by the ratio of the micropore diffusivities of the components being separated. For a useful separation, the size of the adsorbent micropores must be comparable with the dimensions of the diffusing adsorbate molecules. Molecular sieve separations depend on the virtually complete exclusion of the larger molecules and may be considered to be an extreme case of a kinetic separation. An example of the latter is the separation of linear from branched paraffins on 5A molecular sieves, a process which is now in common use for improving the octane rating of gasoline.

3.1.2 Range of adsorbents available

Adsorbents are available in granular, spherical and extruded forms, with sizes generally in the range 0.5 to 8 mm. Other forms are available for special purposes and the manufacture of adsorbents in forms suitable for continuous process operation is one area identified by the author for future research and development.

3.1.2.1 Silica gel

Silica gel is a partially dehydrated polymeric form of colloidal silicic acid with the formula $SiO_2.nH_2O$. Its surface is polar and therefore it adsorbs water, alcohols, phenols, amines, etc. At low temperatures the ultimate capacity of silica gel for water is higher than alumina or molecular sieves. Silica gel is therefore used mainly as a desiccant and little further research on its applications seems necessary.

3.1.2.2 Activated alumina

Activated alumina is a porous high area form of aluminium oxide with the formula $Al_2O_3.nH_2O$. Its surface is more polar than that of silica gel and, reflecting the amphoteric nature of aluminium, has both acidic and basic characteristics. Activated alumina is also used mainly as a desiccant, for warmer gases and air, but has been replaced by molecular sieves. Little further research on its applications seems necessary.

3.1.2.3 Activated carbons

Activated carbons comprise elementary microcrystallites of graphite stacked in random orientation. They are made by the thermal decomposition of various carbonaceous materials followed by an activation process. Micropore diameters are generally less than 20 Å; macropore diameters are generally greater than 500 Å. The surface is essentially non-polar but surface oxidation may cause some slight polarity. In general, carbon adsorbents are hydrophobic and organophilic and they are used for water purification, decolourising, solvent recovery, vapour recovery and air purification. Carbons for liquid phase applications tend to have larger pore diameters. Although activated carbons show little selectivity for molecules of different size, it is possible to control the porosity, surface area and adsorptive capacity in the manufacturing process. Kinetic selectivity has been observed, for example with the separation of methane-ethane mixtures.

3.1.2.4 Carbon molecular sieves

Special activation procedures can produce porous carbons with a very narrow distribution of pore sizes, effective micropore diameters ranging from 4 Å to 9 Å. Raw materials include polyvinylidene dichloride, anthracite or hard coals. Adjustment of the manufacturing process conditions means that it is relatively easy to tailor a carbon molecular sieve for a particular separation process. Good kinetic selectivities may therefore be obtained, although adsorptive capacities are somewhat lower than for activated carbons and there are difficulties in maintaining reproducibility in the manufacturing process. The surface is essentially non-polar. Applications include air separation, principally to produce 99.9% nitrogen, but also for 50 to 90% oxygen, high purity hydrogen recovery from hydrogen-rich gases such as coke oven gas, the separation of ethene from ethane, n-butane from iso-butane, etc. Potential exists for a wide range of selective separations to emerge from the development and use of carbon molecular sieves.

3.1.2.5 Zeolites

Zeolites are porous crystalline aluminosilicates which consist of assemblies of SiO_4 and AlO_4 tetrahedra. Zeolites are distinct from other microporous adsorbents in that there is no distribution of pore size because the crystal lattice into which molecules can or cannot enter is precisely uniform. Each Al atom introduces a negative charge on the framework which is balanced by that of an exchangeable cation. In addition, the Si/Al ratio may be varied from unity to well over 1000. Thus zeolites with widely different adsorptive properties may be tailored, by the appropriate choice of framework structure, Si/Al ratio and cationic form, to achieve the selectivity required for a particular separation. Many zeolites are extremely polar and thus separations may be effected using both molecular sieving and surface properties. The kinetic selectivity is determined by the free diameters of the windows in the intracrystalline channel structure. Excellent potential exists for a wide range of selective separations to continue to emerge from the development and use of zeolites.

3.1.2.6 Polymers, resins, clays and miscellaneous adsorbents

A wide range of synthetic non-ionic polymers in bead form it still being developed for analytical chromatography. For preparative and industrial use, available resins are generally based on copolymers of styrene/di-vinyl benzene and acrylic acid esters/divinyl benzene to give a range of surface polarities. Some possess the macro-reticular pore structure which is available in ion exchange resins. Selective sorption properties are obtained from the structure, controlled distribution of pore size, high surface area and chemical nature of the matrix. By controlled pyrolysis of certain polymers, carbonaceous adsorbents with molecular sieving properties may also be obtained. Polymeric adsorbents are available for selective adsorption from gaseous and liquid (aqueous and non-aqueous) streams. Applications include the recovery of a wide range of solutes from the aqueous phase (phenol, benzene, toluene, chlorinated organics, Polychlorinated biphenyls (PCBs), pesticides, antibiotics, acetone, ethanol, detergents, emulsifiers, dyes, steroids, amino acids, etc.). Regeneration may be carried out by a variety of methods including steam desorption, solvent elution and chemical extraction. Good potential exists for selective separations based on polymer/resin adsorbents.

Like zeolites, clays can be synthesized or taken from natural deposits. Unlike zeolites, they are layer silicates which imbibe quest molecules between their anionic siliceous sheets causing their crystals to swell. Naturally occurring clays, like Fuller's earth, are relatively inexpensive and are generally used for re-refining of mineral oils, adsorption of toxic chemicals, removal of organic pigments, etc. Interest in using clays as adsorbents is growing, since they are of low cost and it is feasible to modify them.

Miscellaneous adsorbents include the use of polysaccharides, corn, peat and other naturally occurring materials mainly for the recovery of chemicals from dilute aqueous solution.

3.1.3 Process configurations

Cyclic batch adsorption processes differ mainly in the method of adsorbent regeneration. The choice between individual regeneration methods, or a combination, depends on both economic and technical factors, the principal ones being pressure or thermal swing systems, or displacement.

Continuous countercurrent contact maximises the driving force for mass transfer and should result in more efficient use of adsorbent capacity than in batch systems. Two methods have been used commercially:

(1) actually to circulate the adsorbent in packed or fluidised beds;

(2) to simulate adsorbent circulation by appropriate design of the fluid flow system; such systems include periodic countercurrent sorption in multiple-columns with desorption effected by conventional means, and the Sorbex (developed and licensed by UOP Inc.) simulated counter-current process in which a complex rotary valve arrangement alters the positions at which feed, product and desorbent streams enter and leave a fixed bed of adsorbent.

It is quite probable that, in parallel with developments in the design and manufacture of adsorbents, such processes and further developments in continuous processing will become increasingly more common in the future.

Chromatographic separations, in which the mixtures to be separated are injected as pulses into flowing streams of carrier fluid, are generally restricted in application to relatively small scale processes, such as the production of pharmaceuticals and fine chemicals. Scale-up appears to be difficult but on-going research and theoretical studies suggest that large scale units are feasible.

3.2 Use of Adsorption Processes

Applications of adsorption processes to effect air separations and solvent recovery have been proven to be energy efficient alternatives to conventional technology, and in some cases an economic benefit from reduced capital cost is also clear. It is a powerful technique in that it can be used to remove trace impurities from valuable products, or it can recover valuable components present in a mixture at low concentrations. Typical industrial applications include:

- drying of compressed air, natural gas, organic solvents by silica gel;
- hydrogen purification using activated alumina;
- air separation (N_2 production), hydrogen purification, solvent vapour emission control, CO_2 recovery using activated carbon;
- oxygen enrichment, water vapour removal prior to cryogenic processes, sulphide removal from hydrocarbon streams, separation of olefins from alkanes, ammonia recovery using zeolites;
- removal of metals, dyestuffs, colour, fatty acids, etc. from waste waters using resins, polymers or clays.

3.3 Pollution Control Applications

In addition to the benefits of recovering valuable products, adsorption also has a role to play in the control of environmental emissions. Emissions of Volatile Organic Compounds (VOCs) are a particular concern for today's environmental scientists, as they are precursors for the formation of photochemical oxidants and thus contribute to deforestation and other potentially harmful environmental phenomena. Similarly, odour emissions from food processing plants, gasoline vapour emissions from oil refineries, and oxides of sulphur and nitrogen from combustion processes are all major sources of environmental pollution for which control measures such as incineration, scrubbing, or refrigeration are moderately effective but also energy intensive. Adsorption processes to remove pollutants to a very low level have the potential to reduce atmospheric pollution significantly while at the same time reducing the energy cost to industry of implementing environmental control measures.

3.4 Benefits to the EEC of Improved Separation Process Efficiency

Industry uses more energy in separating and purifying products than in almost any other process operation, with the possible exception of chemical reaction. This is particularly so when separating products to high purity from very dilute mixtures, or where two products are present with similar physical properties but widely differing market values. It is important that these separations are performed as efficiently as possible to maximise yield and selectivity at minimum energy cost.

Examples of energy intensive separation processes that are commonly used in industry today include:

- gas separation, purification and enrichment using cryogenic distillation;
- recovery of volatile organic compounds (VOC's), or gas drying, using cryogenic condensation;

- separation of isomeric, or otherwise closely related chemicals using fractional distillation;
- azeotropic distillation of pure compounds from mixtures with water.

All these processes require substantial energy inputs to achieve the desired level of separation or purity, and there are significant benefits to be gained by developing alternative, low energy separation routes.

4 OBJECTIVES

The overall objective of the proposed research programme is to devise a comprehensive methodology for the development and design of adsorption processes. This implies two distinct goals which can be summarised as follows:

1. To reduce the dependence on empirical methods for the process of adsorbent design, column design and process design, by enhancing the scientific understanding of adsorption processes, developing improved models and validating them on a range of scales.

2. To bring together existing and future knowledge and data on adsorption thermodynamics, kinetics and adsorbent properties in a structured, standardized, and accessible form.

In order to achieve these goals, the research encompasses the whole range of scales involved, from molecular studies of surface phenomena to pilot plant trials to verify design correlations. The benefits to industry will be seen through effective use of adsorption processes in the appropriate applications, and greatly increased energy efficiency of separation compared with traditional gas separations such as cryogenic or distillation processes.

5 TASKS OF PARTICIPANTS

5.1 Basic Data

This facet of the programme makes up the bulk of the work. The emphasis of the projects is the development and validation of alternative methodologies for obtaining multi-component equilibrium and kinetic data. As a result, the individual group contributions are considerably enhanced by the interactions in this programme. By carrying out a thorough cross comparison of results between the various groups, it will be possible to develop guidelines as to the reliability of particular method, and the degree of confidence that can be placed in the resulting data. The projects cover, in varying degrees, the measurement of multi-component data and reconciliation of that data with different models for predicting the results.

Table 1 summarises the key objectives and targets of each project. For ease of reference, the projects have been coded type B (Basic Data), type C (Co-ordination), or type D (Process Design). The proposals have been developed by individual laboratories in close contact with the industrial partners of the proposed consortium and with close consultation with other collaborating laboratories. As a result, duplication of effort has been avoided, and the collaborative links both between research groups and at the academic/industrial interface have been strengthened. The links between the projects are shown in Figure 1.

5.1.1 CNRS - ENSIC, Nancy (Project B1.)

Institut National Polytechnique de Lorraine, Nancy, will develop a method for obtaining multi-component equilibrium and kinetic data using gas chromatography. There is a lack of reliable data on multi-component mixtures, and predictive methods of obtaining such data are weak. This project aims to develop a reliable, standardized method that can be implemented rapidly. Collaboration with other research groups and industry will provide data obtained by other methods for cross comparison, and for validation of the new methodology proposed.

5.1.2 University of Porto (Project B2.)

The University of Porto has extensive skills in the measurement of transport properties of gases on the surface of adsorbents. They intend to develop techniques for the measurement of intra-particle diffusivity, permeability, and thermal conductivity of zeolites and large pore adsorbents. The knowledge gained from such studies will enable better mathematical relationships to be developed to relate the kinetics of adsorption and regeneration to the structure of adsorbent materials. The thermal conductivity data will also be valuable for use in the modelling of adsorbers by computational fluid dynamics. The methods proposed are to be used in synergy with the chromatographic method of Nancy for equilibrium measurements.

5.1.3 Harwell Laboratory (Project B3.)

Harwell Laboratory intends to investigate the kinetics and mechanisms of desorption processes, building on many years' experience in this field, particularly in the study of the desorption of water vapour from a wide range of solids - not confined to traditionally recognized adsorbents. Existing experimental facilities are available to study the rate of desorption of a range of gases, at operating conditions up to 40 bar and 650°C.

These studies will provide much needed basic data on regeneration phenomena, but more importantly they will establish standardised test procedures for evaluating desorption isotherms, and help refine theoretical models of adsorption and desorption. This will reduce the requirements for experimental measurements at the preliminary stages of process development.

The interactions between these three groups will enhance the individual contributions and the results from these studies will assist companies in identifying the most appropriate adsorbent for a specified application.

5.1.4 University of Madrid (Project B4.)

The University of Madrid will undertake a study of the equilibria of gases on zeolite molecular sieves. Building on their extensive experience of obtaining experimental data and developing predictive mathematical models, the group proposes to compare the behaviour of different types of zeolites. Different zeolite structures can lead to ideal gas mixtures becoming non-ideal under certain conditions, and *vice-versa*, which affects the choice of theoretical methods appropriate for modelling of multi-component equilibria. Understanding how this behaviour can be influenced will provide valuable knowledge from which guidelines on adsorbent selection can be based. The data will also be used for cross-comparison with the results of Nancy and München.

5.1.5 Technical University of München (Project B5.)

The University of München aims to develop a generalised method of predicting ternary equilibrium data from binary data, and also kinetic data, from detailed study of the system CO_2:C_2H_4:C_2H_6 on 5A zeolite. This is a complex, non-ideal mixture for which established models fail, and is therefore a very good system for analysis. It is also an industrially relevant mixture, with more attention focussing nowadays on the use of adsorption for light hydrocarbon separations as an alternative to cryogenic distillation. The equilibrium data obtained by experiment will be used for cross-comparison with those of Nancy and Madrid.

5.1.6 CNRS - LIMSI, Orsay (Project B6.)

In addition, the ***Centre Nationale de Recherche Scientifique (CNRS), Orsay*** also has experience of working on multi-component adsorption systems. They will develop a model to describe simultaneous heat and mass transfer for multi-component gas flowing in an adsorber. This model will then be validated in collaboration with IFP (see section 5.2.2), and cross-checked with that of München, particularly with respect to extracting thermo-kinetic data from experimental measurements.

5.1.7 Rhône-Poulenc Récherches (Project B7.)

To ensure that consistent results can be obtained, it is important that the quality of the adsorbents in use can be standardised across the working groups. ***Rhône-Poulenc*** Recherches will provide adsorbents, fully characterised from common batches, to the research workers, and to measure a range of equilibrium data using classical methods for comparison with other groups.

5.2 Process Design

Good process design methodology is based on a sound understanding of the fundamental scientific principles involved, tempered with an appreciation that detailed analysis on a micro-scale may not always be justified in the design of large process plants. To this end, the studies are intended to build on the fundamental basic data but balancing this scientific knowledge with empirical relationships where appropriate.

5.2.1 Bath University (Project D1.)

The University of Bath will model the dynamics of pressure swing adsorption (PSA) systems, with specific attention paid to the pressurisation and blow-down steps. Although PSA is firmly established as a proven technology, much remains to be achieved in developing the process towards its optimum efficiency. A key parameter in optimizing the process is the cycle time, and reduced cycle times can give rise to significant benefits in reducing plant size and operating cost. As the cycle time is reduced, the dynamic response of the system becomes more complex, and current PSA models are unable to take full account of this as cycle times become reduced. A rigourous model is therefore required which can be used to design rapid cycle PSA plants, as well as to study the controllability of the system.

In this project, Bath will collaborate closely with ***The University of Porto***. The discrete step models developed by Bath will be incorporated into a simple equilibrium model developed by Porto, and tested experimentally using equipment already available to Porto. These studies will also be compared with the results of experiments performed at IFP (see section 5.2.2 below).

5.2.2 Institut Français du Petrole (Project D2.)

Institut Français du Petrole (IFP) has a wide range of laboratory and pilot plant facilities, and will use its facilities to validate models for hydrocarbon separations (normal/iso paraffins) and for fuel gas fractionation. These models will be made available to industrial collaborators for incorporation into in-house process design and simulation tools for testing on real industrial applications.

5.2.3 Harwell Laboratory (Project D3.)

Harwell Laboratory has for many years been at the forefront of process design technology, by developing thoroughly validated methods for the design of equipment based on experimental results and scale-up studies. This expertise will be brought to bear to consolidate the results from the fundamental studies described in the previous sections. This will result in a comparison of adsorption with classical and conventional separation processes such as distillation and cryogenics, leading to the identification of suitable candidate processes for further study and development as demonstration adsorption plants. Out of this work will emerge the key process parameters and properties which are necessary to select and design an adsorption process.

5.3 Project Co-ordination (Project C1.)

Harwell Laboratory will manage the overall project, co-ordinating the interactions between the individual projects through regular progress reviews and reports. Co-ordination will be aided by a Technical Advisory Committee (TAC), consisting of representatives of all participating organizations, including industrial sponsors. This will ensure that the best experts in the various technical areas are available to advise on the direction of projects and the interpretation of the results. It will also ensure liaison between the main project areas, and link where necessary with other relevant areas of research commissioned by the CEC under this programme. Results of the research will also be presented at appropriate CEC meetings.

6 PRELIMINARY RESULTS

Approval for the project has only recently been received. A meeting of the technical advisory committee has been held to agree common systems for study and to formally launch the project. The research groups are currently establishing the experimental facilities, recruiting the appropriate staff and planning the detailed experimental and theoretical programme. There are no meaningful results to report as yet.

7 FUTURE R&D

Because the project is at such an early stage, it is not possible to draw conclusions from any results concerning future R&D requirements in this field. That there are many more highly relevant areas to be explored is not in question; it will, however, be necessary to prioritise these in the light of results obtained from the present programme in due course. For the moment, possible areas of study might include:

- An extension of basic data studies to compile a readily accessible, properly validated data bank with interfaces to common process modelling software
- Studying combined adsorption/reaction systems
- Coupling the work with Computational Fluid Dynamics (CFD) studies
- Extension of the programme to include liquid phase systems
- Model reduction, to reduce the computational requirements of process models and provide readily available, short cut design tools
- The study of kinetically driven adsorptive separations
- A general expansion into the study of chromatographic processes
- Characterisation and understanding adsorptive materials
- The study of carbon based systems for pollutant removal.

It is certain, however, that the use of adsorption processes as an alternative separation route for gaseous products holds great potential for reducing the energy requirements of some industrial sectors by a significant factor. The project team assembled to undertake the current programme of research includes some of the best chemical engineering R&D expertise available in Europe today, and it is only by supporting such multi-disciplinary projects that European industry will be able to compete with the work underway in Japan and North America. Therefore the participants in this project will be seeking to extend the work in industrially relevant fields by building on the collaborations that have been made possible by the JOULE programme.

8 REFERENCES

Crittenden, B.D. *Selective adsorption.* Review of adsorption research commissioned by UK Science & Engineering Research Council (1987)

Reay, D., Pilavachi, P.A. *Needs for strategic R&D in support of improved energy efficiency in the process industries.* EEC Report EUR 11920 EN (1989)

Fair, J.R. *Adsorption/desorption technology review.* Fluid mixture separation technologies, Chapter 5, pp. 154 - 184 (1988)

TABLE 1.
Summary of Main Targets of Proposed Research

Project Code	Lead Laboratory	Year 1 Targets	Year 2 Targets
B1	Nancy	Data analysis software development Experimental design Measurement of multi-component equilibrium data Results comparison	Continue measurements Refine experimental set-up and software as required Simultaneous perturbation and desorption measurements Results comparison
B2	Porto	Establish experimental facilities Measurement of transport properties PSA experiments	Measurement of transport properties (cont) PSA experiments (cont) PSA modelling Comparison of results with Bath
B3	Harwell	Review existing regeneration models Data collection	Development of predictive tools Comparison of models with experimental data Scale up from powders to larger beds of pellets
B4	Madrid	Establish experimental procedure Equilibrium data measurements Comparison of data with theory	Characteristic adsorption equilibrium curves Evaluation of predictive models Conclusions on adsorbent selection and use of predictive models
B5	München	Establish experimental technique Measurement of equilibrium data Model development	Model refinement Predictive modelling in comparison with experiments Comparison of results with other groups Short cut design procedure
B6	CNRS- LIMSI	Experimental measurement of kinetic data for gases on bidisperse adsorbents Analysis of results Model development	Model testing and validation Comparison of results with other groups
B7	Rhône-Poulenc	Supply and characterisation of adsorbents Measurement of equilibrium data	
D1	Bath	Establish fundamental mathematical model Test model experimentally	Refinement of models and experiments Comparison of results with Porto
D2	IFP	Acquisition of experimental data at bench scale and pilot scale	Simulation of experiments using collaborators models Validation of models
D3	Harwell		Critical evaluation of programme results Determination adsorbent selection guidelines Specification of appropriate experimental procedures Methods to determine bulk process parameters
C1	Harwell	Definition of common systems for experiments Co-ordinate progress reports Chair TAC Meetings	Further progress reports Liaison with other JOULE projects Collation and assessment of results Preparation of final report

FIGURE 1.
Links between Projects

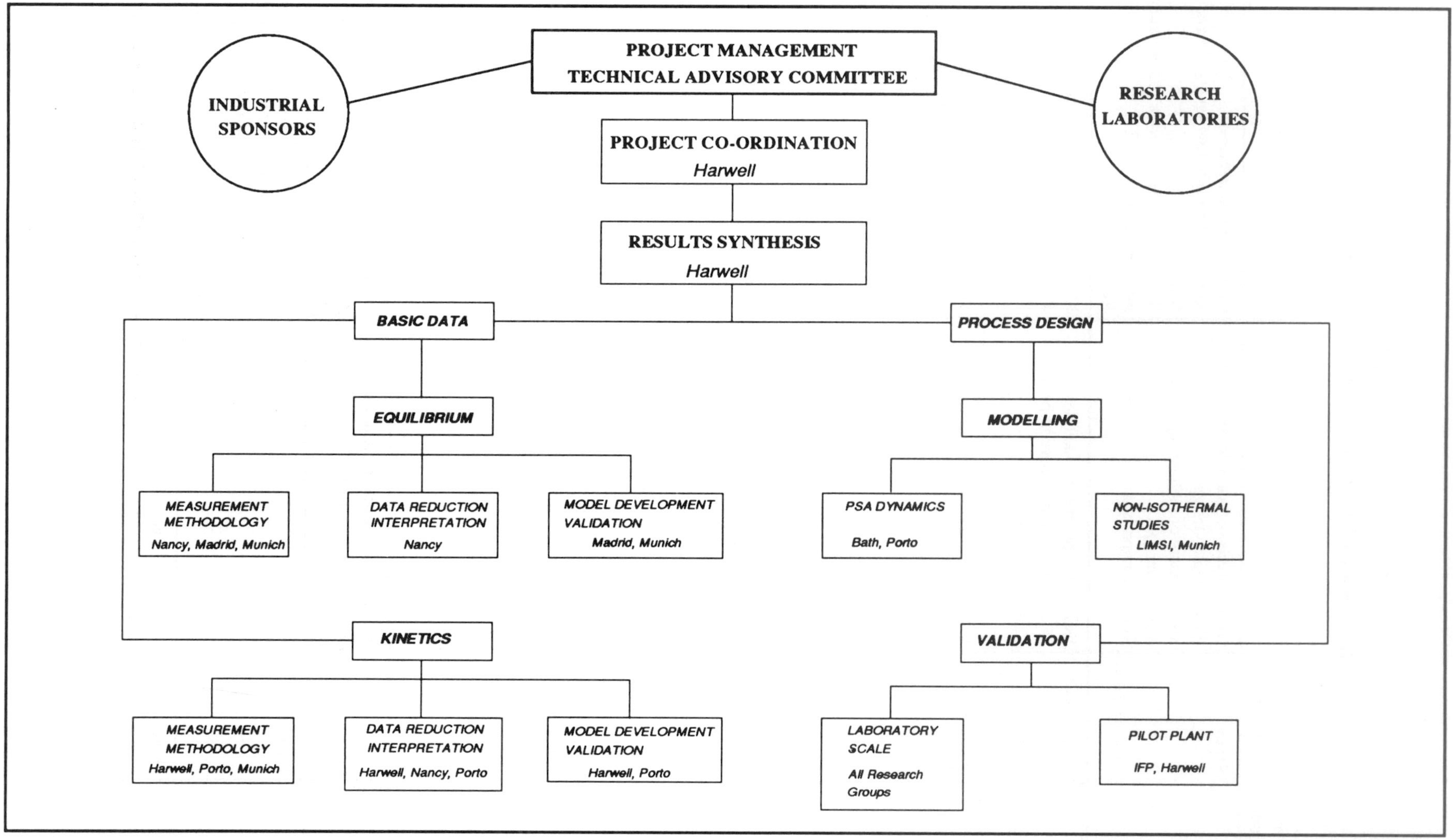

INDUSTRIAL SPONSORS

PROJECT MANAGEMENT
TECHNICAL ADVISORY COMMITTEE

RESEARCH LABORATORIES

PROJECT CO-ORDINATION
Harwell

RESULTS SYNTHESIS
Harwell

BASIC DATA

EQUILIBRIUM

MEASUREMENT METHODOLOGY
Nancy, Madrid, Munich

DATA REDUCTION INTERPRETATION
Nancy

MODEL DEVELOPMENT VALIDATION
Madrid, Munich

KINETICS

MEASUREMENT METHODOLOGY
Harwell, Porto, Munich

DATA REDUCTION INTERPRETATION
Harwell, Nancy, Porto

MODEL DEVELOPMENT VALIDATION
Harwell, Porto

PROCESS DESIGN

MODELLING

PSA DYNAMICS
Bath, Porto

NON-ISOTHERMAL STUDIES
LIMSI, Munich

VALIDATION

LABORATORY SCALE
All Research Groups

PILOT PLANT
IFP, Harwell

IMPROVEMENT OF MELT CRYSTALLIZATION'S EFFICIENCY FOR INDUSTRIAL APPLICATIONS

PARTICIPANTS

Dr. G.J. Arkenbout
TNO - Division of Technology for Society
Department of Chemical Engineering
P.O. Box 342
7300 AH Apeldoorn, The Netherlands

Contract JOUE-0031-C

Prof. Dr. P. Bennema
University of Nijmegen
Laboratory of Solid State Chemistry

Dr.ing. J. Ulrich
Universität Bremen
Verfahrenstechnik/FB Produktionstechnik

Dr.ing. G. Wellinghoff
BASF Aktiengesellschaft
Technische Entwicklung, ZET/SR, L549

SUMMARY

Ultrapurification of organic chemicals is very difficult and energy consuming when conventional methods are used (e.g. distillation) as is the separation of close boiling mixtures. Melt crystallization appears to be an energy- and cost efficient separation method for these applications. To be able to profit fully from the potential savings in energy and costs, a single step separation process should be aimed at. Therefore, this EC JOULE project will focus on the investigation of the basic mechanisms of mass transfer between crystals and liquid to improve the separation efficiency of this new technology.

The following topics will be studied:
- the mechanisms by which, and the process conditions under which, molecules of impurities are incorporated or included into crystal lattices;
- whether and under which conditions molecules of impurities can be transferred from the crystal phase to the melt.

These items will be investigated in the case of:
* crystals in suspension like in a crystallizer
* crystal layers grown on the wall of a heat exchanger and
* crystals e.g. in a packed bed in crystal-liquid separation columns.

A comparison between processes based on the growth of crystals as layers or in suspension will be made. It is expected, that the increased knowledge will result in higher product purity, higher yield and lower production costs.

INTRODUCTION TO PRESENT RESEARCH

General

Melt crystallization appears to be an energy- and cost efficient method to ultrapurify organic compounds and to separate organic mixtures having close boiling points. Melt crystallization seems to be the only feasible technique for the ultrapurification of quite a number of monomers needed for the manufacture of high-tech polymers.

In melt crystallization, solid material is crystallized from the liquid feed without the use of an auxiliary agent like a solvent. The solid material is melted under the process conditions and the melt taken off as the product. The separation effect is large due to the high selectivity by which molecules from a melt may be built into a crystal lattice. The status of development of melt crystallization has been reported at the previous European Seminar on improved energy efficiency in the process industries [1]. The possibility of upgrading fine chemicals by melt crystallization has already been demonstrated on a laboratory scale for more than 200 compounds using the zone melting technique [2]. The feasibility of upgrading bulk organic materials has already been indicated for about 25 compounds like acrylic acid, phenol and caprolactam corresponding with a total world capacity of about 30 millions tons per year. A survey of industrial applications of melt crystallization is given in [3].

Energy saving potential

A study on the energy saving potential of melt crystallization has been reported recently [4]. In general terms it may be said, that melt crystallization's energy requirement in principle is low, because the large separation effect results in a very limited need of reflux. Moreover, the heat of transition in crystallization is 2 to 5 times less than in distillation. In practice, the energy requirement in distillation per kg. product corresponds with 1.2 to 4.0 times the heat of vaporization. However, these requirements can be reduced by heat integration (sometimes up to a maximum of 80%) [4]. The melt crystallization processes, applied in the chemical industry at present, usually show a limited separation efficiency. In such a multistage crystallization process a repetition of the crystallization operation is needed then. The energy consumption per kg. product may increase to 10 or more times the heat of crystallization. The energy requirement of melt crystallization could be reduced considerably, when the purification wanted could be established in one single crystallization operation. Therefore, this EC project was started to improve the process efficiency of melt crystallization. The main interest of chemical industry in melt crystallization focusses on specific separation problems, which cannot be solved by distillation at all. Some examples are:

- ultrapurification of organic compounds like pharmaceuticals, fine chemicals and starting materials for new polymers. The need for ultrapure organic compounds increases strongly. Purities up to 99.999 wt% are required;
- separation of organic mixtures, which cannot be realized by distillation like aromatic isomers and azeotropic mixtures, especially those containing water;

- replacing of crystallization from a solution by crystallization from the melt. In solution crystallization the solvent has to be recycled by distillation. Replacing of solution crystallization by melt crystallization may result, therefore, in a substantial energy saving. Moreover, the removal of the solvent is of great environmental importance, because the required recirculation of solvent may easily lead to an unwanted pollution [5]. So the interest of chemical industry in melt crystallization increases, as this technique shows exclusive features to solve industrial separation problems in an energy- and cost efficient way. The added value of increased product purity, the increase of recovery due to less product decomposition, an improved process efficiency, a lower environmental impact, energy saving and cost reduction are the driving forces to develop further the technology of melt crystallization.

Kinetic limits of purification

The separation efficiency of melt crystallization may be limited both by thermodynamics and kinetics. The limiting effect due to crystallization kinetics may become very large, especially when the concentration of impurities is high. The mass transfer from solid to liquid is difficult to realize under normal conditions in melt crystallization processes. Therefore, the process is usually repeated using the impure product as a starting material, when the purity aimed at is not obtained in one single operation. This repetition, however, is costly and decreases the possible economic advantage over competitive techniques. Therefore, this EC JOULE research project on melt crystallization is focussed on improving the process efficiency. In literature, a model has been reported [6,7] to predict the impurity content of the crystals in dependance on linear crystallization rate, the mass transfer coefficient and the concentration of impurities in the melt.
The relation between k -eff: the effective distribution coefficient (being the ratio between the impurity contents of crystals and melt) and the linear growth rate for a mass transfer coefficient of $2.5.10^{-5}$ m/s is shown in figure 1. It follows from figure 1, that k -eff increases strongly, when increasing the linear growth rate. This means, that a high purity in one single crystallization stage is feasible only when sufficiently low linear growth rates are applied. When crystallizing a melt containing 10 wt% of impurities and aiming at a product purity of 99.99 wt%, an effective distribution coefficient k -eff of 0.001% has to be obtained. Such a low effective distribution coefficient can be established in one single crystallization operation when dealing with eutectic systems showing no solid solubility, but only when linear growth rates of lower than 10^{-7} m/s are applied as follows from figure 1 and the experimental data reported in literature.

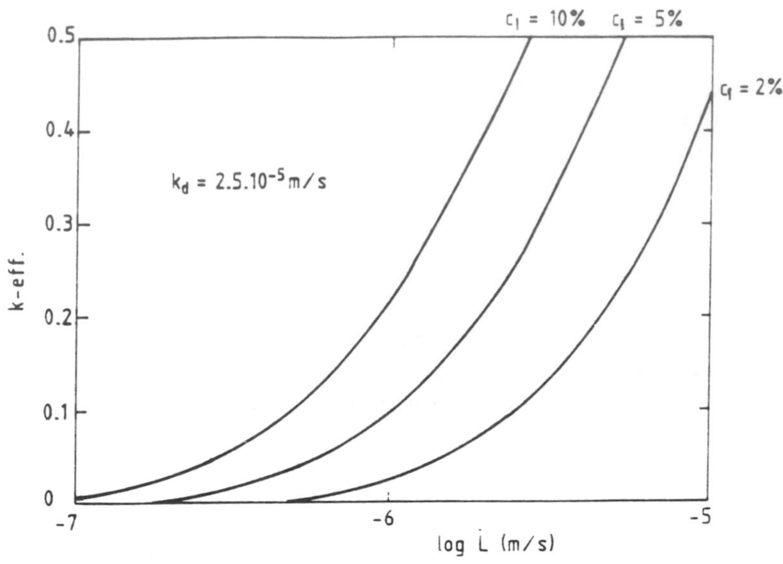

Figure 1. The relation between k -eff and linear growth rate for several concentrations

k -eff: effective distribution coefficient;
$\dot{L}$: linear growth rate [m s^{-1}];
k_d : mass transfer coefficient [m s^{-1}]
c_l : concentration of impurities in the melt [kg m^{-3}]

Process options

Two types of technical processes can be distinguished [1,7,8]. The first type is characterized by the formation of a crystal layer on the heat exchanger wall (see figure 2). Well known examples are the Proabd refiner and the Sulzer MWB process. This type of processes shows the strong advantage that no solids handling is required. The drawback, however, is the relatively low separation efficiency due to the large growth velocity applied. A rate of layer growth of only 3.6 mm per hour resulting in 3.6 kg per m² heat exchanging surface per hour already corresponds with the large linear growth velocity of 10^{-6} m/s resulting in a substantial incorporation of impurities due to kinetics. Technical equipment may contain heat exchanging pipes with a length of 5 m. and an inner diameter of 25 mm. providing a heat exchanging surface of 30 m²/m³ with a crystal growth capacity of 100 kg/m³ hour. The crystal layer is usually grown from a liquid film. Unfortunately, optimal hydrodynamic conditions resulting in a large mass transfer coefficient cannot be established in such a liquid film reducing the upgrading efficiency due to the kinetic incorporation of impurities as was shown in the foregoing section. As a result the process has to be repeated several times with partly upgraded feedstocks to obtain high purity, decreasing the energy and cost effectiveness of this upgrading technique. The separation efficiency may be improved by sweating and by in situ washing. Quite a number of technical applications have been reported using layer growth processes, especially in Europe. The installed capacity for organics in North America is expected to be 400.000 metric tons per year at the end of 1992 [9] showing the market need for this type of processes.

Figure 2
Principle of crystal layer growth

1 heat exchanger tube;
2 cooling/heating;
3 feed;
4 residue, sweating liquid, product;
5 pump;
6 cooling;
7 crystal layer;
8 liquid film

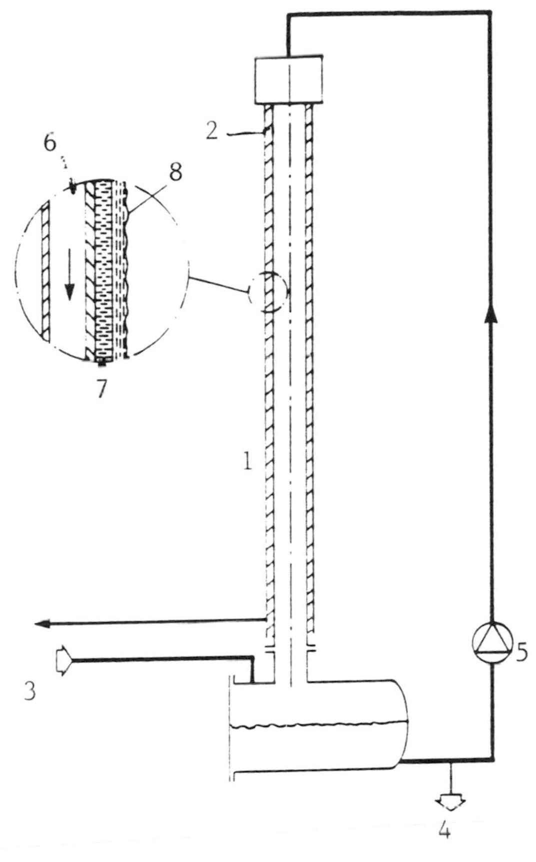

Figure 3
Principle of suspension growth

1 crystallizer containing two scraped heat exchangers;
2 further purification of crystals;
3 separation of crystals and melting;
4 feed;
5 suspension;
6 waste;
7 product

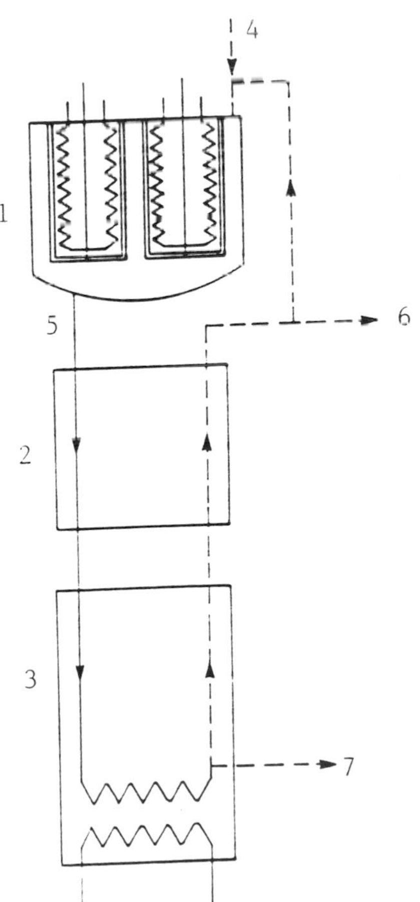

In processes based on suspension growth (see figure 3) a liquid feed enters the crystallizer, where the crystals are grown in suspension by indirect cooling through a heat exchanger wall. When assuming a suspension containing 30 vol% of crystals and the crystals being spheres with a diameter of 200 μm it can be easily calculated, that the surface area of the crystals amounts to 10.000 m^2/m^3 suspension. A low rate of linear growth of say 10^{-8} m/s will result in a crystal mass of 360 kg/m^3 hour. As follows from figure 1 such a low growth rate makes the attainment of a high upgrading efficiency in one single crystallization feasible for eutectic systems provided, that a complete separation between crystals and melt can be established. The average particle size obtainable in suspension growth processes, is the result of both the nucleation- and the growth rate. As will be clear, a high nucleation rate will hamper the growth of satisfactorily large crystals. The nucleation rate may be strongly influenced by the chemical composition of the system. The average crystal size obtained determines the choice of the required solid-liquid separation device. An efficient separation of crystals from the melt can be realized using packed or non-packed separation columns [1,7,8]. Companies in Japan prefer the use of non-packed columns whereas TNO promotes the use of packed columns, as a complete separation between crystals and melt can be established more efficiently using such a separation column.

A number of technical applications can be mentioned for suspension growth processes. Generally spoken it must be said however, that suspension growth processes are less mature than layer growth processes.
Substantial projects are proceeding, however, especially in Japan, aimed at a further development because of their promising features. From the point of energy- and cost efficiency it is important, that the ultrapurification aimed at can be attained in one single crystallization operation.
Unfortunately, the mechanisms of including and extracting impurities in and from crystals are not yet understood satisfactorily. Such a basic knowledge has to be gathered before the rate of further purifying crystals can be increased to satisfactory values. Therefore, this joint European research project focusses on the collection of basic knowledge to improve the energy efficiency of the melt crystallization.

OBJECTIVES OF PRESENT RESEARCH

The objective of this project is to improve melt crystallization's efficiency by elucidating the mechanisms of incorporating impurities into crystals and of extracting impurities out of crystals into the melt phase. Improved design procedures and/or devices resulting from this study will lead to higher product purity, higher yield and lower production costs (decrease of investment costs and energy savings). A comparison between processes based on the growth of crystals as layers or in suspension will be made and guidelines will be drafted for the selection of equipment. It is also expected that, due to increased knowledge, it will be possible to make better estimates on the feasibility of melt crystallization for new compounds.

TASKS OF PARTICIPANTS

The research program will be carried out in close cooperation by TNO-MT, Apeldoorn, NL, University of Nijmegen, NL, University of Bremen, DE, and BASF, Ludwigshafen, DE. Prof.dr. J.N. Sherwood and Dr. K. Roberts of the University of Strathclyde, Glasgow, GB and Prof.ir. E.J. de Jong, NL will be consultants in the project. The scope of the project is surveyed in table 1 and the outline of the program summarizing the tasks of each participant in table 2. The tables 3, 4, 5 and 6 outline the contributions of each participant. As follows from these tables the four research groups carry out four complementary programs. The results of each group will be of large interest to all four participants.

By a strong integration of the four sub-programs it is aimed at to obtain a maximum out of the research efforts.

PRELIMINARY RESULTS

The main activities in this first period of 2 months were focussed on:
- selection of experimental techniques
- choice of test materials
- defining of analytical procedures
- integration of research contributions.

The University of Bremen and BASF will apply test equipment being already available. TNO has redesigned and manufactured a small 100 ml. crystallizer permitting crystal growth and recrystallization tests without nucleation. Moreover TNO has redesigned and manufactured a 3 litre crystallizer allowing the application of the MSMPR (mixed suspension mixed product removal) theory in the crystallization kinetics tests. The University of Nijmegen designs a rotating disk crystallizer to carry out single crystal growth tests under well defined hydrodynamic conditions. This crystallizer will provide possibilities to grow a crystal both under the conditions of a layer growth process and a suspension growth process. Two test substances will be applied. The first compound is caprolactam. It is agreed upon to use a product quality sample to which a known amount of a distinct impurity is added. It has yet to be decided whether cyclohexane or cyclohexanone will be chosen as the impurity depending on the availability of the physical data of both compounds. Naphthalene is considered as the second test compound and biphenyl as the impurity to be added. At present, it is verified whether a suitable product quality sample can be obtained and whether the physical data needed for the evaluation of the experimental results will be available. The four research groups will all use test samples composed of the same batch of main compound and apply identical analytical techniques. The groups will check the analytical data obtained from each other. It is aimed at to do the tests at well defined process conditions permitting a comparison of the results obtained by each group.

FUTURE R&D

Besides from the EC, NOVEM (Netherlands Agency for Energy and the Environment) and TNO financial contributions were obtained for project JOUE-0031-C from 5 large chemical industries (1x BE, 2x DE, 1x IT, 1x NE) and 3 equipment suppliers (3x NE) showing the interest of chemical industry in the technology for melt crystallization. It follows from interviews with representatives of the chemical industry, that industry is very interested in the suspension growth option as this process option offers the outlook to attain ultrapure organic compounds in one single crystallization operation [see also 4]. In Japan, a couple of companies like Tsukishima Kikai Co., Nippon Steel Chemical Co. and Kureha are involved in the further development of suspension growth processes whereas Grenco PT/NE is the only equipment supplier being active in this field in Europe and no specific processes are being developed in the United States. A number of chemical industries started applied research projects in the course of their own research programs to evaluate the technical feasibility of suspension growth processes. It appears, that still some basic knowledge is lacking hampering the further development of suspension growth melt crystallization. This missing knowledge could be collected very efficiently in a precompetitive R&D program partly financed by the EC. In consultation with chemical industry TNO has collected a number of research topics suitable for such a R&D program. The items collected have been grouped to two concept projects summarized in the tables 7 and 8. The first project deals with improving the procedures for separating crystals from the melt and for further purification of the crystals. The second project concerns the evaluation of crystallizer types, control of crystal size and development of design criteria. We propose to compose the actual program of a number of research items selected from the tables 7 and 8 with the help of industry. We propose to incorporate the specific expertise of some leading crystallization groups of Universities in the EC. Besides the crystallization groups of the Universities of Nijmegen, NE, and Bremen, DE, the crystallization groups of Prof.dr. J.P. Klein, Université Claude Bernard Lyon 1, F, [10] and Prof.dr. Garside, UMIST, Manchester, UK, could give very essential contributions to such a program.

REFERENCES

[1] Melt Crystallization, Arkenbout, G.J., Energy Efficiency in Industrial Processes, Future R&D Requirements, Report EUR 12046 EN, 1988, P.A. Pilavachi Ed, p 67-97

[2] Fractional Solidification Vol 1., Ed by M. Zief and W.R. Wilcox, Marcel Dekker, Inc, New York, 1967

[3] Die Schmelzkristallisation von organischen Stoffen und ihre grosztechnische Anwendung, Rittner, S., Steiner R., Chemie Ingenieur Technik 57, 91-102 (1985)

[4] Melt Crystallization - Theoretical Presumption and Technical Limits, Wintermantel K, Wellinghoff G., Proceedings of the 11th Symposium on Industrial Crystallization, Ed by A. Mersmann, VDI, Verlag GmbH, Düsseldorf, FRG, 1990, p 703-708

[5] Rittner, S., Workshop on Melt Crystallization, 11th Symposium on Industrial Crystallization, Garmisch Partenkirchen, FRG, September 1990

[6] Die effective Trennwirkung beim Ausfrieren von Kristallschichten aus Schmelzen und Lösungen - eine einheitliche Darstellung, Wintermantel K, Chemie Ingenieur Technik 58 (6), 498-499 (1986)/MS 1493/86

[7] Improving Melt Crystallization's Upgrading Efficiency, Arkenbout, G.J., Nienoord M., Jong, E.J. de, Paper no. 69b, Annual AIChE Meeting, San Francisco, 1989

[8] On the Choice of Crystallization Processes from the Melt, Arkenbout G.J., Nienoord M., de Jong E.J., Proceedings of the 11th Symposium on Industrial Crystallization, Ed by A. Mersmann, VDI, Verlag GmbH, Düsseldorf FRG, 1990, p 715-720

[9] Techniques of Industrial Crystallization; State of the Business, Jancic S.J., Proceedings Bremer International Workshop for Industrial Crystallization, Ed J. Ulrich, 1990, p. 42-49

[10] On the Industrial Crystallization of Organic Products from the Solution, J.P. Klein, Proceedings Bremer International Workshop for Industrial Crystallization, Ed J. Ulrich, 1990, Session 5, paper 15.

Table 1. SURVEY OF SCOPE OF EC PROJECT

IMPROVEMENT OF MELT CRYSTALLIZATION'S EFFICIENCY FOR INDUSTRIAL APPLICATIONS

- fields of application
  * upgrading to ultrapurity
  * isomers, close boiling systems
- two process options
  * crystal layer growth
  * suspension growth
- process efficiency
  * purity
  * yield
  * energy- and cost efficiency
- objective
  * improvement of melt crystallization's efficiency
- specific objectives
  * study on the mechanisms/kinetics of
    - incorporating impurities into crystals
    - transferring impurities from crystals into the melt
  * comparison of processes based on
    - layer growth
    - suspension growth
  * technical evaluation
- purity crystals (product) limited by
  * solid solution
  * kinetics
  * adhering liquid
- improvement by
  * sweating: removing impurities like included liquid pockets out of crystals and crystal layers under influence of a temperature gradient over the crystal (layer) and/or by partial melting
  * recrystallization: removing impurities out of the crystal lattice by a partial melting and recrystallization under adiabatic conditions
  * washing: removing liquid containing impurities adhering to crystals and crystal layers

Table 2. OUTLINE OF PROGRAM

SURVEY OF TASKS OF EACH PARTICIPANT

Study on the mechanisms/kinetics of

- crystal growth

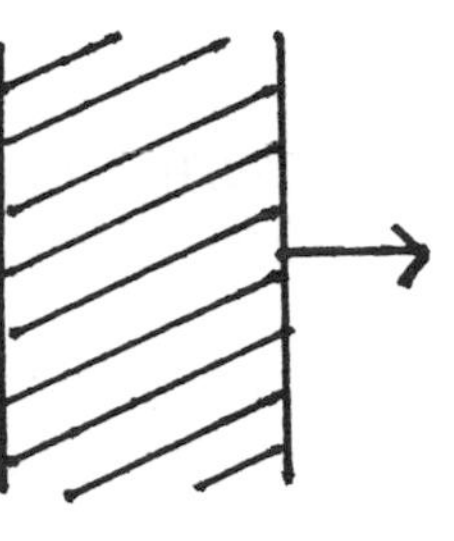

- sweating,
  recrystallization

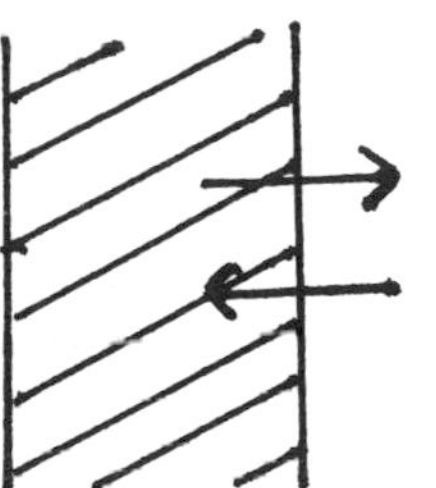

in the case of:

* single crystal: U of Nijmegen

* suspension: TNO/U of Nijmegen

* crystal layer: U of Bremen
  BASF

* separation from melt: TNO

Table 3. OUTLINE OF TNO'S CONTRIBUTION

TNO'S CONTRIBUTION FOCUSSES ON THE INVESTIGATION OF CRYSTALS IN SUSPENSION AND CRYSTALS TO BE PROCESSED IN SEPARATION COLUMNS

- Crystals in suspension

  * kinetics distribution coefficient
  * recrystallization, sweating
  * crystal growth kinetics

- Crystal separation columns

  * sweating crystal bed, recrystallization
  * sweating, recrystallization's suspended crystals
  * two stage operation

- Technological evaluation
  together with BASF and U of Bremen

Table 4. OUTLINE OF THE CONTRIBUTION OF THE UNIVERSITY OF NIJMEGEN

THE CONTRIBUTION OF NIJMEGEN FOCUSSES ON SINGLE CRYSTAL GROWTH AND FUNDAMENTALS

- inventory basic data
- kinetics single crystal growth
  in dependance on concentration and supercooling
- prediction of crystal habit
- measurement of driving forces for growing and melting a single crystal
- influence of stress fields on melting rate.

Table 5. OUTLINE OF THE CONTRIBUTION OF THE UNIVERSITY OF BREMEN INVESTIGATION ON LAYER CRYSTALLIZATION PROCESSES

- crystal layer growth at the wall of a pipe
  * analysis of temperature and concentration profiles in the boundary layer
  * procedure for growing crystal layers without pores
  * kinetic distribution coefficient.
- sweating; mechanism, kinetics
- layer washing at the wall of a pipe
- study on establishing an optimal structure of the crystal layer considering the two following steps of sweating and washing.
  The crystal layer growth units applied have pipes of three different diameters, each temperature controlled either on the inside or on the outside. The units are available in four different lengths.
- conclusions, together with TNO and BASF

Table 6. OUTLINE OF BASF'S CONTRIBUTION INVESTIGATIONS ON LAYER CRYSTALLIZATION PROCESSES

Research work:

1. Experiments (lab.scale + pilot plant) to determine the influence of
   - growth and structure of crystal layers
   - diffusion processes in the pores of a crystal layer
     a. during the growth of the crystal layer
     b. during the washing operation

   on the separation efficiency. Evaluation of the mechanisms of the diffusion and washing processes.
   In the lab.scale tests crystal layers are grown at the bottom of a one liter vessel, whereas in the pilot tests technical scale tubes with a length of 5 m. are applied.
2. Development of optimization strategies for layer crystallization processes on technical scale.

Table 7. **CONCEPT-PROJECT 1**

IMPROVED PROCEDURES FOR SEPARATING CRYSTALS FROM THE MELT, FURTHER PURIFICATION OF CRYSTALS

Ultrapurification of organic chemicals in a cost-efficient single operation is feasible provided, that a complete separation of crystals from the melt can be attained. Such a complete separation of crystals can be established using a packed bed separation column, provided that the temperature of the mother liquor is not more than 15 °C. below the crystallization temperature of the pure compound. When a larger temperature difference is met, the separation of the crystals can be realized using a cascade of two separation columns. The control of such a cascade is rather complicated. Therefore it would be preferable to establish such a separation of the crystals in one single device. Moreover, it would be desirable to attain a further purification of the crystals, when needed, in such a device. Fortunately, our joint EC research project will provide new know-how on the mechanisms of mass transfer to improve the rate of further purifying crystals within short. The main objective of the proposed program is therefore to define a cost-efficient multipurpose procedure for separating crystals from the melt. Specific objectives are the single stage separation of crystals from a mother liquor containing a high concentration of impurities and the further purification of crystals by recrystallization in such a separation device. It will be verified, whether the collected data will provide rules for predicting the performance of crystal separation columns in a simple way. The following tasks could be considered:

1. Single stage separation of crystals
verification whether a complete separation of crystals from a mother liquor containing a large concentration of impurities can be established by coupling zones of densely packed crystal beds with zones of non packed beds;
evaluation of non packed separation columns

2. Feasibility of recrystallization
inventory of the parameters promoting recrystallization in a crystal separation column;
study on the enhancement of the rate of recrystallization in a crystal separation column

3. Further basic knowledge
evaluation of the dependance of the performance of crystal separation columns on the crystal shape, the crystal size distribution and the compressibility of the crystals; analysis of the process of crystallizing the "wash liquid" on the crystals; improvement of model description, selection of design criteria

4. Development of design criteria
fluid dynamics of solid and liquid flows in a separation column especially near the filters, in dependence on the column diameter; column diameters of e.g. 0.1 and 0.3 m will be considered; comparison of hydraulic and mechanical forces to transport the crystals in a packed separation column;
studies on the axial dispersion in packed and non-packed crystal beds;
studies on the concentration and temperature profiles in packed bed columns

Table 8. **CONCEPT-PROJECT 2**

EVALUATION OF CRYSTALLIZER TYPES, CONTROL OF CRYSTAL SIZE, DEVELOPMENT OF DESIGN CRITERIA

In melt crystallization processes based on suspension growth, the heat is commonly withdrawn in an indirect way using scraped heat exchangers preferably installed in the crystallizer vessel. Scraped heat exchangers appear to be, however, costly and troublesome devices. Therefore it is proposed to investigate whether both the cost efficiency and the reliability of these crystal growth procedures can be improved.

When growing crystals in suspension, a satisfactory purity of the crystals can in principle be obtained usually as a low growth rate can be applied to limit solute incorporation. However, the final crystal size being determined both by nucleation and growth rate may easily become a critical parameter. A reasonable crystal size is essential for obtaining a satisfactory separation of the crystals from the melt. So, a particle size of 100 to 200 µm is usually needed for low viscosity melts, when packed bed separation columns are applied. Such a particle size is not always easy to obtain, when the crystals have to be grown from very impure mother liquors and short residence times of 15 to 30 minutes are aimed at. This is due to the limited width of metastable zones of organic systems favouring the birth rate of new crystals.

When aiming at a broad application of melt crystallization, the availability of cost-efficient procedures for crystal growth in suspension is essential.
The main objective of the proposed program is to define a cost-efficient and reliable procedure for growing satisfactorily large crystals with an average size of 100 to 200 µm using residence times of 15 to 30 min. It will be verified whether the collected data on crystallization kinetics will provide means for predicting the performance of melt crystallization in a simple way.

In order to meet its objectives, the study must perform a number of well defined tasks. The following tasks could be considered:

1. Evaluation of crystallizer types

test of a direct cooling method based on evaporating a solvent at the crystallization temperature for the growth of crystals in suspension from the melt; collection of data on the technical and economic feasibility of direct cooling; preventing incrustation in indirect cooling using more simple mechanical means than scrapers

2. Control of crystal size

determination of the dependence of the crystal size on the position of the heat exchanger (in the crystallizer vessel or in the bypass) in the case of indirect cooling; selection of crystallizer system (single crystallizer, cascade: countercurrent or cocurrent) in dependence on crystallization kinetics; evaluation of procedures for fines removal or product classification to obtain a satisfactory particle size

3. Development of design criteria

determination of crystallization kinetics parameters at two different scales of operation (e.g. crystallizer volumes of 2.5 and 100 l) as a first step in developing scaling-up rules; study on the influence of hydrodynamic conditions on the purity and the size of the crystals; prediction of the kinetic parameters from simple basic tests

PHASE EQUILIBRIA AND PROCESS SIMULATION FOR HIGH-PRESSURE SUPERCRITICAL EXTRACTION PROCESSES

Aa. FREDENSLUND and J. M. SØRENSEN
Institut for Kemiteknik, The Technical University of Denmark (DTH)
DK-2800 Lyngby, Denmark

Contract JOUE-0053-C

PARTICIPANTS

Gabrielle di Giacomo, Università de L'Aquila (UDLA), Italy
Enrique Martinez de la Ossa, Universidad de Cádiz (Cádiz), Spain

SUMMARY

The objective is to improve the understanding of low energy consuming processes using supercritical extraction to obtain pure alcohols and other oxyorganic compounds from aqueous mixtures. The research to be carried out includes:

- Measurement of phase equilibria in mixtures with a supercritical solvent (e.g. carbon dioxide or propane), water, and an oxyorganic compound (e.g. ethanol, propanol or acetic acid).
- Modelling of phase equilibria using equation of state with parameters based on the group-contribution approach.
- Bench scale extraction experiments.
- Steady state and dynamic simulation of extraction processes.

INTRODUCTION

Extraction with Supercritical or Near Critical Carbon Dioxide (SCD) is one of the energy efficient, new techniques of recovering or separating organic chemical products from aqueous solutions (Stahl et. al., 1988). An overview of potential applications of supercritical extraction is given in Table 1. In addition, a list of reviews of supercritical fluid extraction processes is given in Appendix 1. It may be seen from Table 1 that an application is in the downstream processing of fermentation broths for the production of several industrial products, like acetic, propanoic and butanoic acids, acetone, butanol and substituted thiophenes. Another important application of Supercritical or Near Critical Solvents (SCS) is the dehydration of azeotropic mixtures, notably the production of anhydrous ethanol.

The objective of this project is to improve the understanding of low energy consuming processes without loss of product quality in the above mentioned areas by using SCD or other suitable SCS or solvent mixtures. For the dehydration of ethanol, SCD extraction is combined with salt effect produced by inorganic salts.

Preliminary computer process simulations carried out at DTH (Brignole et al., 1987) have shown that it may be possible to recover anhydrous ethanol from fermentation broth using propane as a supercritical solvent/entrainer. The energy savings of the new process compared with conventional azeotropic distillation appear to be considerably more than 50%. We wish in this project to measure fundamental data, develop phase equilibrium models and to carry out more conclusive process simulations in order to verify the above statement for dehydration of ethanol and other supercritical extraction processes, such as purification of acetic acid using supercritical carbon dioxide and production of anhydrous ethanol using salted aqueous solution.

This research is divided into three parts:

1. Experimental
2. Modelling
3. Process simulation

THERMODYNAMIC BACKGROUND

For two phases in equilibria, phases α and β, the following equation holds for each component i:

$$f_i^{\alpha} = f_i^{\beta} \qquad i = 1, 2 \ldots N \tag{1}$$

where f_i is the fugacity of component i in the mixture.

The component fugacities are traditionally calculated form either <u>activity coefficient</u> (γ) models:

$$f_i = z_i \gamma_i f_i^0 \tag{2}$$

or from fugacity coefficient (ϕ_i) which may be obtained from equations of state:

$$f_i = z_i \phi_i P \tag{3}$$

In equation (2) and (3), z_i represents the mole fraction of component i in phase α or β, f_i^0 the reference fugacity (pure component i at the temperature and pressure of the system), and P the pressure.

As may be seen from Table 1, one of the phases, say phase α, may be either a solid phase (denoted below by S) or a liquid phase (denoted by L), whereas phase β then is the supercritical fluid phase (denoted below by F).

Supercritical extraction of solids for two phases (S and F) in equilibrium, Eq. (1) becomes

$$f_i^S = f_i^F \qquad i = 1, 2 \ldots N \tag{4}$$

For the solubility of a solid in supercritical fluids, it is normally assumed that the solid phase is pure. The supercritical fluid phase is treated as a compressed gas phase using Eq. (3). The solubility of a solid (2) in supercritical fluid (1) y_2, is then given by:

$$y_2 = \frac{P_2^s}{P} \left[\frac{\phi_2^s}{\phi_2} \, exp\,(V_2^s (P - P_2^s)/RT) \right] \tag{5}$$

where P_2^s is the sublimation pressure of pure solid 2 at the temperature of the system, ϕ_2^s is the corresponding fugacity coefficient, and V_2^s is the molar volume of pure solid 2. The term in the square brackets is termed the enhancement factor. P_2^s / P is the ideal solid solubility.

At normal process conditions the enhancement factor is nearly unity. In near-critical fluid extraction, the enhancement factor may become considerably large.

Consider, for example, the solubility of solid naphtalene in ethylene at 15 K above the critical temperatures of ethylene as shown in Fig. 1 (Bruh et al., 1982). The large difference between the ideal and the actual solubility of naphtalene in ethylene above approximately 60 bar is due to a sharp increase in the enhancement.

Supercritical fluid extraction may also be used to selectively extract components from a liquid mixture. Some of these applications mentioned in Table 1 are: Tertiary oil recovery and recovery of oxygenated hydrocarbons from water. In this case, one of the fluids (e.g. ethanol + water) is liquid-like, and the other fluid (e.g. ethane) is dense-gas-like. In this case, we may write the equilibrium relationship as follows:

$$f_i^L = f_i^F \qquad i = 1, 2 \ldots N \tag{6}$$

where L is the liquid-like and F is the dense-gas-like, supercritical phase.

In this case we can use Eq. (2) to describe the liquid phase and Eq. (3) to describe the vapor phase, in which case Eq. (6) becomes:

$$x_i \gamma_i f_i^0 = y_i \phi_i P \qquad i = 1, 2 \ldots N \tag{7}$$

One may also use Eq. (3) for both phases L and F; in which Eq. (6) becomes:

$$x_i \phi_i^L = y_i \phi_i^F \qquad i = 1, 2 \ldots N \tag{8}$$

As an example of application of Eq. (8), we will consider the extraction of ethanol from water using near-critical fluid extraction (Brignole et al., 1987). Simulation of such processes requires an equation of state to predict the component fugacity coefficients. The group-contribution equation of state (GC-EOS) by Skjold-Jørgensen (1984) was used by Brignole et al.

Based on the predictions of the GC-EOS better understanding of the behaviour of supercritical extraction solvents like CO_2 and ethane is possible. Fig. 2 shows predicted ethanol distribution coefficients between a 10 wt% ethanol aqueous solution and CO_2. The critical coordinates of CO_2 are T_c = 305.2 K and P_c = 73 bar. At 75 bar the distribution coefficient shows a steep decrease with temperature in the ambient temperature range. The same behaviour, but less pronounced, is found at 100 bar. At 150 bar the distribution coefficient is no longer strongly affected by temperature. In the case of ethane, a similar variation of the distribution coefficient with temperature is observed in the ambient temperature range (Fig. 3). The critical temperature of ethane is 305.4 K.

In this work phase equilibrium data will be measured so that we may develop models (equations of state) for the prediction of ϕ_i^L and ϕ_i^F in Eq. (8). These models combine the activity coefficient approach, Eq. (7) with the equation of state approach, Eq. (8). The models will be used for steady state and dynamic simulation of supercritical extraction processes.

OBJECTIVES

The results of the research program will be:

- experimental information for better understanding supercritical extraction processes
- software for dynamic and steady state simulation of such processes
- process analyses for specific cases regarding energy efficiency and controllability, particularly in pure ethanol production.

TASKS OF THE PARTICIPANTS

The following work program has been set out and initiated:

1. Experimental measurements of phase equilibria in synthetic mixtures containing a supercritical solvent (e.g. carbon dioxide), water and an organic compound:

   1.1 Carbon dioxide with aqueous solutions of ethanol, propanol and butanol (ternary mixtures) in a wide concentration, P and T range (UDLA).

   1.2 Carbon dioxide with aqueous solutions of acetic acid in a wide concentration, P and T range (UDLA).

   1.3 Construction of phase equilibrium apparatus in Cádiz (Cádiz).

   1.4 Propane with aqueous solutions of alcohols or acetic acid (same solutes as in 1.1 and 1.2) (Cádiz).

2. Validation of phase equilibrium data by comparison with data from literature and consistency check (UDLA, Cádiz).

   (This means that to a very limited extent measurements will be repeated with data available in literature).

3. Transfer of selected experimental data from UDLA and Cádiz to DTH, including data listed above (no. 1 and 2) and data previously measured (UDLA and Cádiz).

4. Modelling of phase equilibria

4.1 Correlation of the experimental data measured under task 1 using a non-predictive, model which should be applicable, after parametrization, in the whole range of industrial operating conditions (UDLA and Cádiz).

4.2 Development of a generalized group-contribution model for the prediction of phase equilibria in mixtures containing a supercritical solvent and polar compounds (DTH).

4.2.1 Equation of state model development. (This will include special considerations near the critical point).

4.2.2 Determination of gas-gas and gas-solvent parameters from literature phase equilibrium data, e.g. for mixtures with alcohols, and experimental results as transferred from (3).

4.2.3 Determination of model parameters for carbon dioxide with aqueous solutions of alcohols (1.1).

4.2.4 Determination of model parameters for carbon dioxide with aqueous solutions of acetic acid (1.2).

4.2.5 Determination of model parameters for propane (Instead of carbon dioxide) with the same substances as mentioned in 4.2.2 and 4.2.3 (1.4).

4.2.6 Assessment of the model predictions (DTH with an industrial consortium). Fifteen companies such as Shell, BP, ICI, IFP, ENI, Linde, DSM participate. These companies will advise on the project and provide feedback to improve final results.

5. Extraction experiments (UDLA and Cádiz)

5.1 Extraction of alcoholic fermentation broth using carbon dioxide and propane as near-critical or supercritical solvents.

5.2 Extraction of anhydrous ethanol using salted aqueous solutions (1.5).

6. <u>Process simulation</u> (DTH in collaboration with industrial consortium)

6.1 Implementations of the models developed in Tasks 4.1 and 4.2 in steady state and dynamic simulation computer programs (SEPSIM and DYNSIM) for studies of the energy efficiency and control systems for supercritical extraction processes.

6.2 Verification of steady state process simulation by comparing with results from 5.1 and 5.2 as well as process information found in literature or provided by industries.

6.3 Use of dynamic and steady state simulations (SEPSIM and DYNSIM) to examine and compare the energy efficiency and controllability of supercritical extraction processes. Examples of processes to be studied are:

Supercritical extraction of alcohol, phenol, organic acids and other oxyorganic components from water or biomass.

Supercritical extraction of naturally occurring organic compounds, i.e. olive oil, lemon oil and other citrous products.

UDLA has already experience with the following processes:

- separation of main components of lemon oil and other citrus products using supercritical carbon dioxide;
- extraction and refining of olive oil with supercritical carbon dioxide at pressures lower than those presently used.
- separation of mixtures of alcohols, phenolic compounds and other oxyorganic compounds from water and biomass using supercritical carbon dioxide.

These will be provided for the present project.

FUTURE R&D

The following areas of research and development within Supercritical Fluid Extraction (SFE) processes remain open for further investigation:

- measurement of phase equilibrium data in the relevant temperature and pressure ranges for industrially important systems,

- extension and revision of parameter tables for group-contribution and molecular models describing the thermodynamic properties of the systems in question,

- detailed simulations of the steady state and dynamic behaviour of industrially relevant SFE processes in order to verify their performance with respect to energy requirements and operability.

REFERENCES

Brignole, E. A., P. M. Andersen and Aa. Fredenslund, IEC Research 26, 254-61 (1987).

Brignole, E. A., P. M. Andersen and Aa. Fredenslund, IEC Research 26, 1304-1312 (1987).

Bruh, M. R., R. W. Corbett and S. Watanasiri, paper presented at the 47th API midyear Refining Meeting, New York, 1982.

Gearhard, J. A. and L. Garwin, "Resid-Extraction Process Offers Flexibility", Oil Gas J., 74 (24) 63-6 (1976).

Hull, P., Oil Gas J. p. 57. 17 August (1970).

Kuk, M. S. and J. C. Montagna, "Solubility of Oxygenated Hydrocarbons in Supercritical Carbon Dioxide", in "Chemical Engineering at Supercritical Fluid Conditions".

Metcalfe, R. S. and L. Yarborough, SPE. Journal 242 (Aug. 1979).

Moses, J. M., K. E. Goklen and R. P. De Filippi, "Pilot Plant Critical-Fluid Extraction of Organics from Water", AIChE Annual Meeting, Paper No. 127c Los Angeles (1982).

Paulaitis, M. E., V. J. Krukonis, R. T. Kurmik and R. C. Reid, Reviews on Chem. Eng. 1 (2) 179 (1983b).

Peter, S. and G. Brunner, Angen. Chem. Int. Ed. 17 746 (1978).

Skjold-Jørgensen, Steen, Fluid Phase Equilibria. 16, 317 (1984).

Stahl, E., K. W. Quirin and D. Gerard, "Dense Gases for Extracting and Refining", Springer-Verlag, Berlin, 1988.

Vitzhum, O., Hubert, P. and Sirtl, W., "Production of Hops. Extracts", US Patent 4104409 (1978).

Zosel, K., Angew. Chem. Int. Ed. 17 702 (1978).

NATURAL PRODUCTS	SUPERCRITICAL FLUID	REFERENCE
Decaffeination of green coffee beans	CO_2	Zosel (1978)
Extraction of spices, e.g. peper, nutmeg and chili	-	Vitzhum et al. (1978)
Production of hop extract for the brewing industry	-	Vitzhum et al. (1978)
Fractionation of glycerides and fatty acids	-	Peter and Brunner (1978)
Oil extraction from seeds and foods	-	(Cited by Paulaitis et al. (1983), p. 228)
Fractionation of cod-liver oil	-	Zosel (1978)
Extraction of flavours and fragances	-	Caragay (1981), Schultz and Randell (1970)
Defattening of fryed potato chips and other snack foods	-	Paulaitis et al. (1983), p. 230
Extraction of nicotine from tobacco	-	Vitzhum et al. (1978)
PETROLEUM AND COAL		
Deasphalting of heavy petroleum fractions	pentane propane	Gearhart and Garwin (1976), Zhuze (1960), Zosel (1978)
Tertiary oil recovery	CO_2, C_2, C_3	Hull (1970), Metcalfe and Yarborough (1979)
Coal processing for conversion to liquid fuels	toluene water	Paulaitis et al. (1983) part III
PETROCHEMICALS		
Recovery of chemicals from water streams (ethanol, isopropanol, butanol)	C_2H_6, C_3H_8 and others	Moses et al. (1982), Kuk and Montagna (1983), Brignole et al (1987)

Table 1. Overview of Potential applications of supercritical extraction processes.

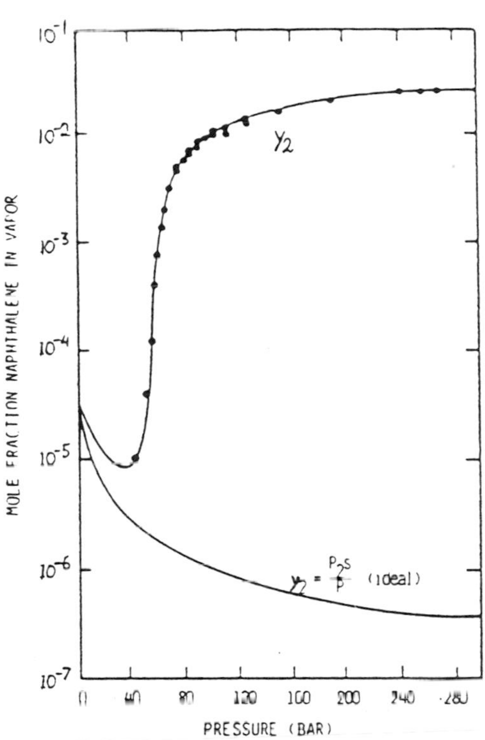

Figure 1. Solubility of naphtalene in ethylene at 297 K.

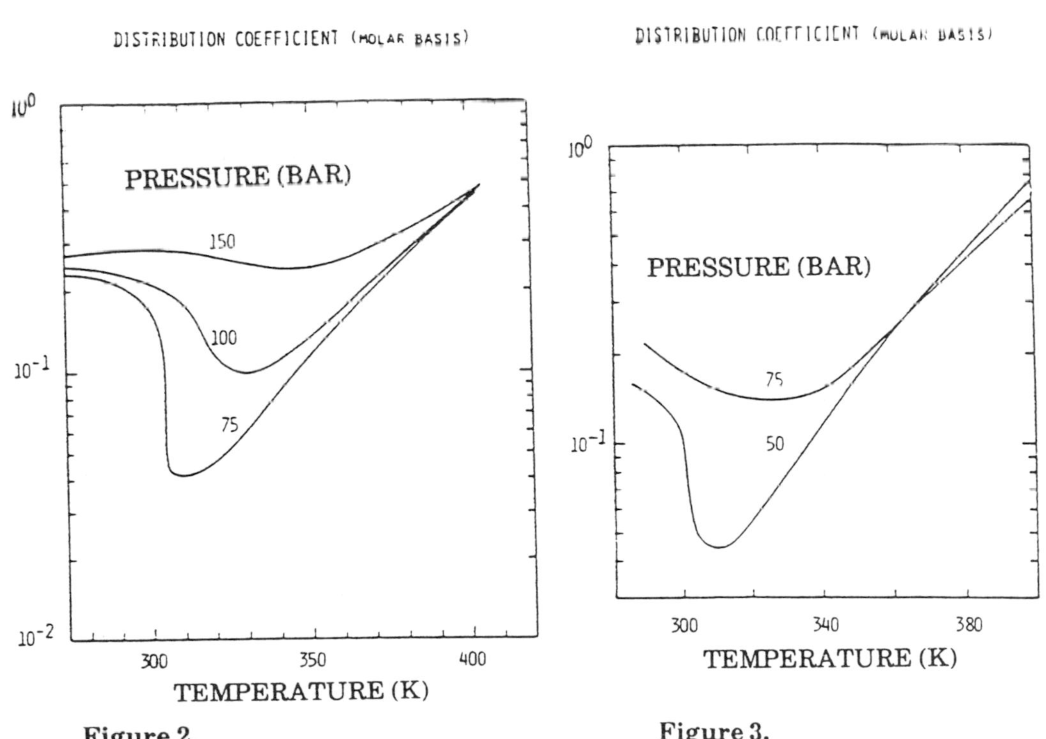

Figure 2.

Figure 3.

Ethanol distribution coefficient between CO_2 (fig. 2) or ethane (fig. 3) and water. Ethanol in aqueous phase = 10% W / W.

APPENDIX I

REVIEW OF SUPERCRITICAL FLUID EXTRACTION PROCESSES

Essen-Symposium, June 1978: Extraction with Supercritical Gases. ed. G. M. Schneider et al., Verlag Chemie 1980.

London, Febr. 1982, Chemistry and Industry, 19 June 1982, pg. 385-405.

Separation Science and Technology, 17, 1982, pg. 1-233.

Cambridge 1982, Fluid Phase Equilibria, Elsevier Scientific Publishing Company, Amsterdam, 10, 1983, pg. 141-344.

Chemical Engineering at Supercritical Fluid Conditions, ed. M. E. Paulaitis et al., Ann Arbor Science Publishers, Ann Arbor, Michigan, 1983.

A Review of Supercritical Fluid Extraction, Dec. 1983, of James F. Ely and Jolene K. Baker, Chem. Eng. Science Div., Nat. Eng. Lab., National Bureau of Standards, Boulder, Colorado 80303.

Königstein/Taunus-Symposium, April 1984, i Berichte der Bunsen-Gesellschaft für Physikalische Chemie, 88, Sept. 1984, pg. 784-923.

Erlangen-Symposium, Oct. 1984, ed. Verein Deutscher Ingenieure, GVC-VDI-Gesellschaft Verfahrenstechnik und Chemieingenieurwesen, Postfach 1139, Düsseldorf.

San Francisco-Symposium, Nov. 1984, Proc. Symp. of Supercritical Fluid Technology, Elsevier Science Publisher BV, Amsterdam.

F. M. Taylor, Carbon Dioxide, The solvent for the food and related industries. Wolwiston Consultancy Services Ltd., 50, Cricket Lane, Lichfield Staffs, England WS14 9ER.

CHEMICAL REACTORS

Chairman: Mr. R. Dumon

REVERSED FLOW SYNTHESIS OF METHANOL

J. Jochems
European R&D Projects
NV DSM
The Netherlands

Contract: JOUE-0032-C

PARTICIPANT: Prof. Dr.Ir. G.F. Froment
Managing Director Laboratory for Petrochemical Technique (LPT)
Rijks Universiteit Gent
Belgium

1. SUMMARY

The study on the reversed flow methanol synthesis within the JOULE context aims to make a technical-economic feasibility study on this new chemical technological concept.
For that purpose a rigorous reactor model has to be generated.
The study includes:

- Non-pseudo steady-state evaluation of the reaction kinetics.
- Bench-scale testing of the methanol synthesis under reversed flow conditions for reaction modelling and testing of catalyst behaviour.
- Combination of the (transient) reaction kinetics and the reactor model for simulating of the entire reversed flow methanol process.
- Technical-economic process evaluation.
- Estimation of energy savings, compared with the conventional methanol synthesis process.

An energy saving of 5 to 10 % compared with nowadays methanol processes is expected.

2. INTRODUCTION

This project deals with the assessment of the reversed flow technology in the context of the methanol synthesis. Reversed flow technology in general can be used for improvements on processes where exothermic (equilibrium) reactions predominate. Especially for the conversion of process streams with low concentrations of substrates (e.g. effluent streams), this principle should be of special importance. The technique is based on reversing the flow through a chemical reactor by changing inlet and outlet streams within a certain cycle time. The adiabatic operation leads to sufficiently high temperatures to obtain desired conversions.

Consider a reactor with a fixed bed of particles, consisting of an inert section, followed by a catalyst bed and again an inert section. In the usual downflow operation of an exothermic reaction in an adiabatic bed, the temperature in the catalyst section increases from top to bottom. To obtain a reasonable conversion, large quantities of the synthesis gas have to be recycled, which costs a lot of energy and high initial investments in compressors and turbines.

If the synthesis gas flow, however, is periodically alternated between downflow and upflow (reversed flow) and (in the upflow situation) the gas will be partially preheated in the bottom inert section, but also in the catalyst section in which of course reaction will occur. Given the relatively low temperature in the top of the catalyst section established in the preceding downflow half-cycle, the temperature in the top of the catalyst section will not necessarily be the highest in that section during the upflow half-cycle. After a number of cycles, temperature profiles exhibiting a maximum in the catalyst section will be obtained, both for the downflow half-cycle and the upflow half-cycle.

This new way of operating a fixed bed reactor causes a number of advantages with respect to the usual operation. The reactor also acts as a regenerative heat exchanger, thereby saving heat exchangers otherwise needed to preheat the feed to the reaction temperature. So with the reversed flow principle it is possible to process even lean mixtures in an autothermal way.

The temperature profile with its maximum is favourable for improving the conversion of an exothermic equilibrium reaction, because the conversion is decreasing towards the reactor exit, in each half cycle. Recirculation of synthesis gas can be significantly reduced. An energy saving of 5 to 10 % (compared with the energy-consumption of a nowadays methanol plant of average 38 GJ/ton) is expected. Multibed adiabatic reactors with intermediate cooling can be reduced to much smaller single bed reactors.

Little is known about the operation of reversed flow reactors, but the technique is claimed to be applied on an industrial scale in the USSR for the production of sulphuric acid. As far as we know, the technique is new for the EC. It has been established by the Russian-group, that in SO_3 synthesis the reactor volume is significantly reduced, while the pressure drop is reduced by a factor of two. The capital investment is lowered by 30 to 80 % and the production costs decreased by 5 to 20 %. Further lean SO_2 mixtures with 4 to 5 % SO_2 can be processed autothermally.

Similar benefits may be expected in methanol synthesis (or ammonia synthesis). It is a generally accepted fact that Western European methanol industry can only remain competitive by aiming (strongly) at a low-cost production of this chemical. DSM is an important methanol producer. This chemical, but also potential energy-vector, is produced from CO and H_2 by means of an exothermic reversible reaction.

The comparison of the experimental and predicted data, based upon simulation models, has suffered from inaccurate kinetic equations, generally determined from steady-state experiments. For unsteady state operation, as applied in the reversed flow process, the kinetic equation of the catalytic reaction should not be based upon the hypothesis of the pseudo steady state and upon the hypothesis of a rate determining step. The rate has to be written explicitly in terms of the intermediates involved in the elementary steps and the kinetics of these steps have to be determined. This requires experiments in the transient state, for which LPT ("Laboratorium voor Petrochemische Techniek") of the RUG ("Rijks Universiteit van Gent") recently purchased special equipment.

3. OBJECTIVES

The aim of the project is to evaluate a new reversed flow technology for the production of methanol. This is an innovation in the area. The aim of the present research work can further be specified as to prove the technical feasibility of reversed flow operation by means of a highly automated bench-scale unit, applied to methanol synthesis. As a result: details and data of the energy savings (and of the reduction of invest-ment costs to be obtained) will be available. The experiments should also provide data necessary to validate a simulation model for the process, a prerequisite for upscaling to larger units and for the economic evaluation of the process.

4. TASKS OF PARTICIPANTS

4.1. General

In the first stage, a bench-scale unit for methanol synthesis will be constructed and operated under reversed flow conditions. The attached figure 1 shows a flow sheet of this unit and the attached figure 2 shows more in detail the reactor. The concept has been developed at the "Laboratorium voor Petrochemische Techniek" (LPT) of the "Rijks Universiteit Gent" (RUG).

At first the unit will be assembled and tested. Thereafter the unit will be operated under various conditions to optimize the operation and to provide data for the establishment of the model for the reversed flow operation. Therefore the resistance of the catalyst to thermal stress has to be checked. Also very detailed information is necessary of the height, exact shape and moving velocity of the temperature wave-front in the catalyst bed.

Further information on the dependance of selectivity in the whole temperature range of reversed flow reactors has to be determined and detailed information on the maximum temperature in the catalyst bed has to be obtained. To do so, DSM has a highly instrumented operational bench-scale unit for the study of methanol synthesis. LPT will investigate the transient kinetics by means of a Brucker FT-IR* spectrometer with on-line reactor cell and the powerful TAP**-reactor-system by Monsanto.

4.2 Detailed description of the experimental work

The project consists of seven tasks and is scheduled to be implemented as follows:

4.2.1 Construction and testing of the bench-scale methanol unit

Responsible: LPT

This unit will be constructed and operated under reversed flow conditions. See attached figures 1 and 2. The concept has been developed at LPT. The unit will be assembled and tested. DSM will bring in it's ten years experience in methanol synthesis research and know-how in industrial methanol production. Knowledge on the many experimental pitfalls in methanol research and know-how on catalyst behaviour and especially catalyst deactivation, sintering as well as poisoning, will mean important time-saving in setting-up the experimental work.

---

*) FT-IR = Fourier Transformation - Infra Red: gives information about type and amount of adsorbed molecules on the surface of the catalyst.

**) TAP = Temporal Analysis of Products: gives information about the nature and evolution of short-living molecules on a catalyst surface.

4.2.2 First "guess estimates" in modelling, using published methanol kinetics

Responsible: LPT

The modelling requires detailed information on the kinetics of the methanol synthesis. In this task published kinetic equations, based upon steady state experiments, will be used. It is likely, however, that modelling of the reaction under non-steady-state conditions requires kinetic equations which are much more explicit as to the dependence on the concentrations of intermediates. Nevertheless, a first approximation will be time-saving by setting-up a global approach and a first rough structure of the model. Later on, fine-tuning of the model on the basis of experimental data will be possible (see 4.2.3).

4.2.3 Non-pseudo steady state modelling by means of FT-IR and TAP

Responsible: LPT

Pseudo steady-state approximations and the existence of a rate determining step are probably not realistic in the present case. LPT is now equipped with a Brucker FT-IR spectrometer with an on-line reactor cell and with the TAP-reactor, developed by Monsanto. This is a reactor which permits the introduction of pulses of feed and intermediates of the order of 100 microseconds and which is connected to a mass-spectro-meter. It is a powerful tool for the rapid development of reaction pathways, since it allows short-life intermediates to be determined. The equipment in Gent is the second of its type. These tools will be used in parallel (and by an independent group) with the bench-scale unit for reversed flow to determine accurate kinetics for the methanol-synthesis. In this work, the experience of DSM with methanol synthesis, both on catalytic and industrial aspects, will be of great value.

This work should result in a valid kinetic reaction model of the methanol synthesis as practiced under reversed flow conditions.

4.2.4 Experimental work on selectivity and stability of the catalyst

Responsible: DSM

At this moment, only information on the selectivity of the methanol-synthesis at high temperatures is available. Because large parts of the reactor work at much lower temperatures than usual information on the dependance of selectivity in the whole temperature range of reversed-flow reactors has to be determined. Normally only trace amounts of higher alcohols and/or dimethylether are found.

An essential difference with the nowadays used ICI quench reactor or Lurgi's tube reactor in methanol synthesis is that the catalyst particles, especially near reactor inlet and outlet, will face continuous and large temperature changes. The resistance of the catalyst to thermal stress has to be checked. Both of the active temperature-sensitive component of the catalyst as well as of the physical resistance of the particle as a whole.

4.2.5 **Initial development of a reactor model**

Responsible: LPT

The generation of a detailed rigorous model is essential to simulate an industrial reactor. Only with a thorough simulation model a technical and economic evaluation of the reversed flow methanol synthesis is possible. While the experimental work will make it possible to show the technical feasibility, the model is also necessary in order to make an economic feasibility study. A model therefore will have to consist of a kinetic reaction model and of a reactor model. The kinetic reaction model has been described in 4.2.3.

As mentioned the development of a reactor model will be necessary as well. It is recognized that the essential feature of a reversed flow reactor is a temperature wave-front in the reactor that will move continuously. This aspect has to be covered with a detailed model.

Very detailed information is necessary of the height, exact shape and moving velocity of the temperature wave-front in the catalyst bed. The total temperature-time history of the catalytic bed as a whole must be known to make it possible to gain quantitative information on the beneficial conversion gain of reversed flow reactors. At the outlet of a reversed flow reactor an extra conversion increase appears as compared to the equilibrium conversion in classical autothermal or isothermal reactors. The exact amount of this conversion gain is determined from the exact shape of the temperature profile at the exit of the reactor.

Detailed information on the maximum temperature in the catalyst bed is necessary because the catalyst has a limited temperature range in which it can be applied. Higher temperatures will lead to fast deactivation. Eventually an intermediate heat exchanger should be applied to guarantee the same catalyst lifetime as is now common-practice in industrial reactors (> 3 years).

In this task, a more global approach of the reactor model will be used to do some first investigations. The results will be necessary for the go/no-go decision, which will take place after this task.

4.2.6 **Go/no-go decision point**

Responsible: DSM

At this point, after the first year of the project, a decision has to be taken whether or not proceed with the project. To be able to take a "go" decision, all the previous tasks will have to be completed successfully, i.e.:

- The bench-scale methanol unit at LPT has to be constructed successfully and will have to obtain proven operability.
- The first approximation of the kinetic model, based upon published data, will have to be set-up as a base for the next task.
- By means of FT-IR and TAP experiments the literature based model has to be adopted to non-steady state reverse flow conditions. This model will have to show potential benefits of the process. Although at this stage no real technical and economic feasibility study will be available, the calculated effects in the model must show the potential benefits by judgement of the experts involved in the project.

4.2.7 **Reactor-model**

Responsible: LPT

In this task the activities of subparagraph 3.2.5 will be continued.

Once it has been verified that a non-steady state kinetic model is necessary, precise information on temperature profiles and hence on increased conversion, the benefit of the reversed flow process, can be evaluated.

The ultimate modelling of the fixed bed reactor operated in a transient mode will require an extensive literature search on the heat- and mass-transfer in catalytic reactors. LPT has a long-time experience in this matter, but a thorough evaluation together with DSM of the available correlations will be necessary.

The modelling of the reactor operated in reverse flow leads to a set of complex partial differential equations. The integration of this set is difficult and will require a serious computational effort. Yet, it is expected that this task could be undertaken in the second year, so that the operation of the experimental bench-scale unit could be simulated towards the project. DSM has adequate facilities and a long experience on this subject.

The modelling of the process, i.e. the combination of a kinetic reaction model as well as the reactor model, will be based upon continued experimental investigations.

4.2.8 Technical and economic feasibility study

Responsible: DSM

During the last months of the project, a technical and economic feasibility study will be carried out. This will be based on the model of the process. This will include a technical feasibility study of continuous change of flow direction in the reactor (catalyst behaviour, valves) as well as considerations concerning energy savings and reduction of investment costs, for a new methanol plant based upon the reversed flow principle.

5. PRELIMINARY RESULTS

Preparations are made for the construction of the bench-scale methanol synthesis testing apparatus at LPT. LPT and DSM are searching now literature for data on methanol synthesis kinetics. DSM is gathering relevant methanol plant data for initial estimation of experimental conditions.

6. FUTURE R&D

As the reverse flow technology is still new within the EEC there are more opportunities to be expected. The reverse flow synthesis for methanol will be used as a test case for the feasibility of the principle. If successful, other chemical processes based on reverse flow technology may be developed. Important applications such as the reduction of toxic components in waste gases (NO_x, SO_x, hydrocarbons, etc.) need further investigation, as the technology seems very suitable for the economical destruction of hazardous wastes at low concentration levels.

7. REFERENCES

1. Matros, Yu. Sh. (1985). In: Unsteady processes in catalytic reactors, Studies in Surface Science and Catalysis part 22, Elsevier, 1985.

2. Matros, Yu. Sh. (1989). In: Catalytic processes under unsteady state conditions, Elsevier, pp. 347 - 389 (ch. 9).

3. Froment, G.F. (1990). Proceedings of a meeting at Novosibirsk, June 1990, Unsteady State Processes, 'Reversed Flow operation of fixed bed catalytic reactors', pp. 57 - 89.

4. Matros, Yu. Sh., Bobrova, L.N., Unsteady State performance of NO_x-reduction by NH_3, Reaction Kinetics Catalysis Letters, 37, (2) pp. 267 - 272 (1988).

5. Matros, Yu. Sh. (1990), Performance of catalytic processes under unsteady-state conditions, Proceedings of a meeting at Novosibirsk, June 1990, Unsteady State Processes, pp. 131 - 163.

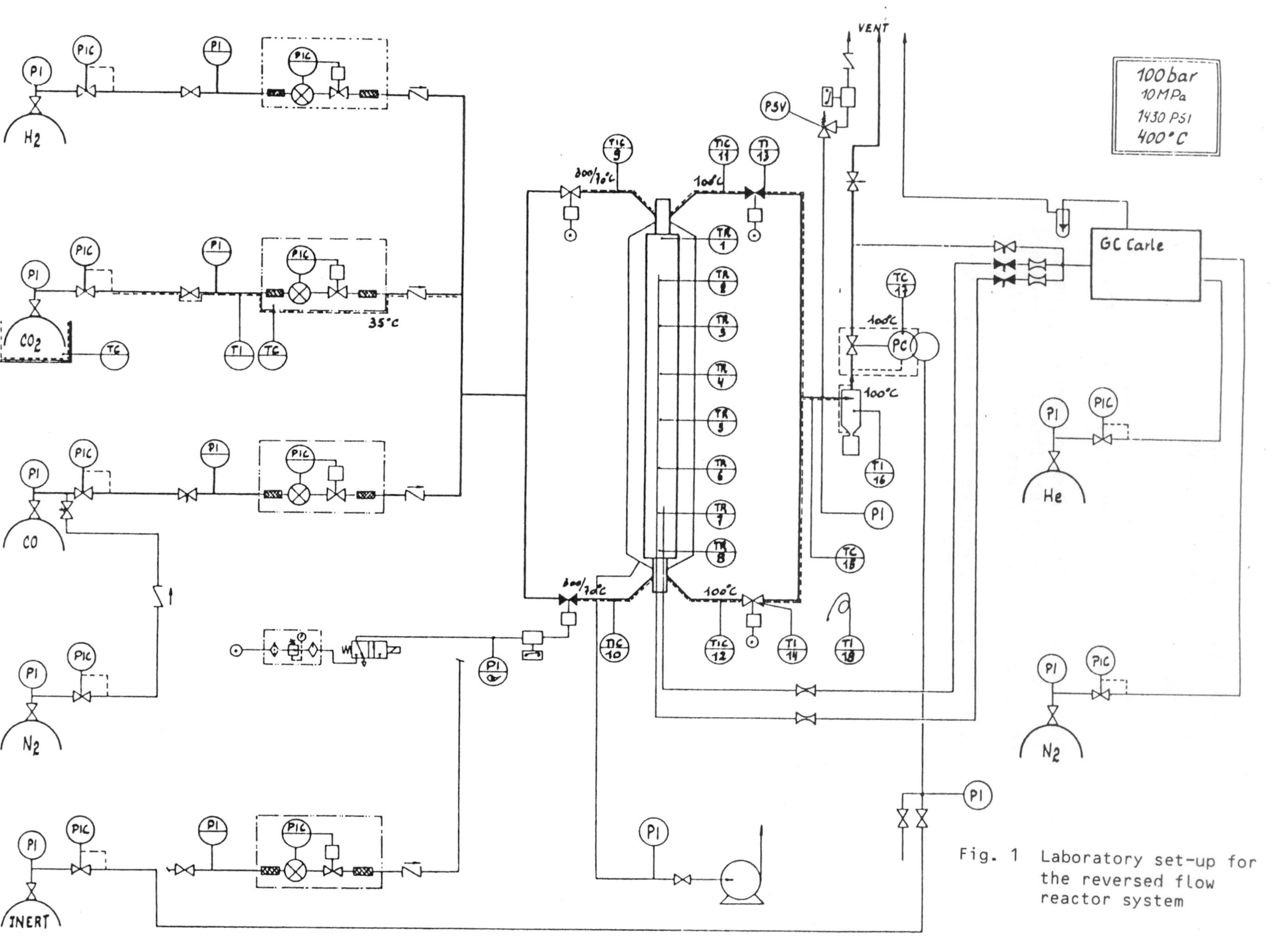

Fig. 1 Laboratory set-up for the reversed flow reactor system

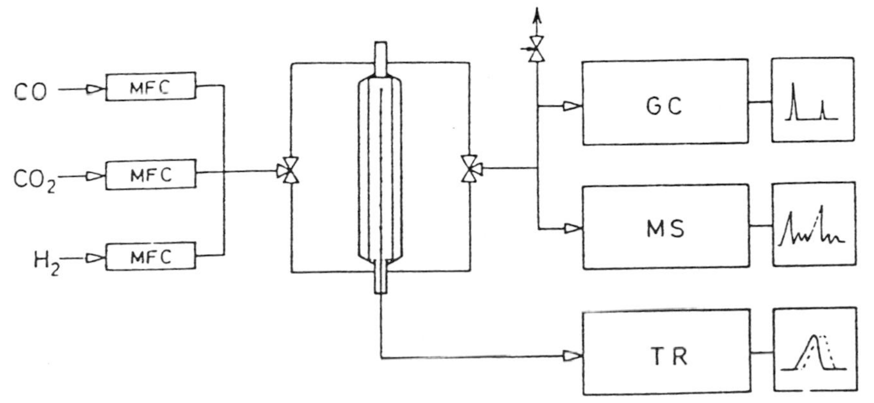

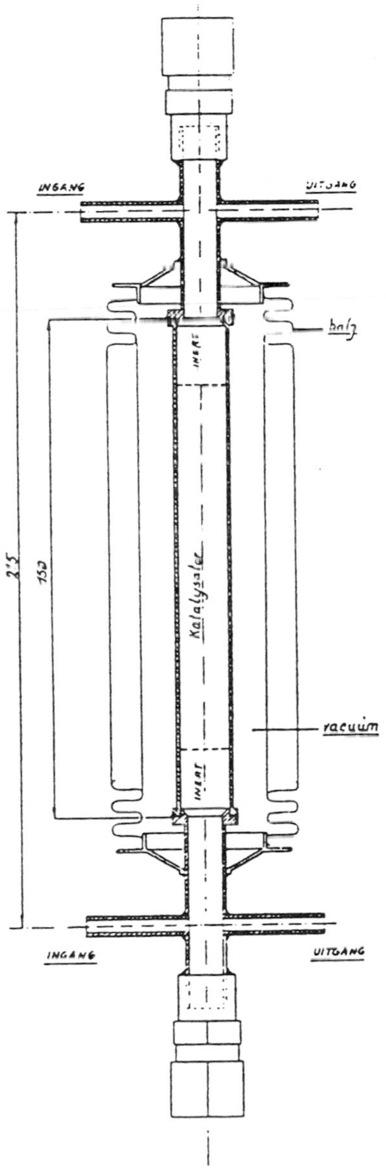

Fig. 2 The reversed flow reactor

FIXED BED REACTOR WITH INTEGRATED HEAT EXCHANGER

Dr. G. Heijkoop
VEG-GASINSTITUUT

Contract: JOUE-0019-C

PARTICIPANTS: Dr. V. Arnhold, Sintermetallwerk Krebsöge GmbH
Prof. J. Geus , State University of Utrecht
Prof. M. Groll, IKE, Universität Stuttgart

SUMMARY

The scope of this research is to integrate heat transfer with (catalytic) reactions for process intensification. In a former research, the basics of a reactor with sintermetals were developed. In this project, the design and development of an application of such a reactor in an industrial environment is made. For this, the super-Claus reaction was chosen and the following steps are taken to come to a complete design:
a. research into a method for varying the voidage of the sintermetal matrix to make an optimal design for heat production and transfer as well as determination of the voidage and heat conductivity.
b. determination of the activity of the catalyst involved.
c. combination of the results of a. and b. into computer models to come to a complete design.
The result of this is a very simple reactor compared to the conventional plant.

INTRODUCTION

There is a great number of gas reactions which take place in fixed bed catalytic reactors. If heat production (exothermic reactions) or heat demand (endothermic reactions) occurs, than there are several solutions which can be chosen for heat transport, for instance:

1. A series of adiabatic reactors and heaters (or coolers) is constructed in which alternately the heat is produced and removed. The number of steps is such that there is sufficient conversion of the input gases without having a temperature rise which causes a wrong equilibrium or undesired products. An example of this is given in figure 1. where a conventional Claus plant is shown.[1]

After partial combustion of the H_2S, sulphur is formed from SO_2 and H_2S:

$H_2S + 1.5\ O_2 \Rightarrow SO_2 + H_2O$ (partial in the combustion chamber)

$2\ H_2S + SO_2 \Leftrightarrow 1.5\ S_2 + H_2O$ (in the combustion chamber and the catalytic reactor stages).

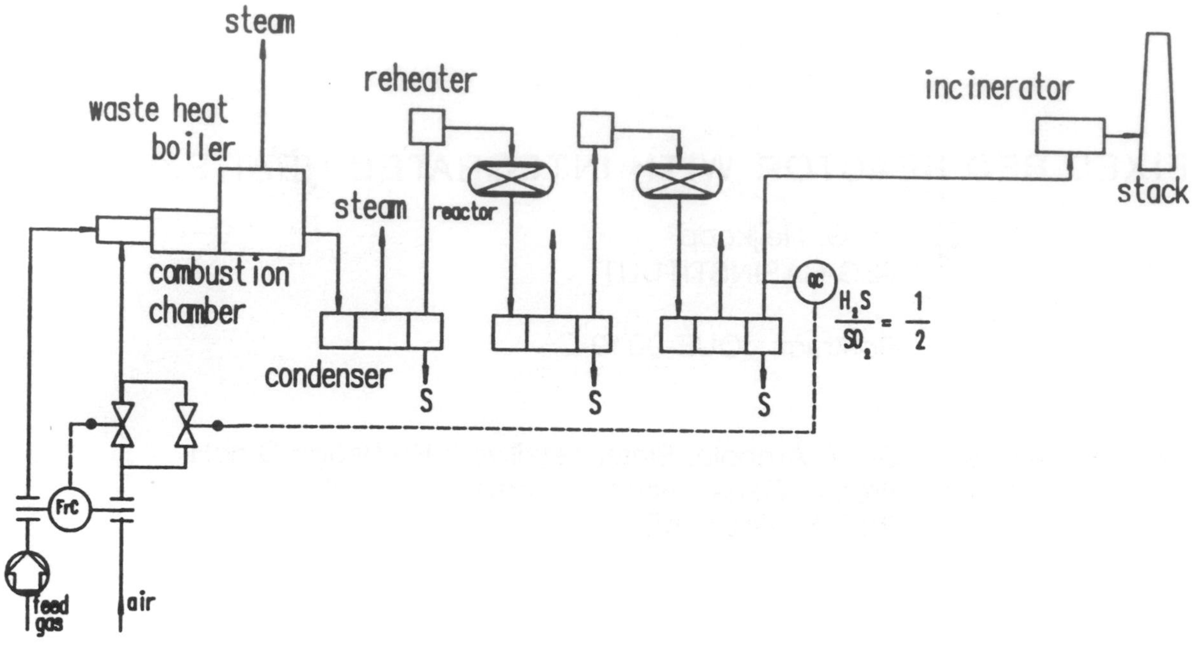

Figure 1. Example of a multiple adiabatic fixed bed reactor: conventional Clausplant

This sulphur is removed in the first condenser. After this there are two (or three) stages in which the remaining H_2S and SO_2 catalytically react to sulphur, which is condensed in a condenser and then the remaining gas is reheated.
2. There are many reactions in which hydrocarbons are catalytically oxidized. The temperature of these kind of reactions is so critical that they are cooled with molten salts to keep the temperature between a few degrees and the reactor dimensions are only of a few catalyst particles [2,3].

These solutions have to be chosen because it is very difficult to get the heat directly out of the bed. This is due to two reasons:
1. The fixed bed catalyst packing has a very poor heat conductance as a result of the many transition resistances from one particle to another.
2. As the catalyst particles have only very little contact with the reactor wall, there is a considerable heat transfer resistance.

Sintermetal matrices don't have these two problems. Because of the sintering the metal powder particles are connected to each other and to the wall (see figure 2.).
The advantages of the use of sintermetals are:
1. Although the construction of a reactor with sintermetals in it is elaborate and

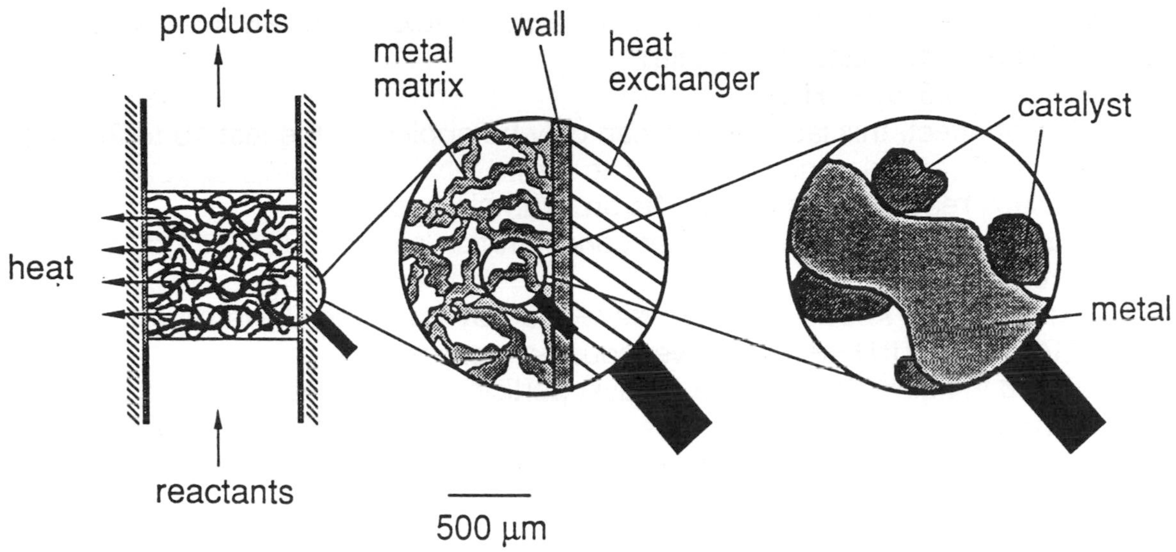

Figure 2. Sintermetal matrix.

therefore expensive, the possibility of integrating the reaction with the heat transfer is making the complete construction of a plant cheap.

2. The sintering of the sintermetal to the wall makes it not only possible to have a good heat transfer out of the catalyst but also provides a carrier for the catalyst so that there is no channelling near the wall and no short cut for not reacted components.

3. In conventional fixed beds catalyst particle size determines the effectiveness of each particle and the pressure drop across the bed. In such beds a compromise has to be reached between these two constraints. In a sintermetal reactor they can be chosen independently because the pressure drop is fixed by the sintermetal matrix while the effectiveness of the catalyst is determined by the deposited catalyst particle size.

4. If fouling occurs in such a conventional reactor it can only be removed by opening the reactor and removing the catalyst and cleaning it separated from the reactor. A sintermetal matrix may be cleaned by giving a gas pulse in the opposite direction of the normal flow thus blowing out the dust particles which have settled down on the catalyst.

As an example of an application of sintermetals, the super-Claus process was chosen: Conventionally, in a Claus plant H_2S is oxidized to sulphur in two steps (see figure 1): Firstly, the H_2S is for a third part burned to SO_2 :

$H_2S + 1.5\ O_2 \ => SO_2 + H_2O$

Secondly the non-burned H_2S reacts with SO_2 to sulphur in the Claus reaction:

$2\ H_2S + SO_2 <=> 1.5\ S_2 + H_2O$

This reaction is an equilibrium reaction so that there is a part of the H_2S that will not react (about 3 to 5%, depending on the number of stages and the inlet concentration). Super-Claus is the name of the use of a newly developed catalyst in which the oxidation of H_2S takes place in one step:

Super-Claus is the name of the use of a newly developed catalyst in which the oxidation of H_2S takes place in one step:

$H_2S + .5\ O_2 => 0.5\ S_2 + H_2O$

Due to the heat effect, this last reaction can only be applied to the last 10 to 20 % of the total inlet H_2S (actual concentration: 1 to 3%).

The super-Claus reaction was chosen as an example because:

1. The yield of the process and the inlet concentration can be increased by using a isothermal reactor.
2. The process is well known as it was developed by the State University of Utrecht and VEG-GASINSTITUUT and will have industrial applications.
3. As explained in figure 3. inside the catalyst particle a side reaction occurs in which sulphur is further oxidized to the undesired SO_2 and therefore the catalyst particle should be as small as possible. In order to avoid problems with pressure drop the application of a sintermetal carrier is advantageous.

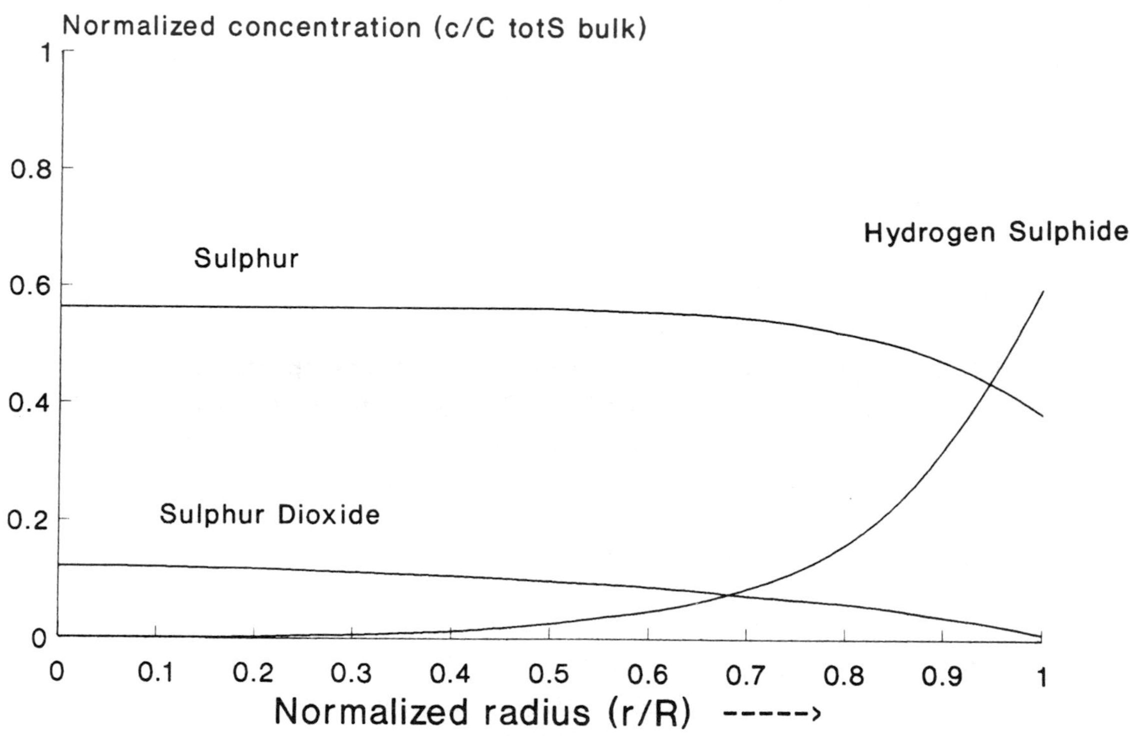

Figure 3. Inside the catalyst particle, S reacts to SO_2.

OBJECTIVES

The main objective of this research is to come to a design of an industrial application of sintermetals, in this case a super-Claus reactor. To do this, several steps must be taken and they are described here.
The expected benefits are not easy to estimate because of the wide variation of reactions, but the economic and environmental advantage and the number of replications may both be large:
There are 200 to 300 Claus plants in the Western world whereas there are 20 to 50 of such processes. Besides, there is a great number of special reactions where sintermetals can be applied too similarly.

TASKS OF PARTICIPANTS

Task 1. Determination of the reaction kinetics. The dependence of the reaction rate on temperature, pressure and concentration of the reactants are needed to come to a reactor design. Besides, the kinetics are influenced by the available porosity of the sintermetal reactor.
The result of this research will be an expression in the following form:

$$\frac{dP_ci}{dt} = F(tau, P, T, P_ci, porosity) \qquad i = 1 \rightarrow n$$

In which $\frac{dP_ci}{dt}$ is the change of component i per unit of time and per unit of volume of the reactor.
Tau is the residence time in the reactor, P the pressure, T the temperature of the reaction, P_ci the partial pressure of the system of component i and n the number of reacting components.
By selecting several temperatures and compositions and testing several catalytic materials in a laboratory differential reactor formula F will be determined. (State University of Utrecht)

Task 2.1. Based on corrosion information from literature, two or three alloys will be chosen. (State University of Utrecht).

Task 2.2. From the alloys selected in task 2.1, an alloy will be chosen based on availability from suppliers. (Krebsöge)

Task 3. The best alloy chosen from task 2.2 will be used for producing several samples of sintered metal. These samples will be different in particle size and pressure during sintering. The porosity and specific pressure drop will be examined .(Krebsöge)

Task 4. The heat conductivity of the samples with different particle size and pressure during sintering, mentioned in task 2 will be measured. (IKE)

Task 5. Formulas describing the porosity and heat conductivity, both as a function of particle size, pressure during sintering and the alloy concerned, based on the investigations of task 3 and 4 will be determined (VEG-Gasinstituut).

Task 6. A two dimensional model will be developed to synthesize the results of task 1 and 5 into an overall model to calculate and optimize the pressure drop, diameter and length of the reactor. The model will include a cooling medium that will have to be chosen outside the reactor tube.

The simulation program for this will be based on Phoenics which will be made available at Comprimo.(State University of Utrecht)

Task 7.1 Upscaling to an industrial design based on the result of task 6 will be done (VEG- Gasinstituut)

Task 7.2 Practical experience like fouling and sulphur condensation will be taken into account in this. (VEG- Gasinstituut)

Task 8.1. A simple reactor element based on sintermetal will be build (Krebsöge).

Task 8.2 The catalyst will be deposited into this reactor.(State University of Utrecht)

Task 8.3 For different temperatures and concentrations the temperature distributions and conversions of H_2S into S will be tested experimentally. (VEG-Gasinstituut)

Task 9. The results of task 6 and task 8 will be compared.(VEG-Gasinstituut).

RESULTS

In figure 4. typical derived activity and selectivity curves for the oxidation of H_2S are given. In the low temperature area, the selectivity asymptotically approaches a constant

maximum value. This implies that the ratio of the produced concentrations of sulphur and unwished SO_2 is constant at low temperatures. Moreover SO_2 is formed while the activity and subsequently the sulphur concentration inside the catalyst bed is low. This means that there is a side reaction in which H_2S is not only converted to sulphur but also to SO_2. According to the power rate law, the rates of these reactions have the same H_2S dependency. If the reactions have the same similar activation energies the reactions also have the same temperature dependency. This explains why the selectivity is constant in spite of the different hydrogen sulphide concentration profiles throughout the catalyst bed at different temperatures.

In the high temperature region the selectivity decreases. Here the activity and therefore the sulphur concentration inside the catalyst bed is high while the H_2S concentration is low. Therefore the follow-up reaction in which sulphur reacts to SO_2 must be responsible for the extra SO_2 production. A higher activation energy is responsible for the higher temperature at which this reaction proceeds. Figure 5 summarizes the reaction paths which are mentioned.

A new method was tried by Krebsöge (Z/S process) to come to a uniform distribution but variable porosity. This method consists of shooting the metal powder with a resin into its shape. In this way a uniform porosity which varies between 40 and 70 % is reached.
To get a close look into the reactor, simulations were done using the Phoenics program. In figure 7., a conventional fixed bed is shown and in figure 8 a sintermetal reactor. As can be seen, there is a considerable slip of not reacted H_2S in the conventional case which is due to slip of the gas along the wall. This has the following disadvantages:

1. There is no catalyst so H_2S will not be oxidized.
2. The pressure drop is lower so that there is a more than proportional amount flowing trough the wall region.
3. The reactor is a tube so that the area of channelling is relatively large.

In figure 8 there is no slip along the wall and the temperature is more uniformly distributed.
To come to a design procedure the (simple) Krischer model was adopted [4]. See figure 9. The Krischer model combines two simplified structures of porous materials: The porous material is seen as parralel plates. In one part the heat flow is parralel to the plates (A), in the other structure the heat flow is perpendicular to the plates (B). From the data of IKE, the a in figure 9 can be estimated.
Both the heat production and heat removal are functions of the porosity: when the porosity is low there is much metal available for heat conduction but little space left for introducing catalyst. (See figure 10).
From the data in table 1., the optimal residence time can be calculated (See figure 11). Using the Ergun-equation the pressure drop across the bed can be calculated:

$$\Delta P=(300/Re+3.5)*(rho_{gas}*w^2*(1-por)*l/(2*por^3*d_p)$$

In which ΔP is the pressure drop, por is the porosity, Re is the Reynolds number based on d_p, rho_{gas} is the density of the gas, w the gasvelocity in the empty reactor and d_p the original particle size.

To remove the heat the reactor tubes can be put into a boiler of about 60 bars so that the temperature is about 550 K and constant.(see figure 12).
With the above information the length and diameter of the tubes can be calculated.

FUTURE R&D

Further steps to be taken are:

Basic research:

a. Further development of the sintermetal optimization method (Z/S verfahren).
b. Development of a better model than the Krischer model for the heat removal for which a considerable amount of sintermetal samples are to be measured for porosity and heat conductivity.
c. Development of a general computer model for all kinds of reactions and shapes.

Development:

Construction of a pilot plant for H_2S oxidation.

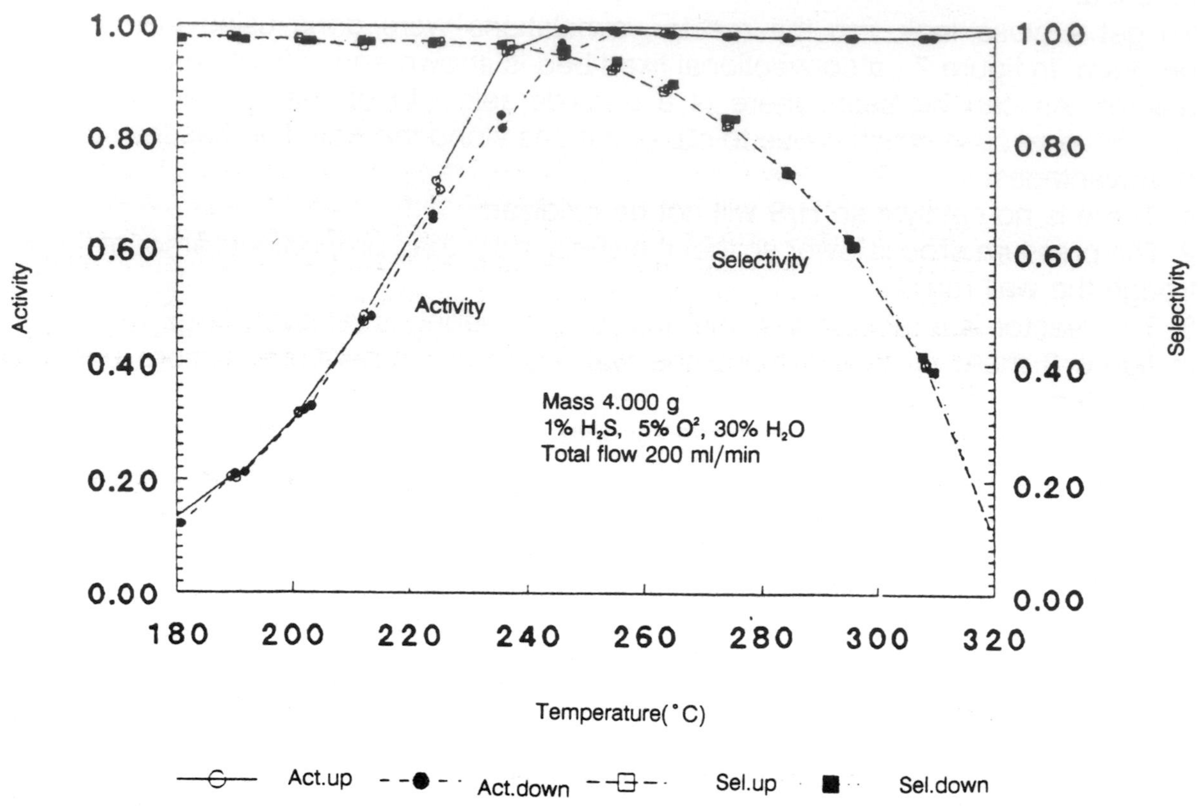

Figure 4. Super-Claus, activity and selectivity.

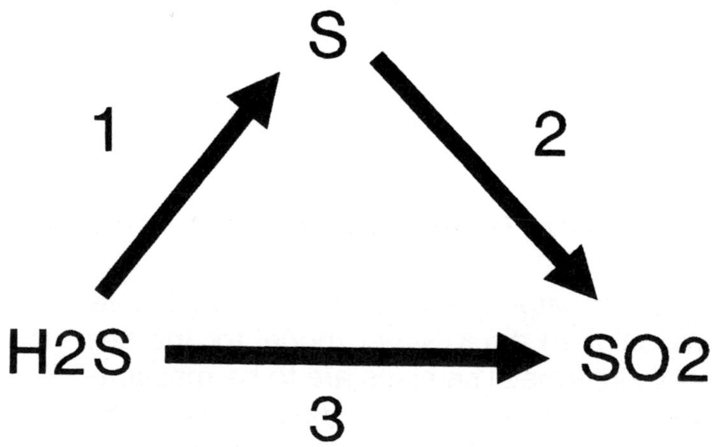

Figure 5. Reaction paths.

In table 1. the main results are summarized.

Table 1. Reaction rates of the three reactions of figure 5.
R1 = exp(21-10220/T)*[H_2S]
R2 = exp(32.1-18600/T)*[S]
R3 = exp(17.4-10220/T)*[H_2S]

The porosity of a sintermetal body which is formed by letting the metal powder flow freely into a shape after which it is sintered is low. Too low to optimize a reactor in which the heat production and heat removal are to be balanced. Moreover the porosity is not the same throughout the body (See figure 6).

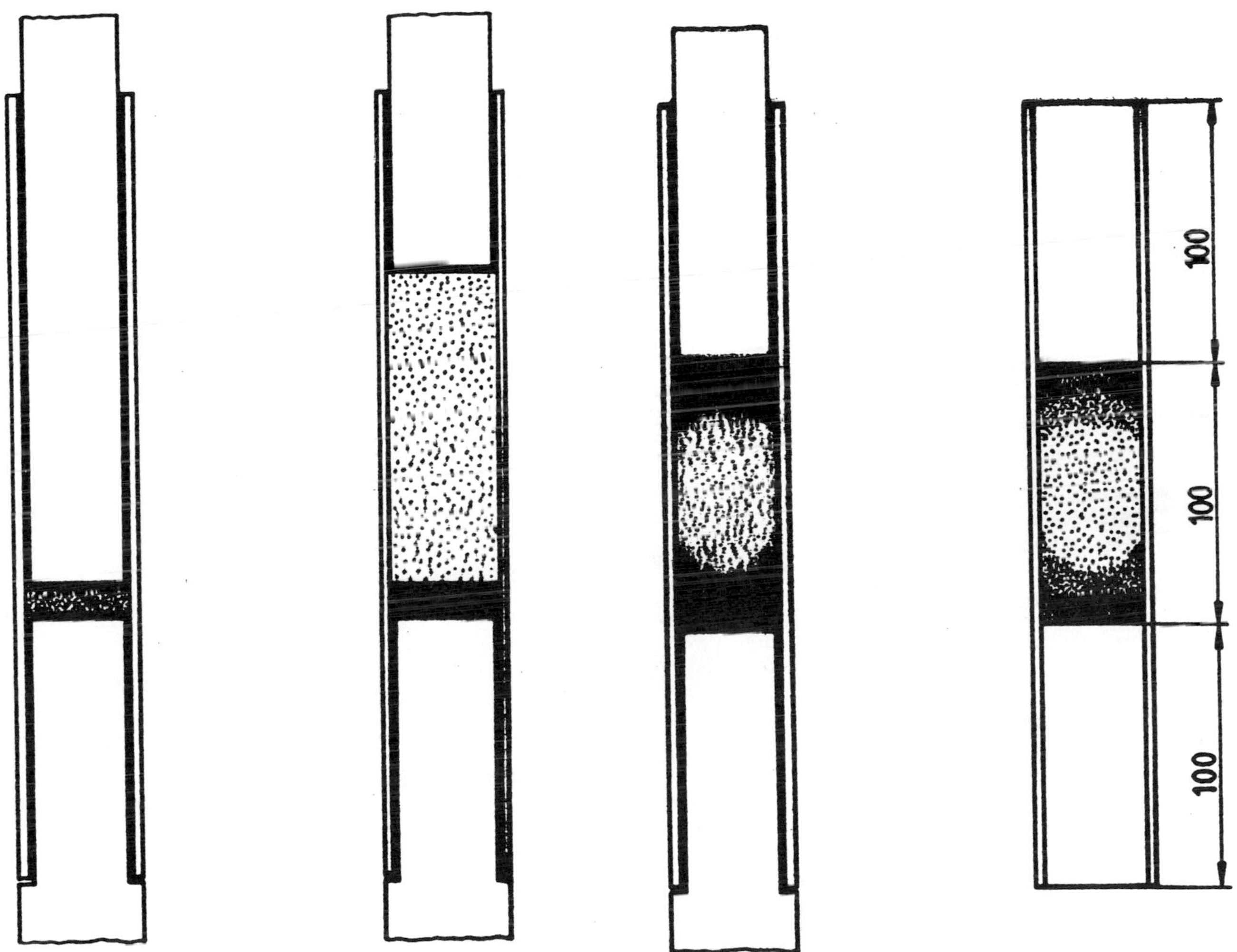

Figure 6. Due to the filling and pressing the porosity in the final sintered body is non uniform.

H_2S

Temperature

Figure 7. Phoenics presentation of a conventional fixed bed.

H_2S

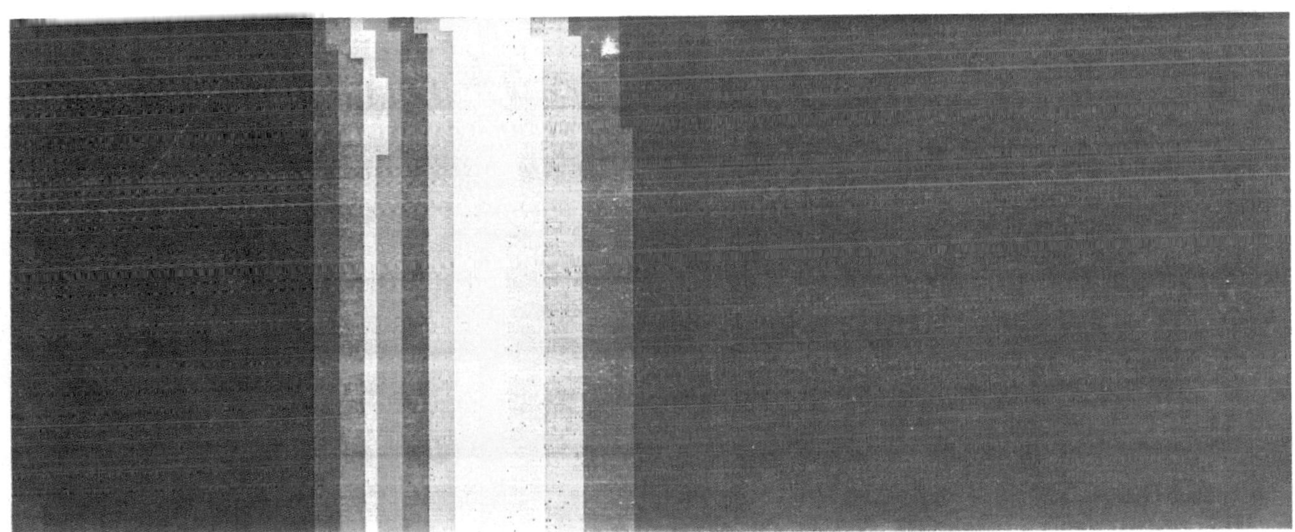

Temperature

Figure 8. Sintermetal reactor in Phoenics presentation.

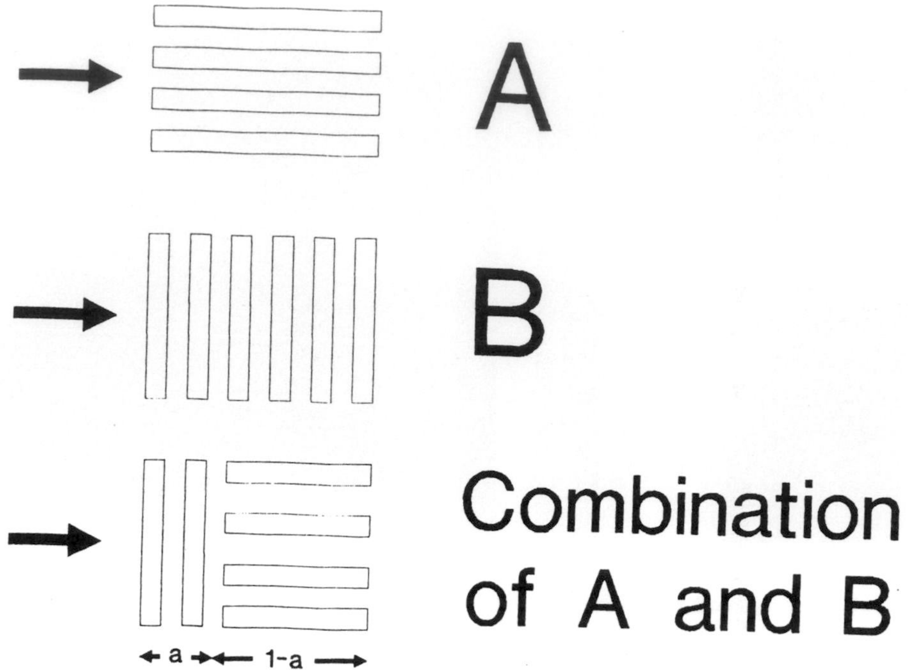

Figure 9. The Krischer model for heat transport in porous materials.

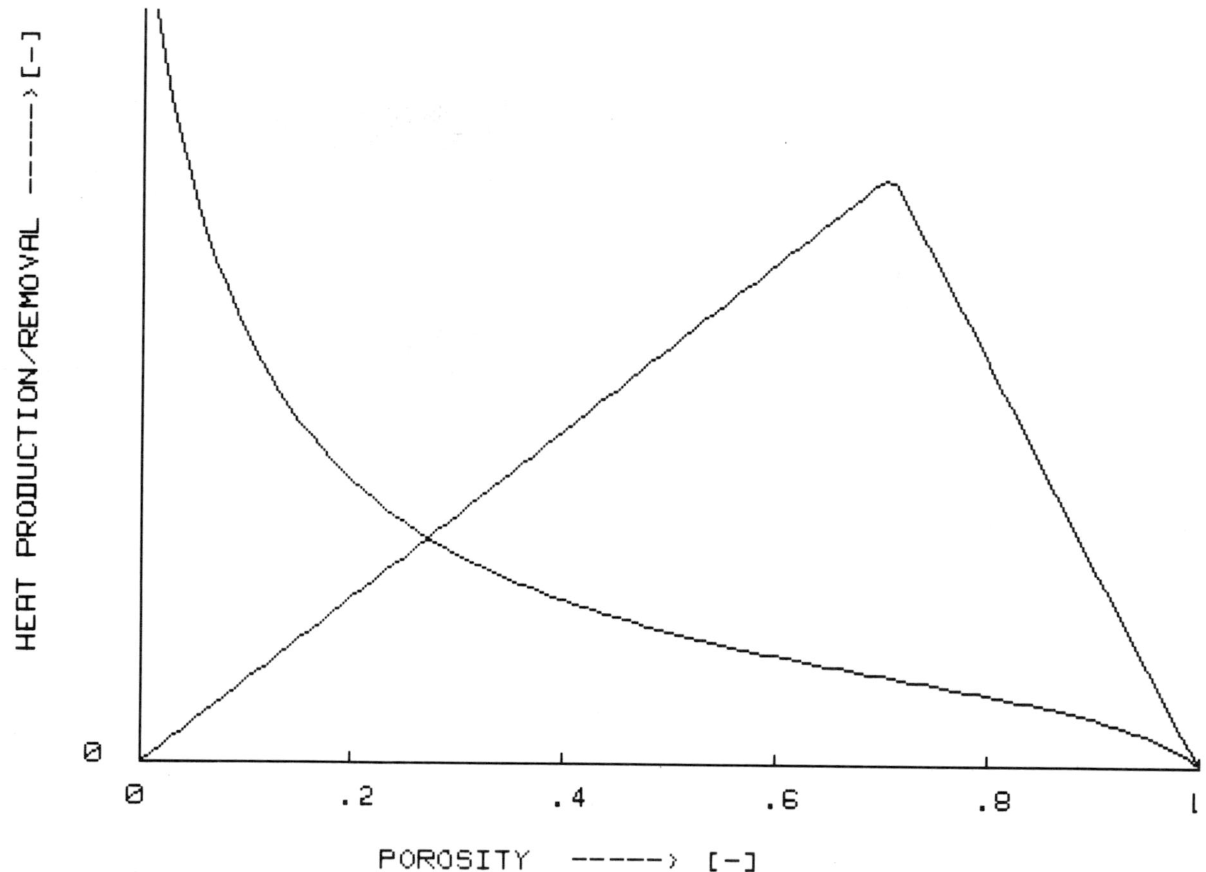

Figure 10. Heat removal and heat production as a function of the porosity.

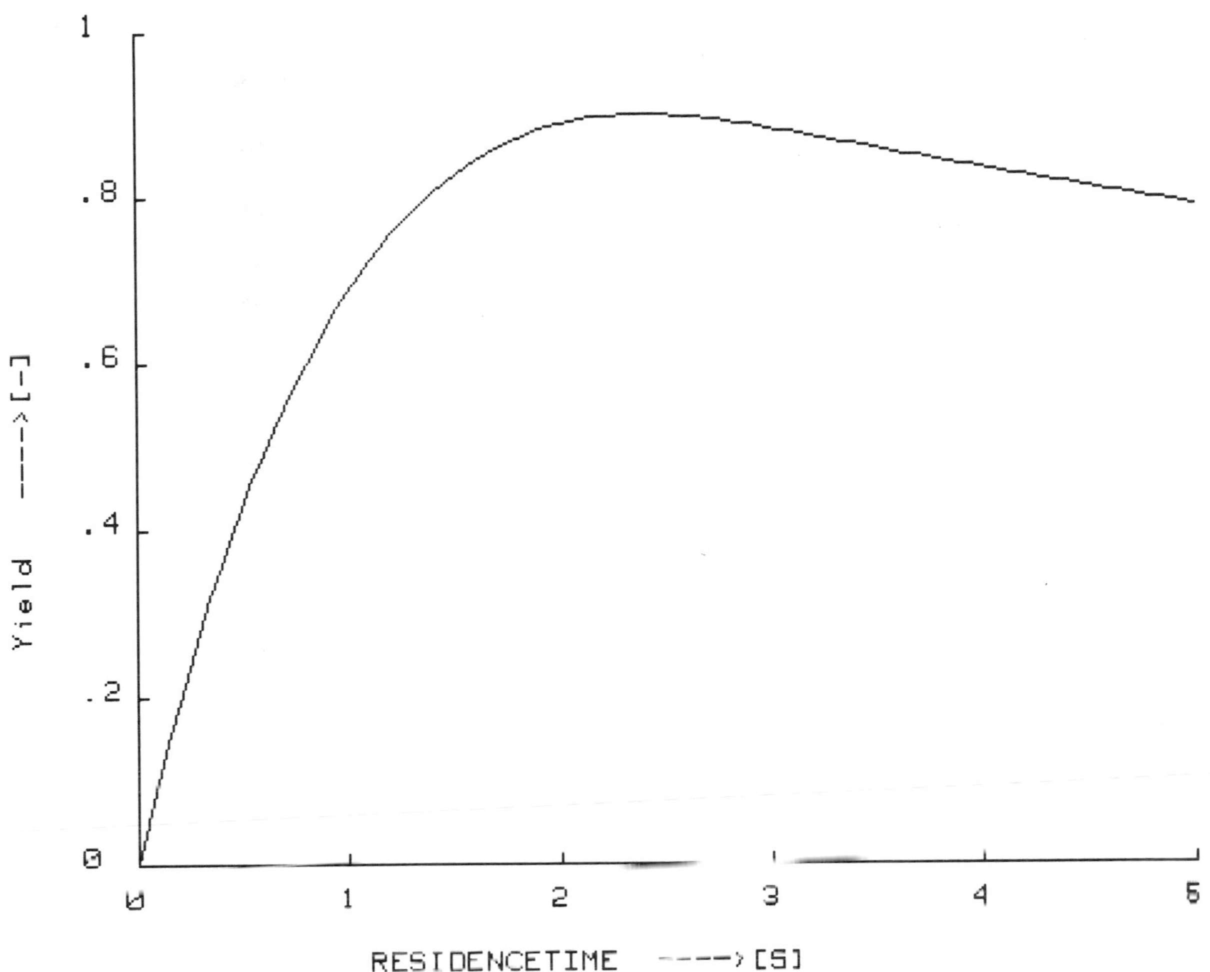

Figure 11. Conversion as a function of the residence time in the reactor.

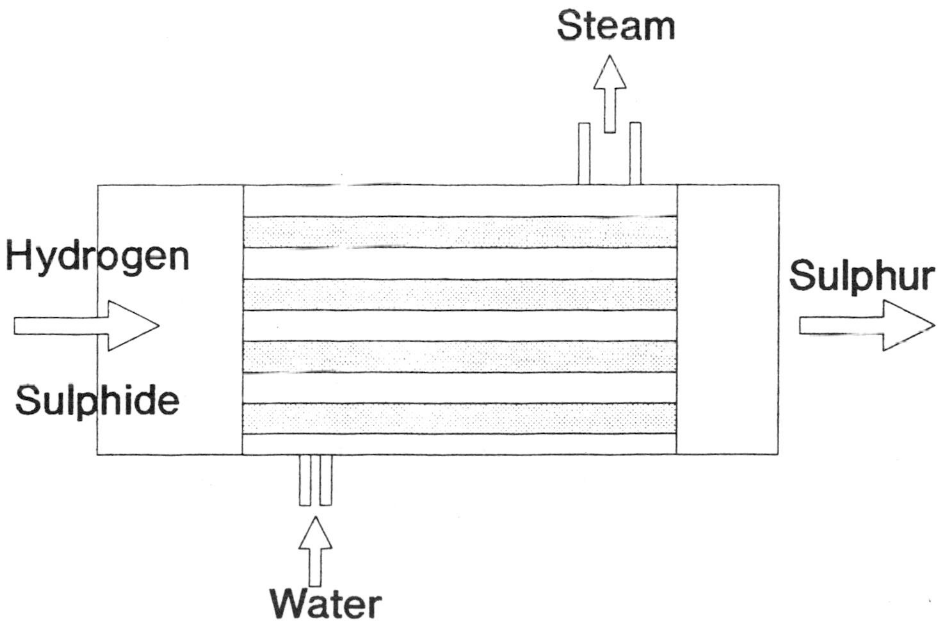

Figure 12. Novel reactor based on sintermetals (compare fig. 1)

OTHER UNIT OPERATIONS

Chairman: Mr. R. Dumon

ABSORPTION-DRIVEN MULTIPLE EFFECT EVAPORATORS

S.YANNIOTIS
HELLAS ENERGY

Contract JOUE-0010-GR

PARTICIPANT

P.Le GOFF
Lab.des Sciences du Genie Chimique
Nancy

SUMMARY

An absorption-driven multiple effect evaporator has been built and operated. The energy savings that could be realized in comparison to a similar conventional steam-heated evaporator ranged from 30% to 45%. A model for a falling film absorber composed of an adiabatic and a diabatic zone has been developed. The concept of Height of Transfer Unit and the Number of Transfer Units has been used to size the absorber. A process control system, which consists of a PC-based central controller performing supervisory control and user interface tasks and a remote unit, the control station, performing local control and data acquisition has been designed.

1. INTRODUCTION

Absorption-driven evaporators represent a new type of evaporators which use an absorbing solution as heating medium instead of steam (2). In these evaporators a hygroscopic solution, i.e. sodium hydroxide or lithium chloride or lithium bromide solution, flows down as a film on the outside surface of the tubes of a falling film evaporator, while the product film flows down the inside surface of the same tubes. Because of the boiling point elevation of the absorbing solution there is a temperature difference between the two films which induce heat transfer and evaporation of water from the product. The vapour generated is transferred to the absorbing solution side through a vapour return line and is absorbed by the solution. The driving force for water vapour mass transfer is provided by the difference in water vapour pressure between the solution and the product. The heat of condensation and dilution which is released during the absorption of water vapour by the solution, provides the heat to sustain the evaporation process. To minimize water vapour mass transfer resistance, non-condensibles are removed from the system by a vacuum pump.

In multiple effect absorption-driven evaporators only the first effect has to be of the absorption type. In this case a vapour return line connects the product side of the last effect with the absorbing solution side of the first effect and the hygroscopic solution absorbs the vapour generated in the last effect. The vapour produced in the other effects is used as in conventional multiple effect evaporators where the vapour produced in one effect is used as heating medium in the next effect.

During operation, the absorbing solution is diluted by the absorbed water vapour. In order to reuse the solution it is necessary to reconcentrate (regenerate) the solution. For this reason, the diluted absorbing solution coming out of the first effect of the evaporator is transferred to a regeneration station where the absorbed water vapour is boiled off.

The regenerator can be coupled with the evaporator and operate in continuous mode or in certain cases it can be profitable to have the regenerator working in a batch process, for example when some low-cost or even free energy sources become periodically available (i.e: solar energy, combustion of residues...). In such cases, the concentrated solution will be stored in a reservoir and be cooled during this storage period.

Absorption-driven evaporators have the following advantages:

1. They give steam economy equivalent to evaporators with many effects without using excessive temperature in the first effect of the product evaporator. This is an extremely important characteristic for heat sensitive materials like foods where the highest temperature can not exceed certain point i.e. 70°C in milk evaporators.
2. They have about 50 % less cooling water requirements in the condenser.

An experimental absorption-driven four effect falling film evaporator coupled with a two effect regenerator has been built under the CEC contract EN3E-0138-GR (Fig.1). Details are given elsewhere (3). The unit was operated as absorption-driven evaporator using sodium hydroxide solution as absorptive/heating medium, but it is very flexible so that other hygroscopic solutions, such as lithium bromide solution, can be used. It was also operated as conventional evaporator using steam in the first effect as heating medium, instead of sodium hydroxide solution. The objective of this work was to compare the energy consumption of the system in the two modes of operation and deduce the energy savings that could be achieved with the proposed system.

The work carried out in this project led to the following conclusions:

1. Absorption-driven multiple effect evaporators are technically feasible.
2. The energy savings that can be realized with a multiple effect absorption-driven evaporator coupled with a two effect regenerator in comparison to a similar conventional steam-heated evaporator range from 30% to 45% depending on the efficiency of sensible heat recovery in the regenerator, the heat losses in the regenerator, the flow rate of the absorptive solution and the overall heat transfer coefficient of the absorber.

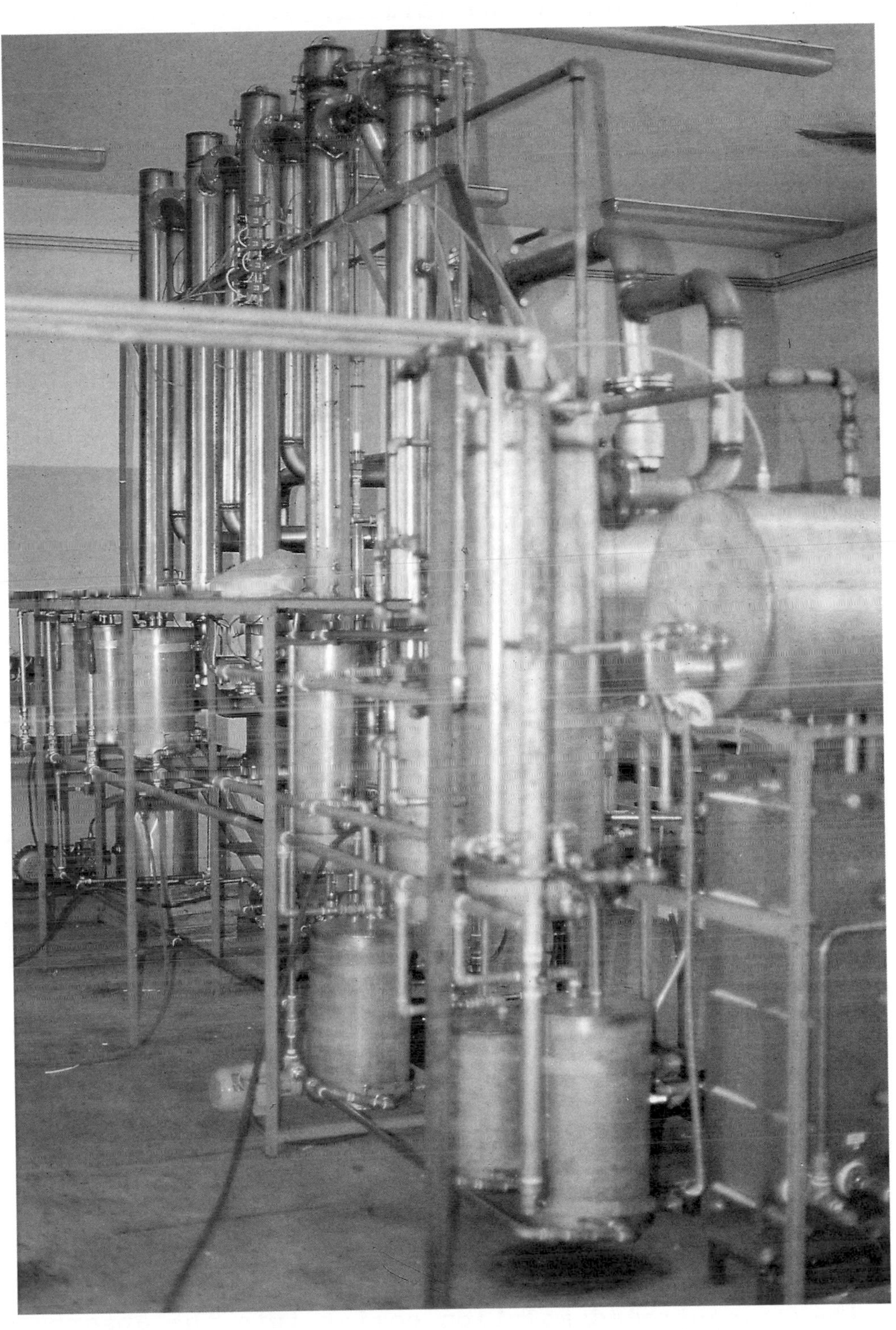

Figure 1. Experimental unit.

Problems that have been identified and need improvement are: a) The overall temperature difference between the absorber (first effect of the evaporator) and the last effect (fourth effect) of the evaporator is much less than the theoretical boiling point elevation of the absorptive solution. b) The concentration of the sodium hydroxide solution can not be high because crystallization of the solution blocks the system when the equipment is shutdown. c) In continuous operation, the amount of water that is evaporated from the absorbing solution in the regenerator must be controlled so that it is equal to the amount of water that has been absorbed in the absorber.

2. OBJECTIVES

The following objectives have been set in the present project:

1. To rebuild the first effect of the absorption-driven evaporator using turbulence promoters in the absorptive solution side of the evaporator tubes in order to increase the heat and mass transfer coefficient.
2. To operate the system using NaOH/KOH mixtures instead of NaOH alone to avoid crystallization of strong solutions at low temperatures.
3. To incorporate in the system a controller to control the water evaporation rate from the NaOH/KOH solution in the regenerator in order to keep the concentration of the solution constant for long runs.
4. To develop a theoretical model for the absorber which will assist in designing scaled-up units and will help to understand better the operation of the absorber.

3. TASKS OF PARTICIPANTS

To achieve the objectives set, the Laboratoire des Sciences du Genie Chimique will design the absorber and develop a theoretical model for the absorber, while Hellas Energy will build the absorber and the controller and carry out the experiments.

4. PRELIMINARY RESULTS

4.1. Theoretical Model

In the present report we will present a mathematical model of the absorbing falling-film, composed of two zones: a first one for the adiabatic heating of the solution, and a second one for the "diabatic" absorption with the heat transfer to a heat-carrying fluid (Fig.2). This kind of absorber is particularly suitable for batch operation , where the concentrated solution coming into the absorber is cool.

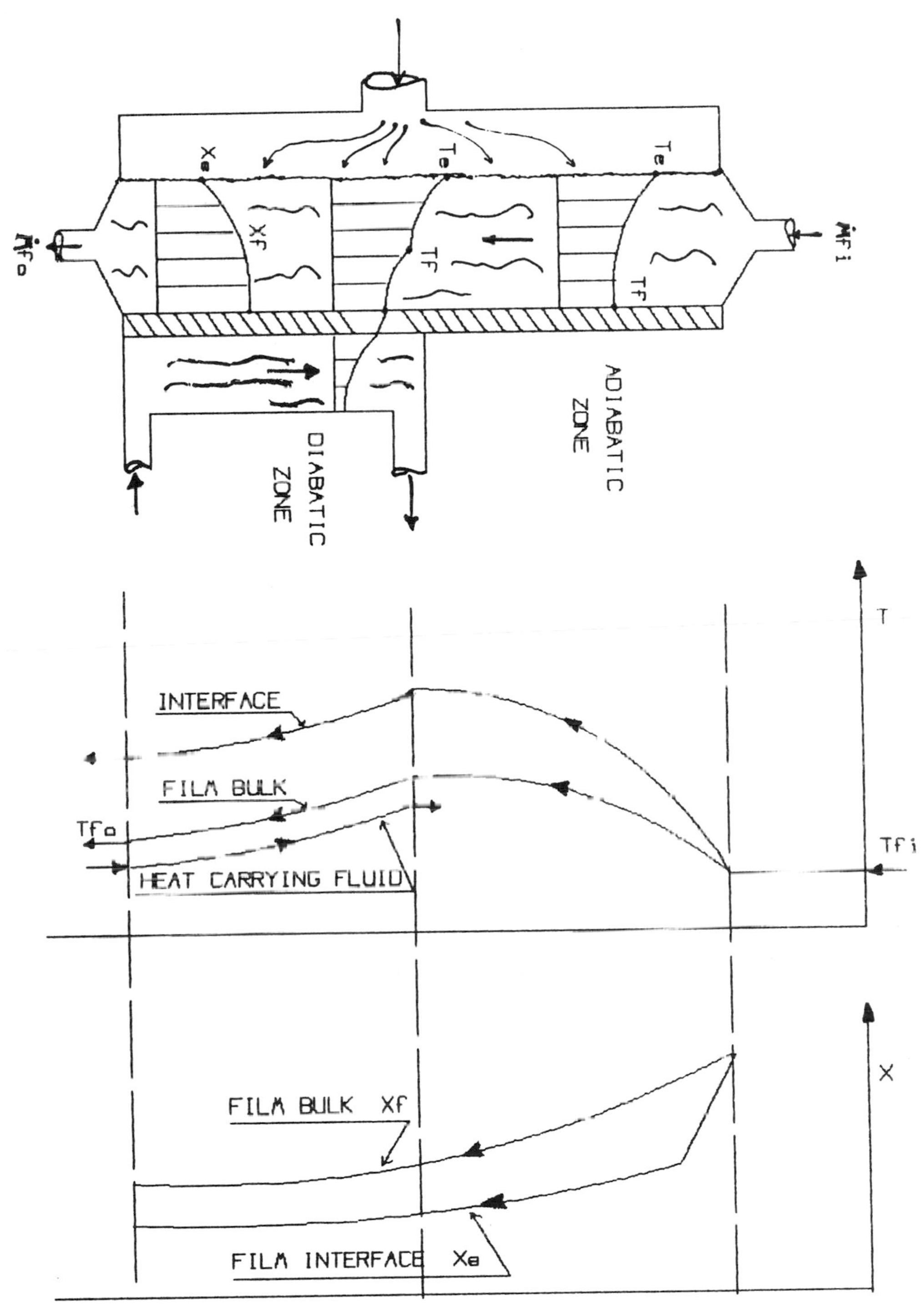

Figure 2. Two-zone absorber with temperature and concentration profiles.

4.1.1. A Scenario of the Absorption Process

At the top of the column, the inlet absorbing solution is represented by the point F_i (Fig.3).

Experience and theory (1) show that within an infinitely short period (non-measurable) the surface of the liquid attains the thermodynamic equilibrium with the vapour phase at the given pressure P_v. This interface is represented by the point E_i. This point is situated on the equilibrium isobar and connected to the entry point F_i, by the interface tie line, whose slope is given by Eq.(1).

As the globule of solution is falling down in the film, thereby mixing with the liquid condensing from the vapour phase, its average temperature T_f increases. The point F, with coordinates $(x_f H_f)$ thus describes the straight operating line F_iV.

This line intersects the equilibrium isobar at a point F_∞ which would be only reached after an infinite time, i.e., at the bottom of an adiabatic column of infinite length.

During such an evolution, the point E representing the interface, and the point F remain connected by a tie line of the same constant slope given by:

$$P_T = \frac{c_m \rho k_{ef}}{h_{ef}} \Delta H_v = \left(\frac{D}{\alpha}\right)^n \Delta H_v \tag{1}$$

In reality at the bottom of the adiabatic zone, of height Z_a, the points reach the positions F_m and E_m.

As the globule of solution descents in the diabatic zone, it is heated by the absorption of vapour, and simultaneously cooled by the heat transfer to the supporting wall. This second effect is stronger than the first one, so that the temperature T_f decreases from T_{fm} till to T_{f0}, at the outlet. The point F describes the curved operating line F_mF_0 but this line is never very different from the straight line F_mF_0, which crosses the ordinate axis at the point V' with coordinates:

$$x = 0, \qquad H_{V'} = H_V - \frac{Q}{\dot{M}_{vd}} \tag{2}$$

For any intermediate level in the diabatic zone, the point (F) is located on a curved line starting from the point F_m and arriving at the point F_0. The chord F_mF, crosses the ordinate axis in a point V" which is different from V'in the general case.But in the particular case, when the heat flux density leaving the column is proportional to the mass

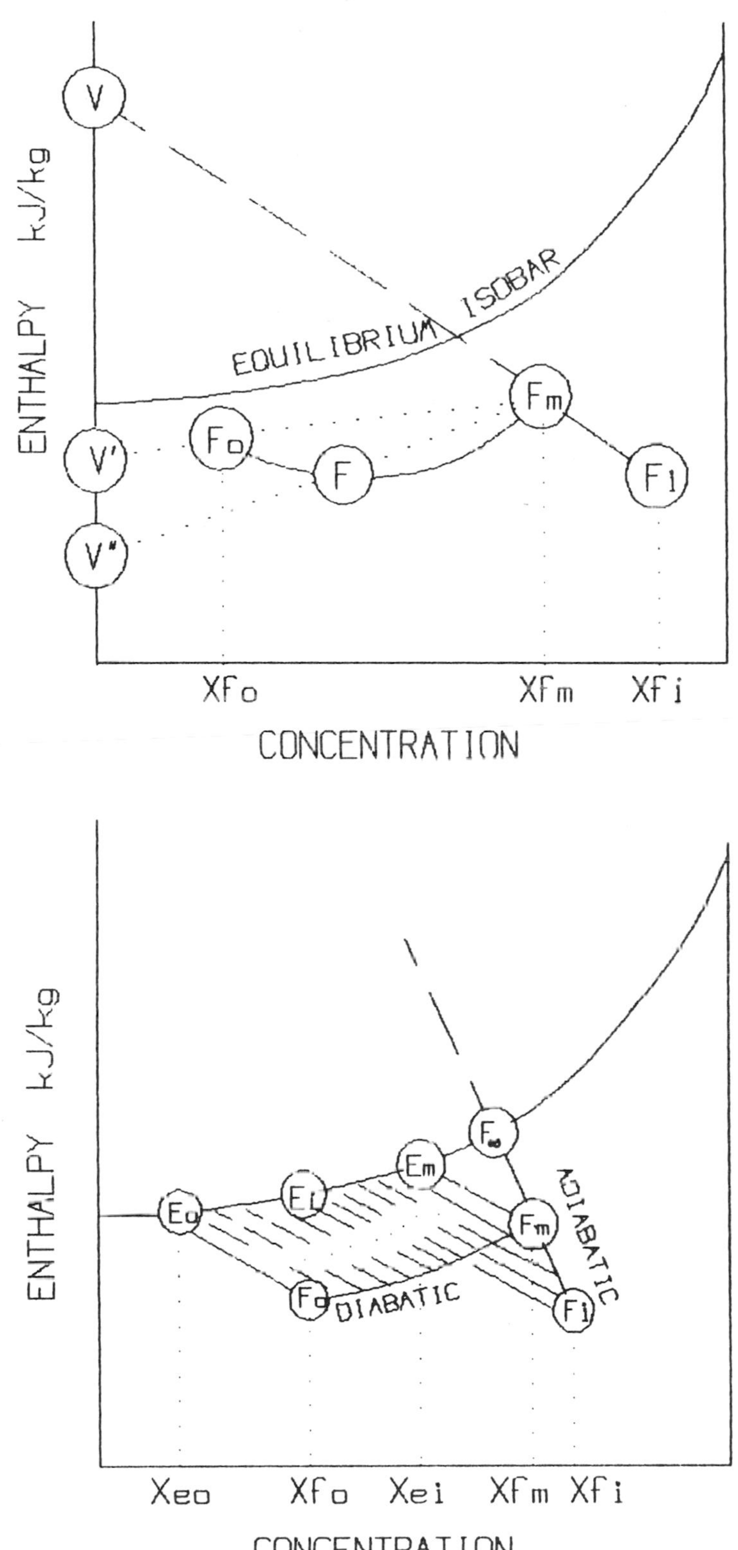

Figure 3. Ponchon diagram for the two-zone absorber.

flux density absorbed at the interface, at each level in the column, the ratio Q_t/M_{vd} is constant over the whole diabatic zone. In these conditions, the point V" is fixed and not different from V'.

In summary, the trajectory of the point (F) representing the bulk of the falling film at any level (which is usually called the "**OPERATING LINE**"), is composed of a rigorous straight line F_iF_m in the adiabatic zone, and an approximative straight line F_mF_0, in the diabatic zone.

4.1.2. Modelling with the "Mass Transfer Unit" Concept

The differential equation for the mass balance of solvent (water) in the film, is:

$$dM_f = \rho k_{ef}(x_f - x_e)\, b dZ = -M_s \frac{dx_f}{x_f^2} \qquad (3)$$

By integration, one obtains:

$$Z = \frac{M_s}{b \rho k_{ef}} \int_{x_{fi}}^{x_{fo}} \frac{dx_f}{x_f^2\,(x_f - x_e)} \qquad (4)$$

or

$$Z = HTU \cdot NTU$$

The HTU can also be expressed as:

$$HTU = Re_f \frac{x_f \mu}{\rho k_{ef}} = Re_f \frac{x_f \mu c_m}{h_{ef}} \left(\frac{\alpha}{D}\right)^n \qquad (5)$$

As the variation of x_f is small along the absorber (i.e. $x_{fi} = 0.50$ and $x_{f0} = 0.47$) the following simplifications can be made:

a) an average constant value x_f is taken off the integral
b) the equilibrium isobar can be linearized in the domain.

As a consequence, NTU can be calculated from:

$$NTU = \frac{1}{\bar{x}_f^2} \cdot \frac{x_{fi} - x_{fo}}{(x_f - x_e)_{lm}} \qquad (6)$$

where $(x_f - x_e)_{lm}$ is the logarithmic mean of the "**mass diffusional driving force**".

4.2. THE CONTROL SYSTEM

4.2.1. Architecture

The overall system architecture is configured as a Supervisory Control And Data Acquisition system. This is a custom designed and fabricated to allow full and integrated implementation of Instrumentation and Control requirements. It is a small scale Process Control System. The front end consists of a PC-XT based Central Controller performing Supervisory Control and User Interface tasks. A remote unit, the Control Station, which performs local control and data acquisition, is based on a single board microcomputer connected to a number of peripheral wiring cards. The two units are interconnected through a RS-232 line.

4.2.2. Measured Variables

The full system instrumentation measures, in addition to the controlled system state variables, a number of variables outside the control loop for analytical purposes.

The system which is of interest to control is shown in Fig.4 and the measured variables are:

- P1:pressure (vacuum) in regenerator R1
- P2:pressure (vacuum) in regenerator R2
- L1:liquid level in regenerator R1
- L2:liquid level in regenerator R2
- C1:concentration of brine in R1
- Q:heat power (resistive-electrical) input to R1
- m1:mass flow rate out of R1 and into the HE
- m2:mass flow rate out of HE and into the absorber A
- m3:cooling water flow rate into the condenser C
- T1:solution temperature out of R1 and into the HE circuit
- T2:solution temperature into the absorber
- T3:cooling water temperature into the condenser
- T4:solution temperature out of the HE primary side
- T5:solution temperature out of R2 and into the HE secondary side
- T6:solution temperature out of the HE secondary side
- T7:solution temperature out of the absorber
- T8:cooling water temperature out of the condenser

4.2.3. Sensors and Transducers

The temperature is measured using Copper-Constantan thermocouples. The level is measured by custom made capacitive, non-contact, transducer. A relatively inexpensive gravimetric method is used to measure the concentration of the solution. The weight (pressure at the bottom) of a fixed liquid column is measured using a differential pressure transducer of range 2m of water and

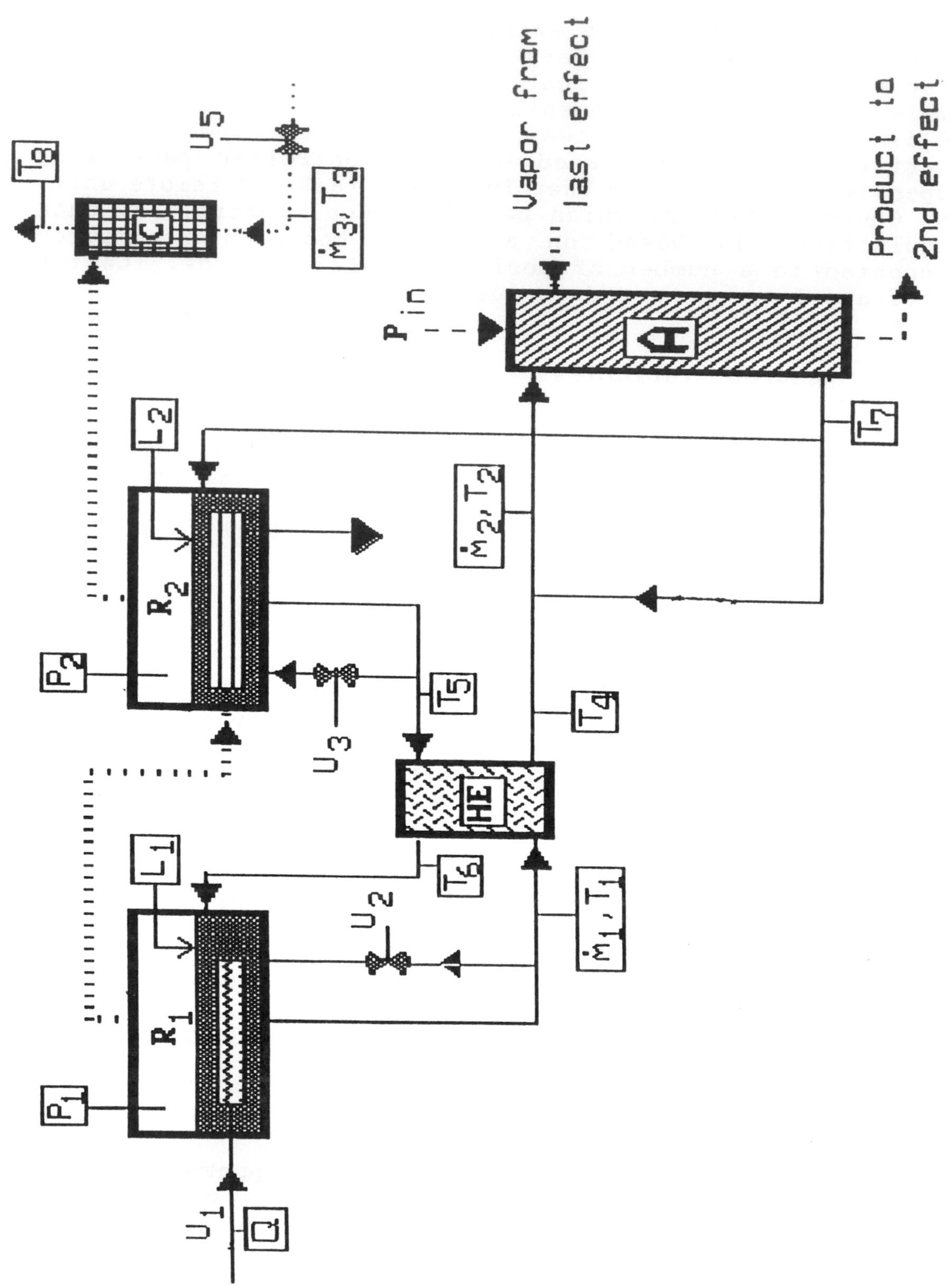

Figure 4. Regenerator/Absorber with control inputs.

0.1% accuracy. The heat input to the system is monitored by V and I (Resistive load Q=V*I). The mass flow rate (m1) out of the regenerator R1 is measured using a commercial magnetic type flow meter. The mass flow rate (m3) of cooling water is measured using an inexpensive flow meter of the "water utility " type onto which a magnetic pick-up has been attached.

4.2.4. Control Inputs

Control inputs that affect the state of the process are (Fig.4):

-U1:This is the heat rate monitored as Q. This variable is analogically controlled because a simple Relay (ON/OFF) control would not provide the required accuracy (overshoot-undershoot ripple). It is controlled through a 3phase thyristor switcher with a DC input signal for phase control. Input U1 is controlled using an independent software PID module in the Control Station. Coefficients for the PID controller are determined after some initial tests for stability are conducted, and then downloaded.

-U2:Is a bypassing control valve used to maintain the desirable flow rate m1.

-U3:Is a bypassing control valve used to maintain liquid level L1.

-U5:Is a cooling water flow control valve used to adjust the condenser power i.e. it controls the concentration C1.

Valve controls U2, U3 and U5 are of the analog (except non-linear) type. For stability reasons the Gain of these elements is adjusted by using "duty cycle" i.e. PWM controlled operation. The appropriate "gain" is found during initial identifying tests
and then downloaded to the CS.

4.2.5. Control Software

As discussed initially the process model is a multivariable system with a high degree of intercoupling between variables. For example increasing (Q) to rise T1 will also affect the concentration C1. This type of intercoupling is expressed in details by the process model equations. Considering the fact that each test-run will target a desirable steady state (i.e. zero all errors) an arbitrary decoupling was decided as it is depicted by the following hierarchy of control sequence. This sequence means in turn:

1. Increase U5 to increase C1 and vice versa.
2. Decrease U3 to increase level L1 and v/v.
3. Decrease U2 to increase flow rate m1 and v/v.
4. Increase U1 to increase temperature T1 and v/v.

5. NOMENCLATURE

b=width of the falling film
c_m=mean specific heat of the solution between interface and bulk
D=the mass diffusivity of the solvent (water) in the solution
h_{ef}=heat transfer coefficient between the interface and the bulk of the film.
H_v=enthalpy of water vapour absorbed
ΔH_v=latent heat of condensation-absorption of the vapour
k_{ef} is the mass transfer coefficient between the interface and the bulk of the film
M_f=mass flow rate of the solution
M_s=mass flow rate of the solute
M_{vd}=water vapour mass flux absorbed in the diabatic zone.
n=exponent approximately equal to 2/3.
Q=heat transferred to the supporting wall
$Re_f=M_f/b\mu$=film Reynolds number
x=solution concentration
α=the heat diffusivity of the solution
μ=viscosity of the solution
ρ=density of the solution

6. FUTURE WORK

A large amount of energy is consumed each year in evaporation in food and chemical industries. Considerable energy savings could be achieved by: a) developing membrane technology further so that reverse osmosis can be used at higher temperatures and pressures than today's membranes can withstand, b) by incorporating heat transfer intensification into evaporator's technology.

With respect to absorption-driven evaporators further energy savings could be achieved by using three effects in the regenerator. The last option is related to work in developing three stage absorption heat pumps.

7. REFERENCES

1. H. Le Goff, A. Ramadane et P. Le Goff. Int. J. Heat Mass Transfer, 29, 625 (1986).

2. Schwartzberg, H.G. Food Technology 31 (3), 67 (1977).

3. Yanniotis S. Industrial Processes. Proceedings of a contractors' meeting. Brussels, 29 June 1988. Ed. P. Pilavachi, CEC publication EUR 12246EN.

ENERGY SAVING AND POLLUTION ABATEMENT IN GLASS-MAKING FURNACES, CEMENT KILNS AND BAKING OVENS

Maria da Graça Carvalho
Instituto Superior Técnico (IST)
Technical University of Lisbon

Contract JOUE - 0051 - C

PARTICIPANTS

Prof. Fred Lockwood — Imperial College of Scie.Techn. & Med. — ICST&M
Prof. Franz Durst — University of Erlangen-Nuremberg — LSTM
Prof. Hector Meunier — Faculté Polytechnique de Mons — FPM
Prof. René Jottrand — Université Libre de Bruxelles — ULB
Dr. Christos Papadopoulos — Centre for Renewable Energy Sources — CRES
Dr. Ubo de Vries — TNO Institute for Cereals, Flour and Bread
Ir. L.W. Koot — TNO Division of Technology and Society
Prof. Ramoa Ribeiro — Instituto da Energia — INTERG
Ir. J.F. Bassine — Institut National Belge du Verre — INV
Dr. J. Richalet — ADERSA
Eng. Barros da Silva — Metal Portuguesa SARL
Dr. Dimitri Hadjicostantis — TITAN Cement Company, SA

SUMMARY

A computer simulation model which can be used for a variety of furnaces, kilns and ovens will be developed and validated. The model will include different fuels (gas, oil and coal) and environmental aspects such as NO_x emissions will be incorporated. The model will be validated with experimental data from a laboratory furnace, applied and adapted to simulate glass-making furnaces, cement kilns and baking ovens.

For the experiments, a variety of sensors will be used. To provide temperature distributions along walls of furnaces, kilns and ovens, temperature sensors operating in high temperature environments will be selected and adapted. In addition infrared wall temperature sensors will be developed. For the measurement of quantities of coal and air supply to the burner, a Coriolis mass flow meter and flow rate regulator will be developed. Development of sensors and monitoring systems for gas temperature, pollutants and moisture content will be carried out.

Modelling and experimental work on electric and gas-fired baking ovens (e.g. bread) will include development of a multisensor system for water vapour partial pressure, level of forced air circulation and crust colour.

The general code will also be applied and adapted to cement kilns; work will include the integration of a NO_x emission model; and modelling of the major chemical reactions; validation of the models will be done against data obtained from the TITAN kilns.

The model will be extended to simulate different parts of a glass-making furnace; the near burner region; the control system; the forehearth of the furnace.

INTRODUCTION

The recent awareness of the limitation of energy resources, the increase in fuel prices and the problem of pollution have turned the attention of combustor engineers towards the importance of improving the design of combustion equipment.

Optimized furnace, kiln and oven operating conditions together with advanced control systems are required to reduce energy consumption and decrease pollutant levels in industrial furnaces, such as those used in glass, ceramic, cement and baking. The design and operation of furnaces and burners have, however, relied almost exclusively on empirical methods. Increased knowledge of the flow and heat transfer characteristics of industrial furnaces, kilns and ovens is an essential requirement to determine improved designs and operating conditions for the furnaces.

The main goal of the present project is to develop "tools" to be used in the glass, cement and baking industry that can lead to energy savings and pollution abatement. The work programme will involve:

- Computer-Aided Exploration of Novel Energy-Saving and Pollution Abatement Equipment and Operational Concepts.
- Feasibility Study for Development of Control Strategies and Expert Systems making use of Mathematical Modelling.
- Application of Sensors in Harsh Environments.

This proposal highlights mathematical modelling as a means of unifying the treatment of the diverse furnace types under consideration here in.

Several research groups involved in the present project, I.S.T., I.C.S.T. & M., LSTM-Erlangen and Metal Portuguesa, were previously involved in a research project in the Non-Nuclear Energy R&D Programme (Energy Conservation) entitled "Improved Design for Glass Smelting Kilns" - EN3E-0153-P.

In the previous research project a computer code for the simulation and design of industrial glass smelting furnaces was developed. This computer code was used to improve the design and operating conditions of already existing industrial glass furnaces operating with oxy-fuel conditions. The present project will extend the previous research with the following priorities:

- To widen the flexibility of flow modelling techniques to increase the range of applications, namely to cement kilns and baking ovens. In spite of the diversification and range of temperature, occuring in a glass-making furnace, a cement kiln and a baking oven, the underlying physical processes are the same (combustion, convective and radiative heat transfer and mass transfer). Therefore, the ruling equations and the numerical algorithm to be used for the three cases are the same.

- To extend the modelling techniques to oil(taking into account the two-phase flow behaviour of the fuel spray) and coal fired furnaces.
- To improve the quality of data from experimental measurements with the aim of refining the models.
- To reduce computer time and to produce a more flexible, general and user-friendly computer code.
- To improve the understanding of interactions between the combustion process and the actual reactions occuring, to enable combustion and process models to be confined effectively.

OBJECTIVES

The aim of the present project is to develop and validate a computer simulation model which can be used for a variety of furnaces, kilns and ovens. Such a code will be used to explore oven concepts and control strategies which can lead to energy savings and pollution abatement. Experimental work aiming at the evaluation of thc model will include testing of sensors suitable for harsh environments.

TASKS OF PARTICIPANTS

The work programme was subdivided in five tasks entitled:

- Development of General Mathematical Modelling and Validation with Laboratory Data.
- Application of Sensors in Harsh Environment.
- Baking Ovens.
- Cement Kilns
- Glass and Ceramic Furnaces.

Development of General Mathematical Modelling and Validation with Laboratory Data

In the present task, a computer simulation model which can handle gas, oil and coal-firing will be developed (IST and ICST&M). The computer code will be validated against data acquired in a large scale laboratory furnace for gas, oil and coal firing (ICST&M). The present furnace is a vertical axially down-fired by a variable swirl burner. The cylinder diameter and length are respectively 0.6 m and 3 m. The near burner cylindrical walls are refractory lined for a distance of 1.5 m from the burner plane and water cooled over their remaining length. These measurements will include details of the near burner field and of char burnout, NO_x emission and the heat transfer to the wall - ICST&M.

Application of Sensors in Harsh Environments

Adaptation of Wall Temperature Sensors

Special attention will be given to high temperature sensors typical of glass-ceramic furnaces and cement kilns.

To provide information on temperature distributions along walls of ovens, kilns and furnaces, various high-temperature sensors are offered on the market. Their application in practice shows that the limitation of the applicability of the sensors in high temperature environments is not known. This hampers their application and raises doubts about the measured progress parameters. In order to remedy this situation, LSTM-Erlangen will select and adapt sensors already available in the market for temperature ranges typical of ovens as well as kilns and furnaces. Their properties will be tested in laboratory experiments and data will be provided that allow the sensor performance to be assessed when employed for wall-temperature measurements in ovens, kilns and furnaces. Performance data will include predicted reliability and life-time. In this way, the behaviour of the sensors in high-temperature environments will be known - LSTM.

Infra-red Wall Temperature Sensors

In ovens, kilns and furnaces, local temperature information of the wall is of interest in order to assess durability of the employed high-temperature materials and/or to assess additional temperature controls. Temperature measurements can be carried out with infra-red sensors but wall temperature measurements can be carried out with infra-red sensing devices, but these are usually disturbed by the radiation of the flame itself and from the gas temperature distribution inside of kilns and furnaces. To reduce these disturbing effects, special focusing optics will be employed to yield local temperature information of wall materials with a higher reliability than that obtainable from conventional infra-red systems. A complete optical and electronic system will be set up and make available for wall temperature measurements in ovens, kilns and furnaces of the participating companies - LSTM.

Coriolis Mass Flow Meter and Flow Rate Regulator

The performance of combustion processes in kilns and furnaces is heavily dependent on the metering of the coal and air supply to the burners. It will be demonstrated that a specially developed Coriolis-flow meter can measure the coal supply from a coal bunker to a supplying line of a burner that provides the mixture of coal and air. The principles of the Coriolis-mass flow meter is based on the measurement of the Coriolis-force of a coal stream entering the meter axially and leaving it radially. The force is interpreted as a momentum of the rotating wheel which is measured as instantaneous information on the mass flow of coal - LSTM.

Videometic and Kinematic Studies of Flame Structures

The energy consumption and emission values of furnaces and kilns will depend on the flame structure which is given by the sum of the convection, diffusion and combustion processes. In order to observe these, a cold probe has been developed that allows videomatic and kinematographic studies of the flame front. Figure 1 shows a picture of the developed video fire probe for furnaces and kilns and Figure 2 shows the application of the probe in a melting kiln.

The project will provide a complete system with camera to be used by the various industries involved in the project. It is planned to have an additional camera available together with suitable processing equipment to quantify the flame structure for assessing its influence on energy consumption and emission rates in furnaces and kilns - LSTM.

Development of Sensors and a Monitoring System for Gas Temperature, Pollutant and moisture Content Measurements

Sensors and a monitoring system for gas temperature, pollutant and moisture content will be developed by TNO - Tech. for Society.

Development of a Multi-Sensor System for Baking Ovens

A multi-sensor system for the water vapour partial pressure, the crust colour and the level of forced air circulation will be developed by - TNO Cereals Flour and Bread.

Applications to Baking Ovens

The mathematical models referred in the First Task will be applied to the particular geometry and operation conditions of baking ovens. The model will take into consideration the heat and mass transfer in the dough during baking, the thermal radiation and the forced circulation inside the oven (IST, INTERG and CRES). Experiments will be carried out using the multi-sensor system for the temperature, the water vapour partial pressure, the crust colour and the level of forced air circulation (TNO Cereals, Flour and Bread). The model will be validated on the basis of the aforementioned measurements in experimental ovens (TNO Cereals, Flour and Bread). A feasibility study of the development of control strategies and expert systems for baking ovens making use of mathematical modelling will be performed by ADERSA. The model will be used to establish performance of the oven under several operating conditions (IST).

Application to Cement Kilns

The mathematical models referred in the First Task will be applied to the particular geometry and operation conditions of cement kilns. However, further additions will be required which will handle the combustion/aerodynamics in a coal-fired cement kiln (IST). A physical model describing reaction kinetics and mass and heat balances will be developed. The model will constitute a first attempt to take into account the major chemical reactions taking place in the kiln (INTERG). NO_x emissions and soot formation will be incorporated into the preceding model for the combustion/aerodynamics (IST). Data will be aquired in the cement kilns of TITAN for model validation (TITAN and CRES). The developed mathematical model will be used to establish performance of the kiln and burners under several operating conditions (CRES).

Application to Glass-Ceramic Furnaces

The developed mathematical model will be applied to the geometry and conditions of one of the ceramic furnaces of Metal Portuguesa. The oxy-fuel combustion will be compared with the air-fuel combustion and with (air+oxygen)/fuel combustion in order to determine optimum operating conditions in terms of energy savings and pollution abatement (IST). A model to describe in detail the near burner region for the conditions of the kiln of Metal Portuguesa will be developed. This model will take into account the two-phase flow behaviour of the fuel spray (IST). Simplified models ("long furnace" models) for batch or transient operation optimization will be used for the definition of control strategies and for on-line computer control (MONS). A feasibility study of the development of control strategies and expert systems making use of mathematical modelling will be performed. This will make use of information derived from the mathematical models to define optimum operating conditions (ADERSA). The flow and heat transfer in a forehearth of the glass melting furnace will be studied. ULB has carried out research on the field of modelling the flow of molten glass in a forehearth of a glass furnace since July 86 under the Contract No. EN3E-0044/B. A model for the velocity and temperature field was developed. The radiative heat transfer was not considered. In the present project, a computer code combining the effects of conduction and radiation as well as the effects of inlet and free convection or segregation induced by the density gradients will be performed (ULB).

CURRENT STATE OF ADVANCED MATHEMATICAL MODELLING OF INDUSTRIAL COMBUSTING ENVIRONMENTS

Prediction codes capable of computing the three-dimensional characteristics of the aerodynamics, mixing, combustion and thermal radiation of industrial gas fired furnaces have been developed.

Carvalho *et al.* (1988-a) presented a completely three-dimensional simulation of an industrial cross-fired glass furnace. The mathematical model comprises submodels for the combustion chamber and the glass tank flow. The first submodel incorporates physical modelling for the turbulent diffusion flame, soot formation and consumption, and thermal radiation. The second submodel incorporates physical modelling for the laminar flow and energy balance of the molten glass, driven by free convection. The combustion chamber and the molten glass flow were studied by cyclic iterative separated calculations, matched by the relation between the heat flux from the flame to the glass surface and its temperature. The whole mathematical model was applied to the cross-fired regenerative furnace shown in Figure 3. The furnace is essencilly a large insulated container in which the batch enters via the dog-house and the molten glass flows from the dog-house near-wall to the opposite end-wall. The firing ports are located along the sides of the furnace. There are four ports on each side, each port containing two fuel jets. The furnace is fired alternately from either side to give more uniform heat flux to the glass and to make the regeneration possible. The combustion products pass through regenerators which are used to preheat the combustion air before entering the furnace to produce higher temperature and heat flux to the glass. Waste ports opposite burners working as outlet ports are demanded by the reversing operating conditions. The roof furnace and side walls are refractory lined. Figure 4 shows the predicted temperature distribution in the combustion chambers on vertical planes normal to the inlet-port containing wall. In the reaction zone the temperature is higher than in the other zones with a maximum value of 1880 K. Outside the flame region the temperature is near homogeneous. Temperatures are higher below the horizontal plane containing the burner than above it. This is due to the upper recirculation zone which slightly directs the flame towards the glass in the first meters after the injection.

Carvalho *et al.* (1988-b) used the prediction procedure described above to improve the design of an industrial glass furnace. Predictions were made for a wide range of the combustion chamber and their effects on the furnace performance were quantified, showing the abilities of the present procedure as a tool to improve industrial glass furnaces designs and operating conditions. The furnace analysed in the present case is similar to the one sketched in Figure 3. Table 1 illustrates some aspects of the comparative study of the combustion chamber performance for the parameters under investigation. Figure 5 shows the fuel concentration on the nearest plane parallel to the oultel port, which is the last plane calculated by the model. The effect of the air preheating can be seen by comparing cases 1, 2 and 3. Figure 5 shows that the level of air preheat does not influence significantly the wasted unburned fuel at the outlet. The effect of the excess air can be determined by comparison of cases 1, 4 and 5. The wasted unburned fuel varies indirectly proportional with excess air in both RUN 4 and RUN 5, as shown by Figure 5. The influence of the position of the fuel jet on the resulting flow and temperature fields and mass fraction distributions can be assessed by comparing RUN 1 and RUN 6. For RUN 6, the fuel injection distance to the glass surface was duplicated. For this case, the furnace displays a much better performance as the fuel concentration at the outlet is almost zero. From this study it appears that the present furnace design is not the best and that many improvements can be achieved with minor changes. The mixing pattern is not very efficient due to the inlet port geometry and the combustion chamber aerodynamics. The cross-stream velocities around the fuel jet are directed in such a way to carry the fuel away from air and towards the glass. The change of the fuel jet position, as made in Run 6, prevents this phenomena because the low pressure inside the recirculation zone pulls the fuel away from the glass, allowing a much better mixing between the fuel and the air. In this way the usability of air input is increased and no wasted unburned fuel leaves the furnace.

Table 1. - Predicted Performance Criteria of the Furnace

RUN	ENERGY INPUT (KW)			Total heat flux to the glass (KW)	Outlet temperature (°K)
	AIR	FUEL	TOTAL		
1	1596	2826	4422	980	1710
2	1720	2826	4546	1032	1865
3	1470	2826	4296	831	1790
4	1797	2826	4623	940	1840
5	1436	2826	4262	925	1817
6	1596	2826	4422	983	1720

Carvalho *et al.* (1987) has applied a three-dimensional prediction procedure to a ceramic glass smelting furnaces with oxygen-rich burning conditions. In this work a two dimensional axisymmetric model was used to simulate the burner region, providing with these results the inlet conditions for the three-dimensional calculations of the combustion chambers. The results were extensively validated with experimental data acquired in the furnace and, as an example, Figure 6 shows the measured and predicted gas temperature and oxygen concentrations along horizontal traversal profiles. Figure 7 complements the previous figure and shows the predicted velocity vectors and temperature contours in a vertical plane acrossing the burner region. The model was used to optimize the furnace operating conditions and, for example, the results have shown an eighteen percent improvement in energy efficiency when oxygen enrichment is applied.

Three-dimensional modelling of refractory brick firing furnace configurations has been performed by the research groups of University of Mons. The charge consists of stackings located in the furnace chamber and the flow through the stacking porosity is the only useful for heating up the charge. In these applications, combustion of gas may be considered as completed at the burner exit port. The stackings are assumed as a porous anisotropic gas-solid medium characterized by its porosity and directional parameters such as surface permeability and fluid-solid 3-D friction factors. Convection coefficients depend on local velocity components. Buoyancy has already been taken into account, since it deeply influences the flow pattern inside the stacking. A turbulent k-ε model has been adopted. Although radiation is still to be included, some interesting results have already been obtained for a refractory brick firing furnace containing one stacking side-heated by two rows of burners. Figure 8 shows an example of graphic 2-D representation of gas temperature and charge temperature. Influence of parameters such as charge porosity distribution, burner momentum, position of the flue exit port is obviously determinated for charge temperature uniformity. Measurements in industrial furnaces and in a $2m^3$ - laboratory furnace are planned for validation.

The work of modelling of flow and heat transfer in the molten glass has been backed up by experimental work (Halloin and Jottrand 1990). Given the difficulty associated with measurements in molten glass, experiments are done in a transparent viscous fluid. The measured velocity and temperature fields are compared to the numerical computations of the general equations of a non-isothermal viscous flow. The velocity field is recorded by photographying the trajectories of microbubbles in the illuminated plane slice of the flow. Velocity profiles were collected in an isothermal viscous flow. Figure 9 shows the flow in the vertical median plane above the outlet orifice made in the bottom of the channel. The velocity measurement technique developed gives a full visualization of the flow as well as an accurate determination of the velocity at any point. It permits the analysis of transient and permanent flows in enclosures of complex geometry.

The works reviewed in the previous paragraphs have concentrated on the optimization of the aerodynamics and combustion efficiency of industrial furnaces and boilers. However, particularly acute is the need to comply with more stringent ecological requirements, by lowering the noxious gas emission without sacrifying production. The large amount of air preheat and consequent elevated flame temperature in many glass and cement forming kilns, ensure that the levels of thermal NO_x emissions are high, which are causing concern within the European Community. Reductions in NO_x emissions are achievable through combustor modifications, but parametric trials on full scale equipment are very expensive and accurate measurements are difficult to be obtained. The number, and so the cost, of trials required to be performed could be considerably reduced with the aid of a reliable mathematical model. Carvalho *et al* (1990) have attempted to calculate for the first time in an industrial glass furnace the concentrations of pollutant NO_x, but considerable research is required in this field prior to be possible to use the models to guide the change of current operating conditions and the design of new industrial furnaces in order to reduce pollutant emissions. Figure 10 shows the NO_x mass concentration in vertical planes parallel to the inlet-port-containing wall inside a cross-fired regenerative furnace similar to the furnace sketched in Figure 3. The results show that the thermal NO_x is formed mainly at the edge of the flame, near the stoichiometric region, where the levels of temperature are high and the oxygen concentrations are still significant. The NO_x concentrations reach their maximum values near the flame front at a distance of about two meters downstream of the inlet port. Further downstream the levels of NO_x are progressively reduced because of the convection and diffusion of NO_x away from the region where it is formed. Inside the upper recirculation zone, the NO_x mass concentration is uniform. At the outlet port, the predicted NO_x concentration is uniform with a value of 3.9×10^{-3} kg_{NO}/kg_{mix}.

To investigate the extent up to which simplified atomization models for oil-fired furnaces can be used and to improve understanding of the atomization process of liquid fuels, detailed studies of fuel sprays have been performed. Semião (1989) describes a calculation method for the prediction of reacting sprays. The initial conditions of the spray are calculated from a Nukiyama-Tanasawa type function for the droplet-size distribution analitically derived from entropy considerations (Carvalho *et al*, 1989). A twin-fluid airblast atomiser correlation for SMD is derived and the predictions tested against experimental data. Furthermore, the radiation heat transfer is accounted for by the use of the discrete transfer method, applied for the first time in its cylindrical coordinates version, along with a simple soot model to characterize optically the flame. The turbulent dispersion of the droplets is accounted for by the use of a SSF model based on that of Gosman and Ioaniddes (1991). The ability of the present procedure to predict the local properties of spray flames is demonstrated by comparison with the experimental data, obtained by Costa *et al* (1989, 90) acquired from a swirling spray flame in a laboratory furnace located at ICST&M. The experimental and predicted results for the temperature profile at an axial distance from the burner of 0.28 m is shown in Figure 11. The fall of gas temperatures noted near the combustor wall is due to the upstream convection by the external recirculation zone of colder gases from downstream. The results show a good agreement between the predicted and measured results except for the near wall region. The discrepancies observed in the temperature profile, namely for large radii of the combustion chamber (r>0.2 m), are influenced by uncertanties in the boundary condition values. In this work, an adiabatic condition was used.

FUTURE R&D

Areas for future R&D within the European Community in the cement, glass and baking industries were identified in the work of Carvalho *et al.* (1988-c) based upon the current scenario of R&D in the present industries and following views of main industries and research experts. From that work it was concluded that the scientific and theoretical capabilities of the research institutions in Europe compare favourably with those in the USA and Japan. However, there are some gaps which could lead to Europe being at a disadvantage in the near future. These are:

a) The lack of well coordinated large computational facilities.
b) The time lag between scientific developments and their industrial implementation.
c) The limited number of well equipped experimental and intrumentation facilities and the limitations on their use.

In reference to a) the computational facilites in the USA give researchers a significant technological advantage over European counterparts. Europe should study ways to provide a more unified approach to research in this area by implementing a large European Computational Centre together with an European computer network.

In reference to b) the continuation of existing efforts to bring together industries, universities and research laboratories should be strengthened. For example, the Japanese experience in the cement industry based upon coordinated research programmes involving the industry, could bring Japan to lead the cement technology.

In reference to c) existing experimental and instrumentation facilities should be reviewed and their used coordinated wherever possible. Better utilization of these facilities through coordinated research programmes, supported by carefully targeted investment to enhance capabilities where needed, will provide a cost effective and rapid route to the development of successful projects in the selected fields.

Future strategic R&D within European Community in the cement, glass and baking industries should emphasise the following priority topics:

- Advanced Flow Modelling.
- Dynamic Simulation of Complex Systems, Including the Development of Control Strategies and Expert Systems.
- Advanced on-line Sensors.

Precompetitive R&D in these areas is expected to lead to significant improvements in the energy efficiency of the EEC process industries, thereby helping to make them more competitive internationally and reducing the EEC's fuel import requirements. It is stressed that the efficient application of some research areas to industrial systems requires further fundamental research topics such as:

- Development of adequate physical models for two-phase flows and pollutant formation.
- Development of advanced diagnostic techniques, including those for two-phase flows.
- Development of multi-sensor systems including those of vision, for industrial environments.

The research to be undertaken in all the areas has a strong multidisciplinary character and, as such, will benefit from being conducted through close international cooperation among many specialists both in universities and industry.

REFERENCES

M.G.M.S. Carvalho, D.F.G. Durão and J.C.F. Pereira, "Prediction of the flow, reaction and heat transfer in an oxy-fuel glass furnace". *Eng. Comput.*, Vol. 4, No. 1, March 1987, pp. 23-34.

M.G.M.S. Carvalho, P. Oliveira and V. Semião, "A three-dimensional modelling of an industrial glass furnace". *Journal of the Institute of Energy*, September 1988-a, pp. 143-156.

M.G.M.S. Carvalho, P. Oliveira and V. Semião "Modeling and optimization of an industrial glass furnace". *Progress in Astronautics and Aeronautics*, AIAA, 1988-b pp. 363-384.

M.G.M.S. Carvalho, D.F.G. Durão and M.V. Heitor, "Energy efficiency in industrial processes in the European Community: Future R&D requirements in glass making furnaces, cement kilns and baking ovens". Presented at the CEC Seminar on "Energy Efficiency in Industrial Processes - Future R&D Requirements", Ed. P. Pilavachi, 30 June - 1st July, Brussels EUR 12046 EN, 1988-c.

M.G.M.S. Carvalho, V. Semião, F.C. Lockwood and C. Papadopoulos, "Predictions of nitric oxide emissions from an industrial glass-melting furnace". *Journal of the Institute of Energy*, March 1990, pp. 39-47.

M.G.M.S. Carvalho, M. Costa, F.C. Lockwood and V. Semião, "The prediction of SMD and droplet size distribution for different atomisers". Proc. of International Conference on Mechanics of Two-Phase Flows, Taiwan, Republic of China, 1989.

M. Costa, P. Costen and F.C. Lockwood, "Combustion measurements on a heavy fuel oil-fired furnace". Internal Report, Imperial College of Science, Technology and Medicine, FS/89/16, 1989.

M. Costa, P. Costen and F.C. Lockwood, "Detailed measurements in a heavy fuel oil-fired large-scale furnace". Internal Report, Imperial College of Science, Technology and Medicine Report, FS/90/04, 1990.

A.D. Gosman and E. Ioannides, "Aspects of computer simulation of liquid - fuelled combustors". AIAA paper No. 81-0323, 1981.

V. Halloin and R. Jottrand, "Experimental study of viscous laminar flow with a laser light". Proc. of Fifth International Symposium on Application of Laser Techniques to Fluid Mechanics and Workshop on the Use of Computers in Flow Measurements, Lisbon, Portugal, 1990.

V.S. Semião, "Modelação da combustão, transferência de calor e emissão de poluentes em sistemas de queima de combustíveis líquidos". PhD. Thesis (in Portuguese), Technical University of Lisbon, 1989.

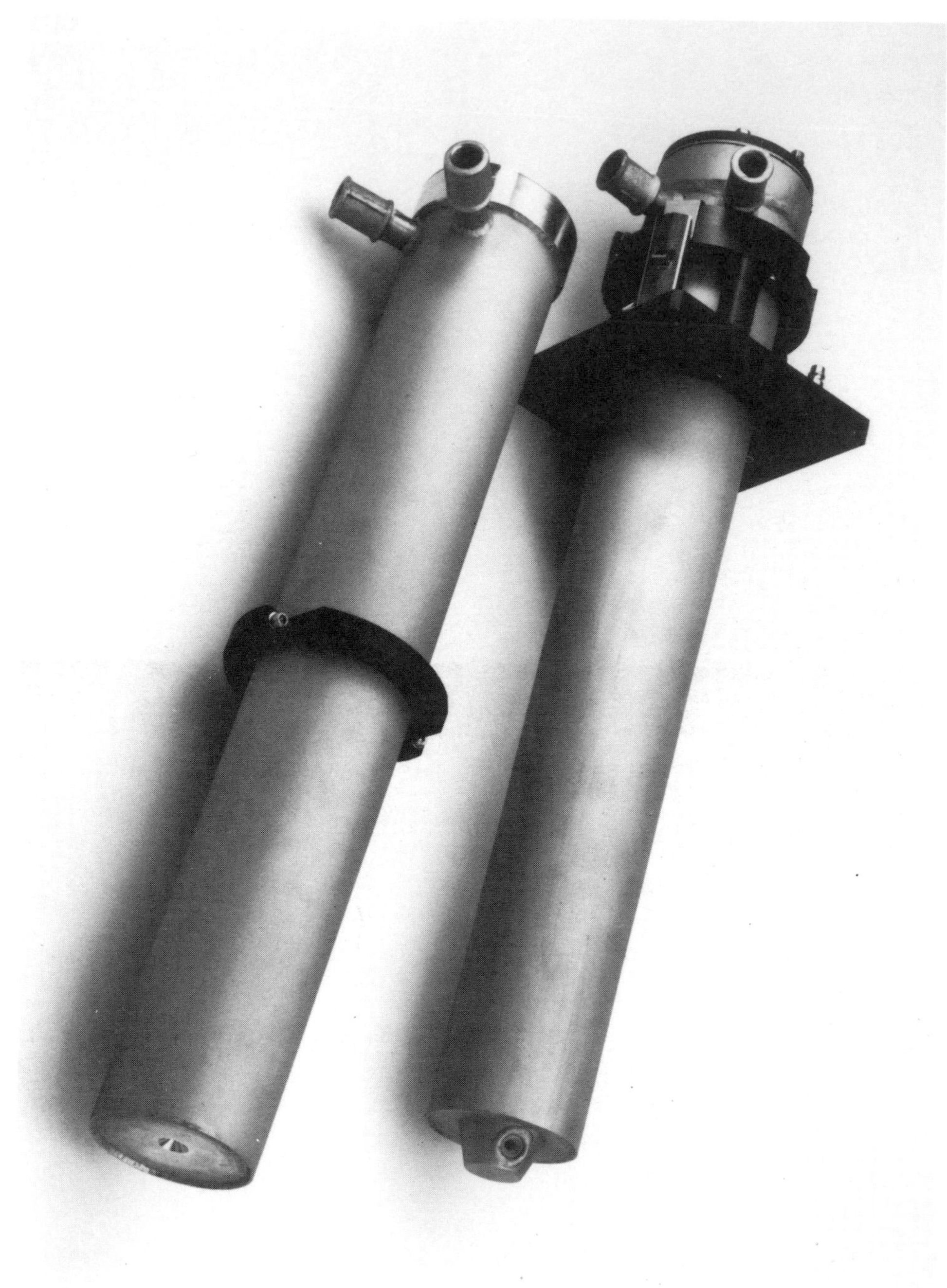

Fig. 1 Video fire probe for furnace and kilns.

Fig. 2 Application of the fire probe in a melting kiln.

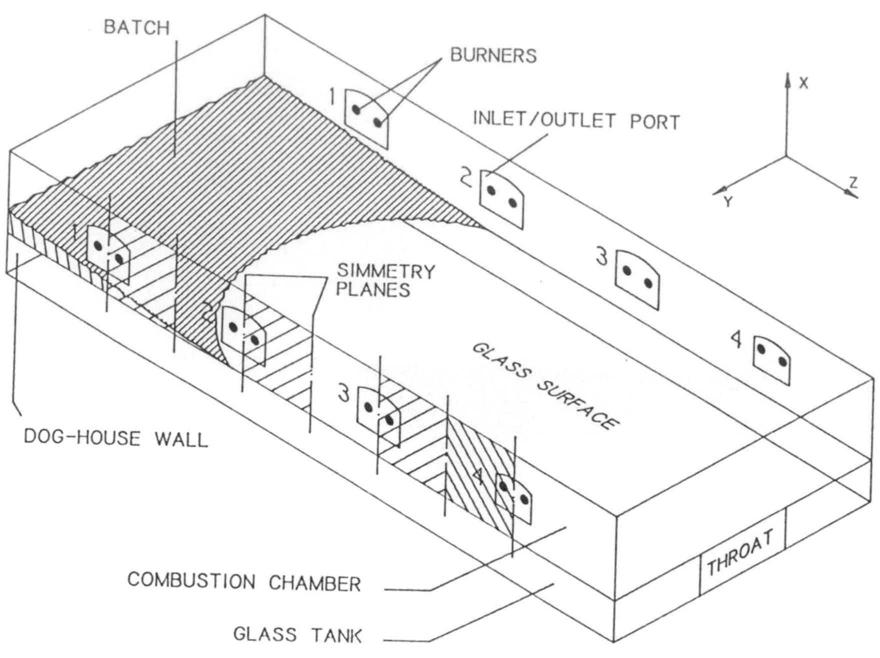

Fig. 3 Sketch of the cross - fired regenerative furnace .

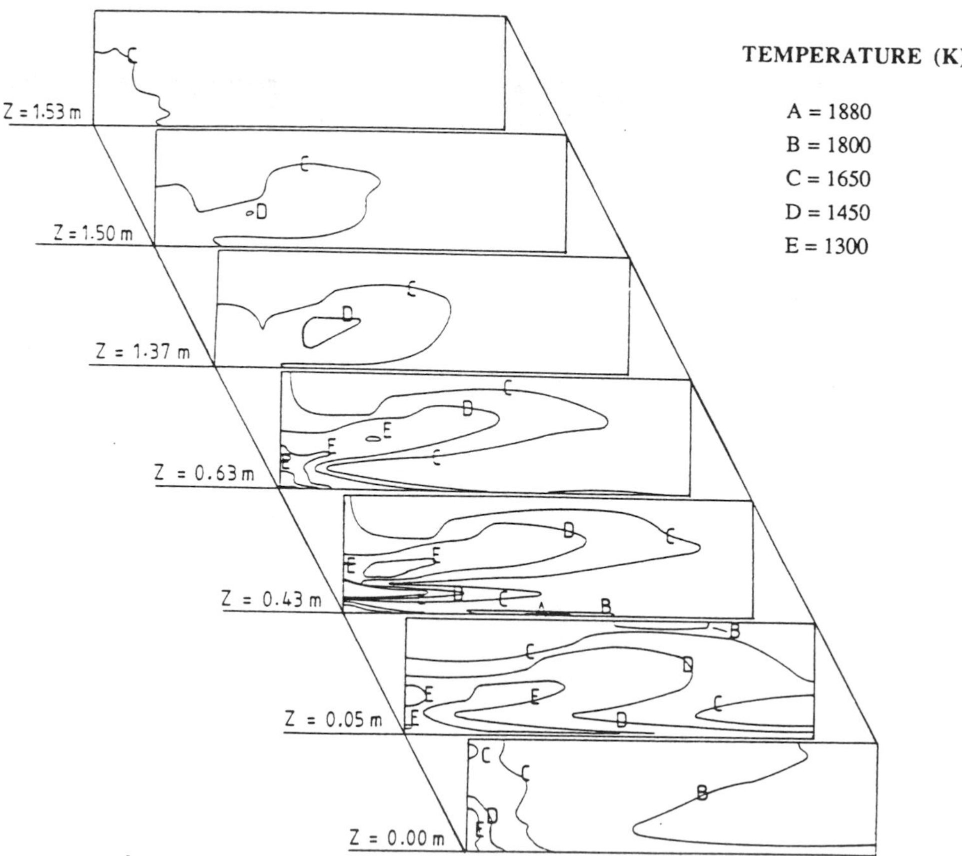

Fig. 4 Temperatures on constant z planes for combustion chamber.

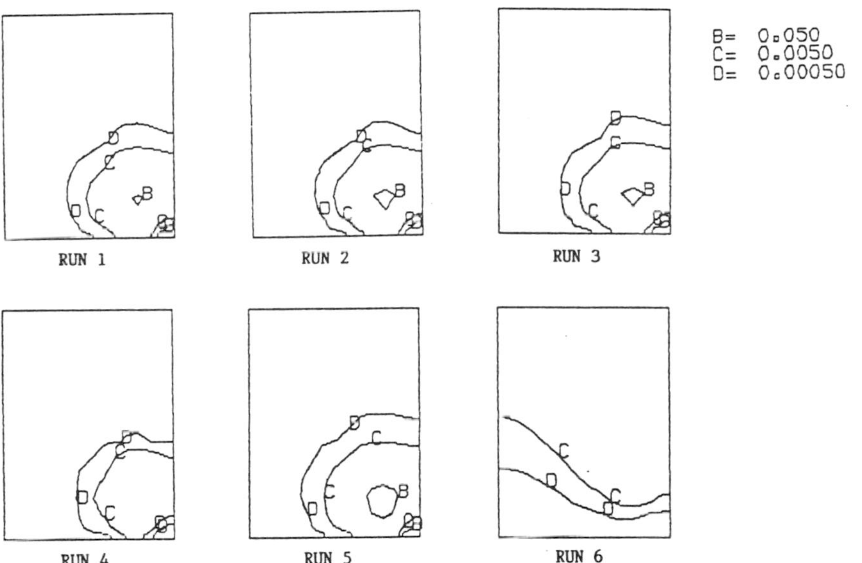

Fig. 5 Fuel mass concentration for all studied cases at the outlet port (combustion chamber; Y=7.00 m).

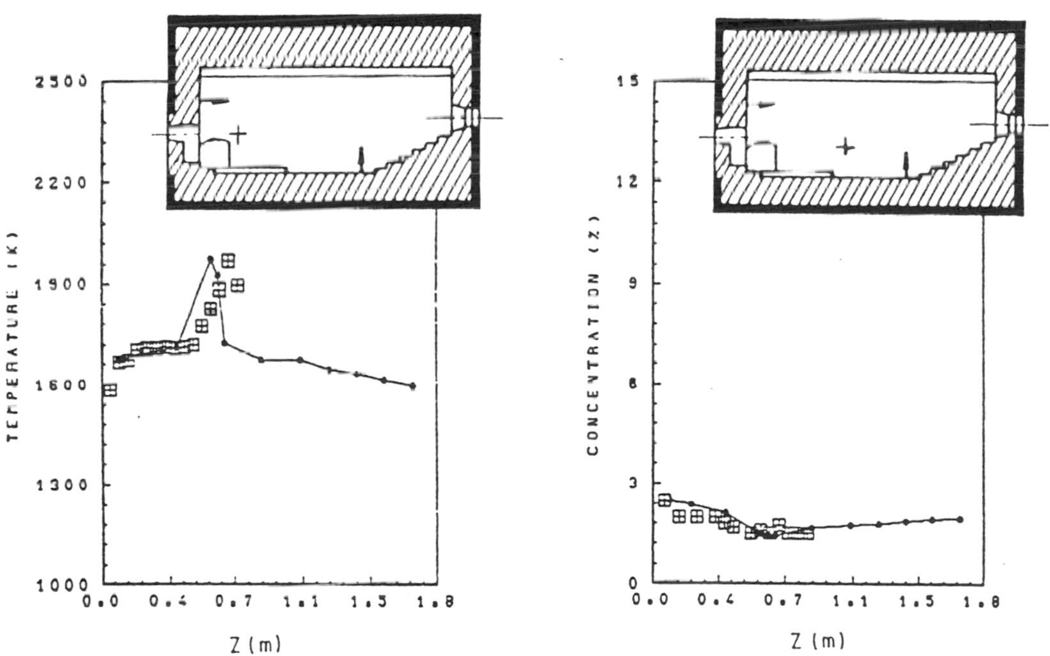

Fig. 6 Transversal profiles of measured and predicted mean gas temperature and oxygen concentration respectively across the flame zone and downstream of the flame.

⊞ — Measured values

● — Calculated values

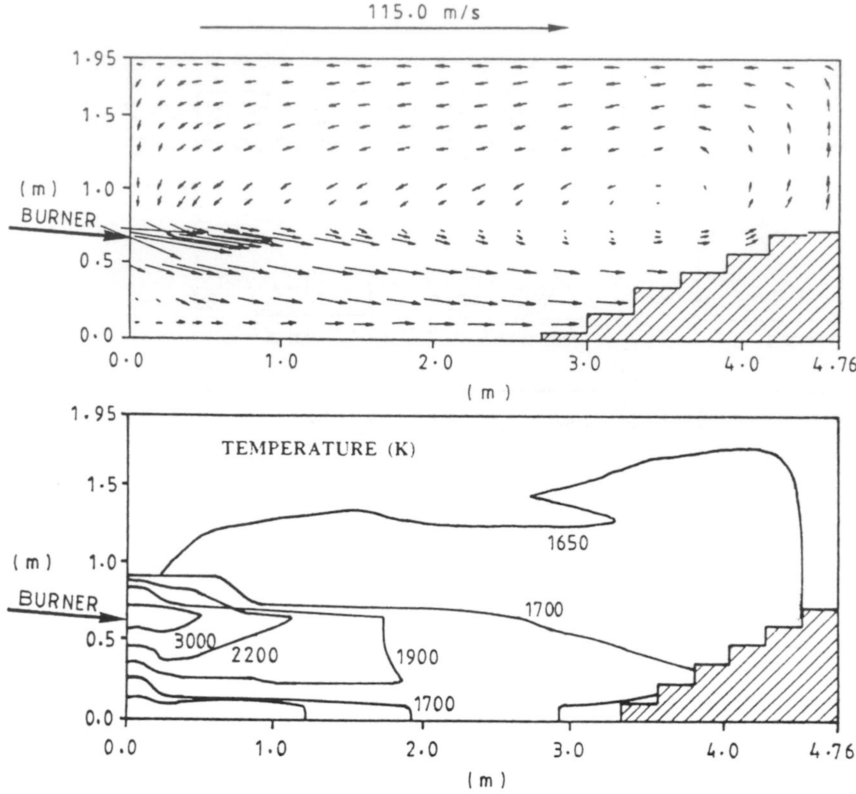

Fig. 7 Predicted mean velocity and gas temperature fields along a vertical plane containing the burner.

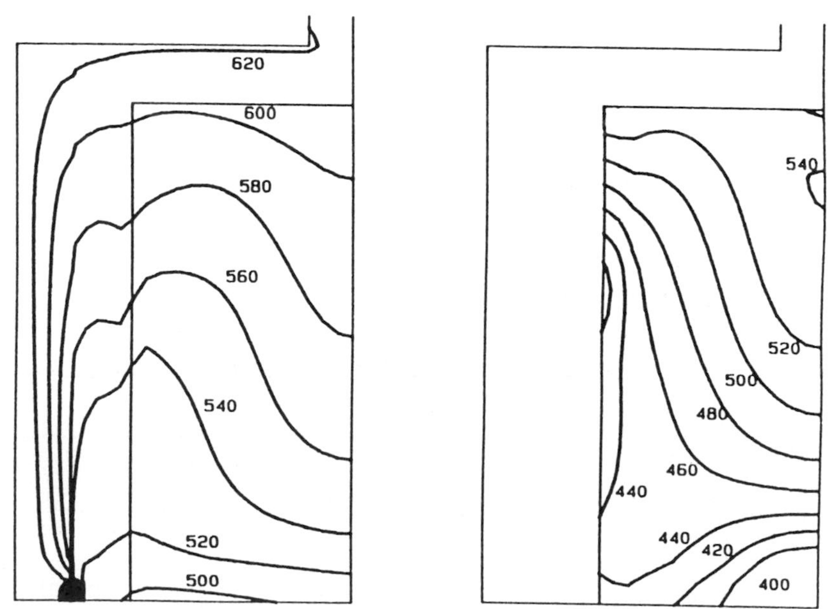

Fig. 8 Temperature Fields Inside a Refractory Brick Firing Furnace.
a) Combustion gas temperature (°C)
b) Charge temperature (°C)

Fig. 9 Flow visualization.

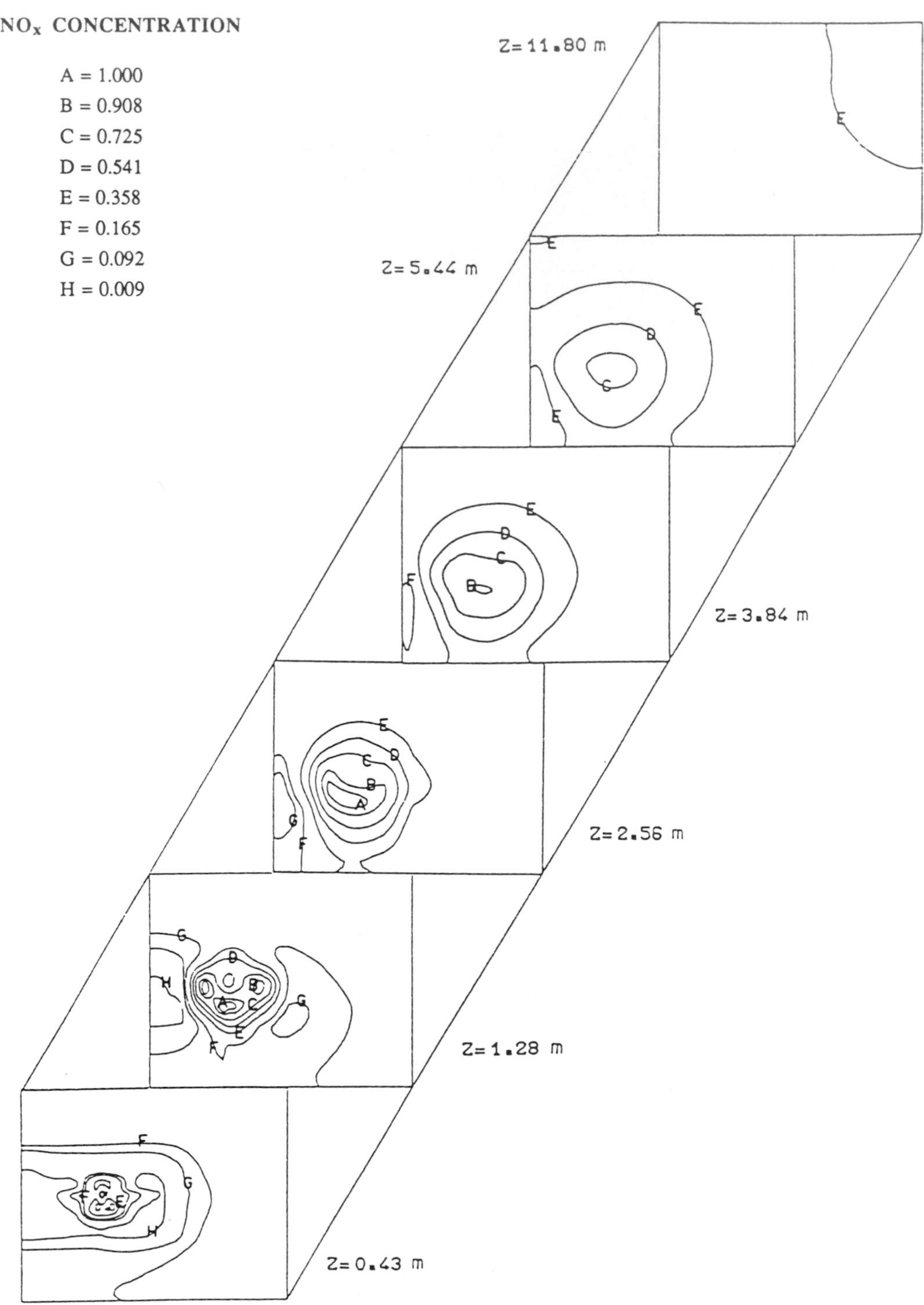

Fig. 10 Mass concentration of NO_X along the width of the furnace (Z) (adimentionalised by the maximum value).

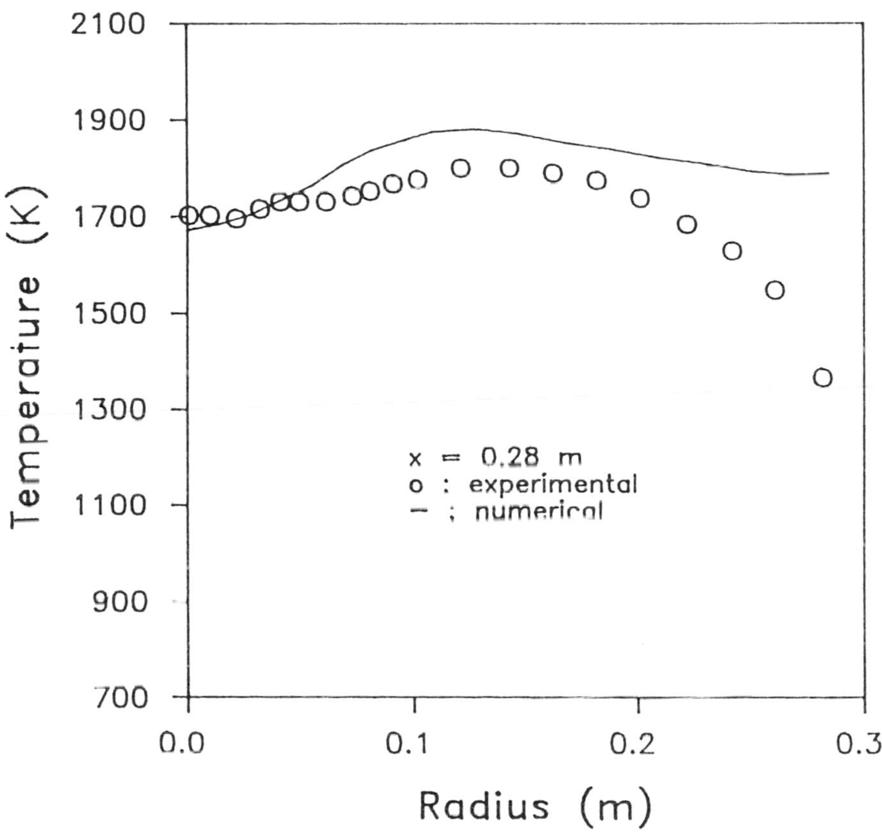

Fig. 11 Comparison of predicted and experimental values for the temperature profile at an axial distance from the burner of 0.28 m.

Advanced Flow Modelling For Applications in the Process Industries

N.C.MARKATOS
Department of Chemical Engineering, N.T.U of ATHENS, GREECE
Contract No: JOUE/0067/C (pending)

PARTICIPANTS

* Dr. S.Huberson, CNRS (LIMSI) France
* Prof. P. Hutchinson, Cranfield IT, UK
* Prof. F.C. Lockwood, Imperial College, UK
* Prof. N.C. Markatos, NTU of Athens, Greece
* Prof. J.C. Pereira, IST-Lisbon, Portugal
* Dr. G.Quarini, Harwell Laboratory, UK
* Dr. M.Sommerfeld, University of Erlangen/Nurenberg, Germany

SUMMARY

The present study will address two areas of process engineering which have been identified as priorities, namely spray dryers and packed beds, and apply Computational Fluid Dynamics techniques to these areas to assess the present utility of this approach, towards improved energy efficiency In each case the work is a combination of the development and evaluation of new physically based approximations to constituent processes of spray dryers and packed-bed reactors and, finally, the validation of the resultant computational models against a selected data base. The work comprises both experimental and theoretical studies in simplified situations as a first step and, when successful, will be followed by a further study in which the then developed models will be applied to predict the performance of industrial units and to test these predictions against experimental data.

INTRODUCTION

This paper describes the work to be performed on assessing the utility of present Computational Fluid Dynamics (CFD) approaches to predict the performance of spray dryers and packed-bed reactors, for improved energy efficiency. CFD is now an important tool for the desing and development of equipment and processes in the fields of mechanical, nuclear and aeronautical engineering. It has great potential for application in the process industries, but so far the number of applications in this field has been relatively limited.The primary field of application has been to the design of power generation furnaces and process heaters.

Many key issues in design for the process industries are related to the behaviour of fluids in turbulent flow often involving more than one phase, reaction or heat transfer. CFD techniques have great potential for analysing these processes and can be of great help to the designer, by reducing the need to resort to "cut and try" approaches to the design of complex equipment. The present state of the art in CFD is such that there is a need for extensive evaluation and validation of CFD models is such that there is a need for extensive evaluation and validation of CFD models before they can be used for design.

The evaluation is aimed at selecting the most appropriate physical approximations and the validation step is aimed at defining those situations in which the resultant approximations can be reliably used to predict the behaviour of engineering processes.It is, therefore, appropriate to select particular unit processes to evaluate the performance of CFD methods in the process industries.The present study will address two areas which have been identified as priorities with respect to improved energy efficiency, namely spray dryers and packed beds, and apply CFD techniques, appropriately amended and elaborated, to these areas to assess the present utility of this approach.

The use of spray dryers in chemical, food and other industries is widespread. Many different designs of spray dryers are in use including for example co-current, counter-current and mixed flow types. Each of these three configurations is suitable for a particular application and has associated with it a few typical air and liquid distributors.

The spray drying process consists of four stages:

- the atomisation of feed into spray
- spray air contacting (mixing and flow),
- the drying of the spray (evapouration of moisture and volatiles)
- the separation of the dried product from the air.

Current numerical modelling of these processes is based on one-dimensional integral models and few studies have considered multi-dimensional differential models. The simplest of these are one dimensional models based around the assumption that there is no effect of the spray on the air velocity or temperature field. Consequently such models are not accurate enough to be useful for design, or performance prediction, or evaluation of spray dryers.

In other applications models have been developed that can be used to simulate the spray air mixing and vapourisation of sprays, for example in studies of diesel engines and furnaces. These models are based on Eulerian descriptions of the fluid phase and Lagrangian or Eulerian descriptions of the dispersed phase, together with various assumptions regarding the vapourisation process. As a result, there is a good basis for the development of multi-dimensional computational fluid dynamics approaches to the modelling of spray dryers.

In general, two phase flows are complex and there is a need to evaluate the basic understanding of the mass, momentum and energy exchange processes in spray in simple geometries. In order to achieve this aim it is necessary to take data bases of the velocity fields of fluid and droplets, the droplet size, obstruction and concentration in simple flow configurations. This data will then be used to evaluate the validity of models which combine a description of the turbulent continuum phase and the dispersed phase. The experimental methods required involve the use of Laser-Doppler anemometry for measurement of the turbulent flow field and Phase-Doppler anemometry for characterisation of the droplet field. These methods are well established at all participating organizations [1-14].

Adsorber-regenerators are used extensively in the process industries for gas cleaning and separation. In the field of gaseous separations, adsorption is used to dehumidify air and other gases, to remove objectionable odours and impurities from industrial gases such as CO_2 to recover valuable solvent vapours from dilute mixtures with air and other gases and to fractionate mixtures of hydrocarbon gases containing substances as methane, ethylene, ethane, propylene and propane.

Liquid separations include the removal of moisture dissolved in gasoline, decolourization of petroleum products and aqueous sugar solutions, removal of objectionable taste and odour from water and the fractionation of mixtures of aromatic and paraffinic hydrocarbons.

Traditionally, a fixed bed of adsorbent beads is supported within a vertical cylinder, with a baffle installed to ensure adequate flow distribution. Gas is pumped throuph the bed, which selectively removes certain components. Bad flow distributions can lead to poor product quality, loss of feedstock and excessive energy use. When the beads are near to saturation, the sorbate is recovered from them by a change in the operating conditions. There may, for example, be a decrease in pressure (pressure swing adsorption) or an increase in temperature (temperature swing adsorption). Adsorbents are necessarily porous solids and the porosity plays an essential role in determining the way in which gases or vapours are adsorbed under various conditions of concentration, temperature etc. However, it is not necessarily the most porous adsorbent which adsorbs the most gas. The structure of the pores, their size, uniformity and arrangement must also be taken into account. Chemical processes introduce a further level of complexity, requiring means of evaluating the relevant heat and mass transfer rates. The above process is used extensively in the European Chemical Industries where typical applications include the cleaning of air of natural gas prior to cryogenic processing [15,16]. Pressure swing adsorption is seen as a future alternative to distillation in the preparation of intermediate amounts of low quality oxygen [17].

CFD techniques have reached a stage that permits, in principle, predictions of flow patterns and heat/mass transfer in industrial equipment of some complexity. However, the constitutive physical expressions for the two-phase flows involved leave a lot to be desired and the performance of such existing models has been insufficiently validated to-date, against reliable experimental data. Therefore, although CFD methods and tools can be used for the study of adsorbers/ regenerators, there remains a lot of research to be done in order to :a)Improve such physical and mathematical models as the wall-interactions and porosity models; and b) Validate the results obtained by the various CFD techniques against experiments.

OBJECTIVES

As indicated above the overall objective of the present study is to assess the utility of current CFD approaches, appropriately amended and elaborated for the processes in question, to predict the performance of spray dryers and adsorbers/ regenerators. More specifically, the study will combine the acquisition of good experimental data and the improvement of mathematical models, in order to lay a firm foundation for the development of sound computational tools for spray dryers and adsorbers, which would be useful in the prediction of performance and the development of improved designs. As a result, the user of these tools will be in a position to a) Recommend improvements to current operating procedures; b) Specify mechanical arrangements to improve the efficiency of current processes; and c) Identify more efficient designs for future use.

TASKS OF PARTICIPANTS

SPRAY DRYERS

The elements of the work specified below combine experimental work by the participants at the University of Erlangen/Nurenberg and IST Lisbon and a combined effort on modelling involving both the groups mentioned above and those at Cranfield, CRES and Imperial College. In order to simplify the computations, it will be important to take good data on the mean and fluctuating velocity of the continuum phase, separately from that of the dispersed phase. This will allow an early test of the accuracy of models for the dispersed phase using experimental data for the behaviour of the continuum phase. The individual contributions in achieving the overall objective of the study are given under the appropriate University name.

University of Erlangen / Nurenberg

For the detailed study of spray evaporation in a turbulent air stream a test facility is available at the LSTM Erlangen [1], which only needs minor modifications for the proposed research. The evaporation of a spray, issuing from a nozzle into a co-flowing heated air stream which enters a test chamber will be studied by the Phase-Doppler technique, which allows a simultaneous measurement of drop size and velocity. Furthermore, the measurement of the air velocity will be possible by seeding the flow with very small droplets and applying a recently developed discrimination procedure [2]. Therefore, this method allows a detailed examination of the evaporation process in turbulent flows. For the examination of the influence of turbulence intensity on evaporation rate the turbulence level of the air flow will be varied. Furthermore, combining variation in the air temperature with sprays of different volatility will give the detailed information necessary for detailed prediction of spray drying in turbulent environment.

The existing information on convective droplet evaporation together with the results obtained in a turbulent environment will be used to improve the evaporation models. The evaluation of the numerical results will be based on the experiments, which provide the mean and fluctuation velocities of gas and droplets and the spatial development of droplet size distribution throughout the flow field.

An existing numerical code [3] will be the basis for the proposed work, and the dispersion models for droplet motion developed at Cranfield and CRES/Imperial College will be incorporated into the code and tested.

Instituto Superior Tecnico, Lisbon (IST).

Two phenomena of interest in the simulation of spray-dryers, and for yielding experimental data of high fidelity to perform numerical model comparison and validation have been isolated:

a) Experimental and mathematical modelling of the turbulent heat fluxes and Reynolds stress in the vicinity of two co-axial jets with or without swirl. The inner jet is cold and the outer hot.

b) Study of the influence of turbulence on droplet dispersion and vice-versa, by replacing the cold jet by a water pressure spray.

IST Lisbon will perform measurements of the mean and turbulent fields, with and without swirl, for (a) above [2,4,5], and will recommend improvements to the modelling of the mean, turbulent and scalar fields investigated [6-9].

They will also perform measurements of velocity and droplet size of a water spray surrounded by an annular heated air system, and will compare them with predictions from an improved stochastic Lagrangian model for the droplet dispersion and evaporation in the shear flow. In addition the variations of the dispersion models developed at Cranfield and CRES/Imperial College will be evaluated. This work will provide quidelines to determine the most effective one point closure representation (eddy-viscosity/diffusivity, algebraic and differential models) for co-axial heated flows with or without the presence of a dispersed phase (spray) and to understand how the improvements in the modelling of the turbulent field are conductive to a better representation of dispersed phase and consequently a better representation of the whole flow.

Cranfield Institute of Technology (CIT).

The group at CIT will perform the following tasks:

- develop an existing Eulerian/Lagrangian model for droplet dispersion by turbulent flows, to take account of the effect of evaporation on the effective diffusion coefficient for the droplets.

- establish a data base of effective droplet diffusion coefficients as a function of the properties of both gas and droplets.

- test the resultant model against data to be gathered by the other partners and available elsewhere in the literature. This will first be achieved by using measured data for the flow field and using the dispersion model to predict the transport of droplets.

- create a module embodying the dispersion model into a form suitable for use by other partners in their computer programmes and for use in already developed codes.

-extend the technique to allow inference of the probability distribution of particle trajectories from the properties of the diffusion equation. [10-12]

Centre for Renewable Energy Sources (CRES), and Imperial College of Science. Technology and Medicine.

The good prediction of industry sprays is not possible in the absence of a sound model which simulates the interaction between the particulate or droplet phase and the turbulence. This interaction disperses both the velocities and spatial locations of the droplets and modifies the turbulence properties of the carrier phase. The effects of the interaction can be so significant that prediction methods which ignore it are of small value to the design engineer. Regretably, the existing simulations are either too simplistic or hopelessly uneconomic.

In the present detailed study of the dispersion of the particulate phase in the sprays of the project by the turbulent flows a novel model called P.E.P. (Predicition of Evolving Probabilities) will be used. This entirely new model, which observes all of the relevant physics, is described in [13, 14]. It has been applied for the prediction of the velocity and spatial distributions of droplets for an open jet flow at small particulate loadings for which circumstances experimental data were available.

The predictions showed excellent accuracy when compared with the experimental data. Very importantly the computer times to obtain these results were orders of magnitude less when compared to the times reported in the literature for similar predictions using all previous models.

As it stands this promising model requires further resting and development to ensure successful application to sprays. In this context, the above groups will:

- prepare a complete review on the existing models that have been used for simulation of the dispersion of particles in a turbulent fluid.

- develop further the P.E.P. model for simulating the dispersion of droplets in sprays. This work will include: new sub-models for the prediction of the concentration of droplets, the calculation of the correlation coefficient for the gas and droplet velocities, and allowances for the varying size distribution of the droplets in turbulent flows.

- assess different closure assumptions for the joint probability density function the validity of these assumptions being assessed by comparisons with the data. At the present time a joint Gaussian presumption is made.

- test all aspects of the performance of P.E.P. against the existing experimental data and those that will be obtained during the course of this project at the University of Erlangen and at the Instituto Superior Tecnico.

- effect direct comparison with the despersion method being developed at Cranfield for identical conditions. The respective advantages and disadvantages of each model will be determined for a range of conditions of particles loading, size distribution, etc.

- prepare a final valuation of the P.E.P. model with special emphasis on the accuracy of prediction and on the computational economy.

- demonstrate the use of the evaluated P.E.P. dispersion model applied to a specific industrial spray that will be determined during the course of the project following detailed discussion with be the partners.

ADSORBERS/REGENERATORS

The work to be performed by the three partners will contribute to the overall objectives of the project by:

- improving specific models, such as the porosity and wall models;
- predicting micro-scale effects in industrial adsorbers;
- simulating numerically heat and mass transfer in adsorbers/regenerators, under

steady-state and transient conditions; and

- validating the numerical results obtained by direct comparison with experimental measurements from literature and industry and with analytical solutions.

LIMSI-CNRS Orsay

The task of this partner will be an attempt to combine different knowledges of the adsorption problem in order to provide an efficient tool for predicting micro-scale effects in industrial absorbers. The resulting tool will be incorporated into the models of Harwell and NTUA which include a global account of the industrial adsorbers.

An adsorption column consists of an assembly of beads. Each bead is an assembly of microparticles, so that there is a three-scale problem: column scale, macropores scale and micropores scale. A bi-disperse model developed at LIMSI [18-24] will be used at the bead scale, this model being non isothermal and including two mass diffusion coefficients. The resulting equations will be solved by a finite-difference formulation in spherical coordinates.

Convection-dispersion equations will be used for the column scale, heat and mass transfer from the bead scale to column scale will be treated through appropriate source terms as in [19]. A numerical solution of the three-scale problem in a 1-D case will be obtained by a finite difference solver for each scale.

A sensitivity study of the solution to the different parameters will be performed.

The model will be used to test the influences of kinetic rates and the influences of geometric and design parameters. For example, it is well known that the bead size influences the column permeability and the bead kinetic rate but what is the exact influence of bead size on the global response of the column?

This model will be compared to results otained at LMSI on the propagation of concentration and temperature fronts in a dead-end column of activated carbon submitted to pressure steps of methanol vapour.

National Technical University of Athens. (NTUA)

The task of NTUA is to develop new and/or validate existing mathematical models for the analysis of the physical aspects related to adsorption, in view of incorporating them in a suitable CFD package. A specific test case will demonstrate the use and the convenience of the package for design purposes. The above work will be divided into the following tasks:

-Steady-state flow study:Temperature and pressure profiles in the vessel containing the packed bed during the adsorption stage.

-Transient flow study:Temperature and pressure profiles during the regeneration cycle.

-Parametric study of vessel geometry effects.

-One of the important parameters needed in the desing of packed bed systems is the particle-to-fluid mass transfer coefficient (ka). Parametric studies of ka will be carried out.

-Adsorbent solids are usually used is granular form, varying in size and shape. Parametric studies of these factors will be carried out.

Important items of the above work include:

1.Improvement of the wall-particle interaction models. 2.Effect of size and shape of particles in respect to fixed bed hydrodynamics (i.e pressure drop, flow characteristics). 3.Use of different Constitutive adsorption equilibrium relations. 4.Use of different models in respect to pore diffusion (pore size distribution, porous structure of solid particles, capillary model, dusty gas model) that take into account the geometries and physics of porous materials 5.Parametric study of porosity distribution functions and flow regimes. 6.Flow regimes in ideal-and-solid particles flow (Poiseuille flow, Knudsen's flow, Slip-flow). 7.Simulation of breakthrough curves for isothermal adsorption in packed bed. 8.Diffusion and reaction in a porous catalyst. Parametric study on the role of pore diffusion in catalysis. 9.Heat transfer in packed beds under unsteady-state conditions. The three models proposed to descrite this phenomenon are the Schumann model, the Continuous-Solid phase model and the Dispersion-Concentric model.

Harwell Laboratory.

CFD analysis will be applied to the entire physical space associated with the adsorber system. This includes the packed bed, gas spaces above and below the bed, and mechanical inserts.Thermal diffusivity equations will be applied to the vessel structure. The treatment of porosity considers the spaces between the beads, and it does not include the micropores and mesopores inside the beads. An individual cell volume will be deemed to contain a number of spheres, which are treated as solid. Porosity is taken as the ratio of the space between the spheres to the total cell colume.

Transport equations can be written to account for porous media. In the Navier-Stokes equations additional terms are required for drag forces. These can be derived from classical experimental correlations, such as those of Ergun or Carmen-Kozeny [25].

Fields of the various parameters involved in adsorbers can be modelled by using the general transport equations (appropriately modified for porosity effects) and adjusting the values of velocity and source terms. The appropriate correlations for heat and mass transfer will be found in standard texts.

In void spaces(porosity=1) the effects of turbulence are likely to be significant. The appropriate diffusivity terms will be amended through the k-ε turbulence model. The turbulence model will be 'switched off' in the porous regions. The empirical correlations for drag force, heat and mass transfer will in themselves include an adequate model of turbulence.

The above task requires a significant amount of code development, since an ergonomic code is vital to the needs of industry. Finally, Harwell will perform extensive validation studies for the following cases:

-There exist four well documended experiments, wherein the breakthrough curves at the outlet of a laboratory scale adsorber have been measured. Here the vessel length is very much greater than its diameter, making the flow one dimensional. In each case, the authors provide sufficient details for their results to be predicted numerically [26-29].

-There exists a truly 3D system [30] for which plots are given of CO_2 concentration versus time at the outlet of a shallow bed adsorber.

-There exists a sister Joule project that will provide facilities to validate models for Hydrocarbon separation.

PRELIMINARY RESULTS.

Preliminary results for adsorbers/regenerators are given in Fig 1 to 5.Figure 1 presents the geometry of the packed bed and its vessel.Figure 2 presents velocity vectors and axial velocity contours from the steady-state adsorption calculation, for a baffle height of 700 mm. Figure 3 presents the same information for a baffle height of 1200 mm and in addition the radial velocity contours.Figure 4 refers to the regeneration cycle and presents velocity vectors, for a distributor height of 900 mm. Figure 5 refers to the regeneration cycle and presents velocity vectors, for a distributor height of 400 mm.

FUTURE RESEARCH AND DEVELOPMENT

As a result of this work, existing mathematical models for single, dispersed and two-phase flows will have been improved and combined to offer a range of approaches to the modelling of vapourising sprays, spray dryers and adsorbers/ regenerators and the accuracy of these models evaluated. Limited testing of the validity of the models in an industrial context will have been commenced and preliminary data on the validity of the approach for use in design established. This project, if successful, will be followed by proposals to test the models more thoroughly, against industrially based data and to assess their validity for use in design and the prediction of performance. In the latter context the CFD codes could also be combined with semi-analytical correlations as well. In the research area a study of the time history of particles and of the chemistry turbulence interactions could be of benefit. Finally, the analysis of physical parameters affecting chemical reaction in a Transport type Fluidized Bed Reactor, as used in the Fluidized Catalytic Cracking (F.C.C) process, will be an interesting future development.

There is considerable European activity in advanced flow modelling, and all future needs can be covered within Europe. There is considerable effort in the U.S as well but directed largely at aerospace problems; hence, products appear too specialized for applications in the process industry.Japan is a user of European and American modelling software and just starts to get active in original development.Europe can sustain a world lead in the application of CFD to engineering problems.

REFERENCES

1. Sommerfeld, M, and Qiu, H,-H :"Detailed Measurements in a Swirling Particulate Two-Phase Flow by a Phase-Doppler Anemometer", submitted to Int. J. of Fluid Flow, 1990.
2. Qiu, H.-H., Sommerfeld, M. and Durst, F:"High Resolution Data Processing for Phase-Doppler Measurements in a Complex Two-Phase Flow; Proc. of the 5th Int. Symp. on Applications of Laser Techniques to Fluid Mech. Paper 24.2, 1990.
3. Sommerfeld, M:"Particle Dispersion in Turbulent Flow: The Effect of Particle Size Distribution"' to appear in Part. and Part Systems Characterization., 1990.
4. D.F.G. Durao, M. V. Heitor and J.C. F. Pereira (1988) "Measurements of turbulent and periodic flows around a square cross-section cylinder". Experiments in Fluids, Vol. 6 pp. 298-304.
5. D.F.G. Durao and J. C. F. Pereira and J. M. P. Rocha (1989) "Evaluation of k-ε Turbulence Model for Predicting Buoyant Free Round Jets", National Heat Conference, HTD Vol. 107, Heat Transfer in Convective Flows, pp. 99-107.
6. J. L. T. Azevedo and J. C. F. Pereira (1989) "Prediction of Particulate turbulent two-phase flows in a plane and co-axial confined jets". Int. Conference on Mechanics of Two-Phase Flows, June 1989, Taipei-Taiwan.
7. J. C. F. Pereira and J. M. P. Rocha (1989) "Prediction of Non-isothermal Turbulent Free Flow with an Algebraic Second-Moment Closure Model", 6th Int. Conf. Numerical Meth. in Laminar and Turbulent Flow, Swansea, 11-15 June.
8. J. C. F. Pereira and J. M. P. Rocha (1990). "A Numerical Prediction of Convective Heat Transfer in Jets and Plumes"; Submitted at Numerical Heat Transfer.
9. J. L. T. Azevedo and J. C. F. Pereira (1990) "Numerical Predictions of Co-Axial and Confined Swirling Two-Phase Flows". Submitted to AIAA Journal.
10. Hutchinson, P., Hewitt, G. F., Dukler, A. E., "Deposition of liquid or solid dispersions from turbulent gas streams; a Stochastic model." Chem. Eng Science Vol. 26, pp. 419-439, March 1970.
11. Collelial, G. A. and Stock, D.E. "Turbulent Particle Dispersions, a Comparison between Lagrangian and Eulerian modelling approaches." Gas Solid Flows 1986.
12. Hutchinson, P., Tan, J. S. C., and Gill, M. E. "Droplet Dispersion in an Isotropic Homogeneous Turbulent Flow using a Diffusion Stochastic Method." Fifth Workshop on Two Phase Flow Predictions, LSTM Erlangen, March 19-22 1990.
13. F.C.Lockwood, C.Papadopoulos. "A new method for the computation of particulate dispersion in turbulent two phase flows' Combustion and Flame Vol. 76, p.403, 1989.
14. C.Papadopoulos, "The Prediction of Two Phase Flows", PhD Thesis, London University 1989.
15. Rathbone T. " Proceedings of the Low Temperature Engineering and Cryogenics Conference. University of Southmapton, July 1990.
16. Acton, A. "Proceedings of the Low Temperature Engineering and Cryogenics Conference. University of Southampton, July 1990.
17. Smolarec J. and Campbell M. Gas Sep. Tech, Process Technology Proceedings, 8 (gas Separation Technology), Proceedings of the International Symposium on Gas Separation Technology, Antwerp, September 1989.
18. H.Q. Wang "Modelisation des transfers de masse en milieu sature a double porosite" Thesis Orsay 1987.
19. L.M.Sun et F. Meunier "Non isothermal adsorption in a bidisperse adsorbent pellet" Chem.Eng.Sci. 1987, 42, 2899-2907.
20. F.Meunier, L.M. Sun, F.Kraehenbuehl et F. Stoeckli "A comparison of experimental and

theoretical Kinetics of Dichloromethane vapour by active carbon" J. Chem. Soc. Faraday Trans 1988, 84, !973-1983.

21. K.Abdallah, Ph. Grenier, L.M. Sun et F. Meunier "Non isothermal adsorption of water by synthetic NaX zeolit pellets" Chem. Eng. Sci. 1988, 43, 2633-2643
22. F.Meunier, L.M. Sun, K. Abdallah et Ph. Grenier "Kinetics of vapour adsorption" Third International Conference on Fundaamentals of Adsorption Sonthohfen RFA 1989
23. A. Torresan, Ph. Grenier, L.M. Sun, F.Meunier, J. Karget et H. Pfeifer "Determination of diffusion Coefficients: comparison between thermo-gravimetric and NMR measurements" Zeocat Conference Leipzig August 1990.
24. G.M. Zhong, F. Meunier et S.Huberson " On the possible influence of pressure drops on the determination of diffusion coefficients in uptake measurements " Zeocat Conference Leipzig August 1990.
25. Coulson J. and Richardson J. " Chemical Engineering, volume 2 " Published by the Pergamon Press.
26. Zheng Dexin et al. "Gas Separation And Purification Journal". December, 1988.
27. Zheng Dexin and Gu Youfan. "Gas Separation and Purification Journal".March 1988.
28. Sowerby B. and Crittenben B. "Gas Separation and Purification Journal".June 1988.
29. Graham I. P. "Gas Separation and Purification Journal". June 1989.
30. Kier S. C. and Lavin J. T. " Gas Separation and Purification". 1987 vol. 1. September.

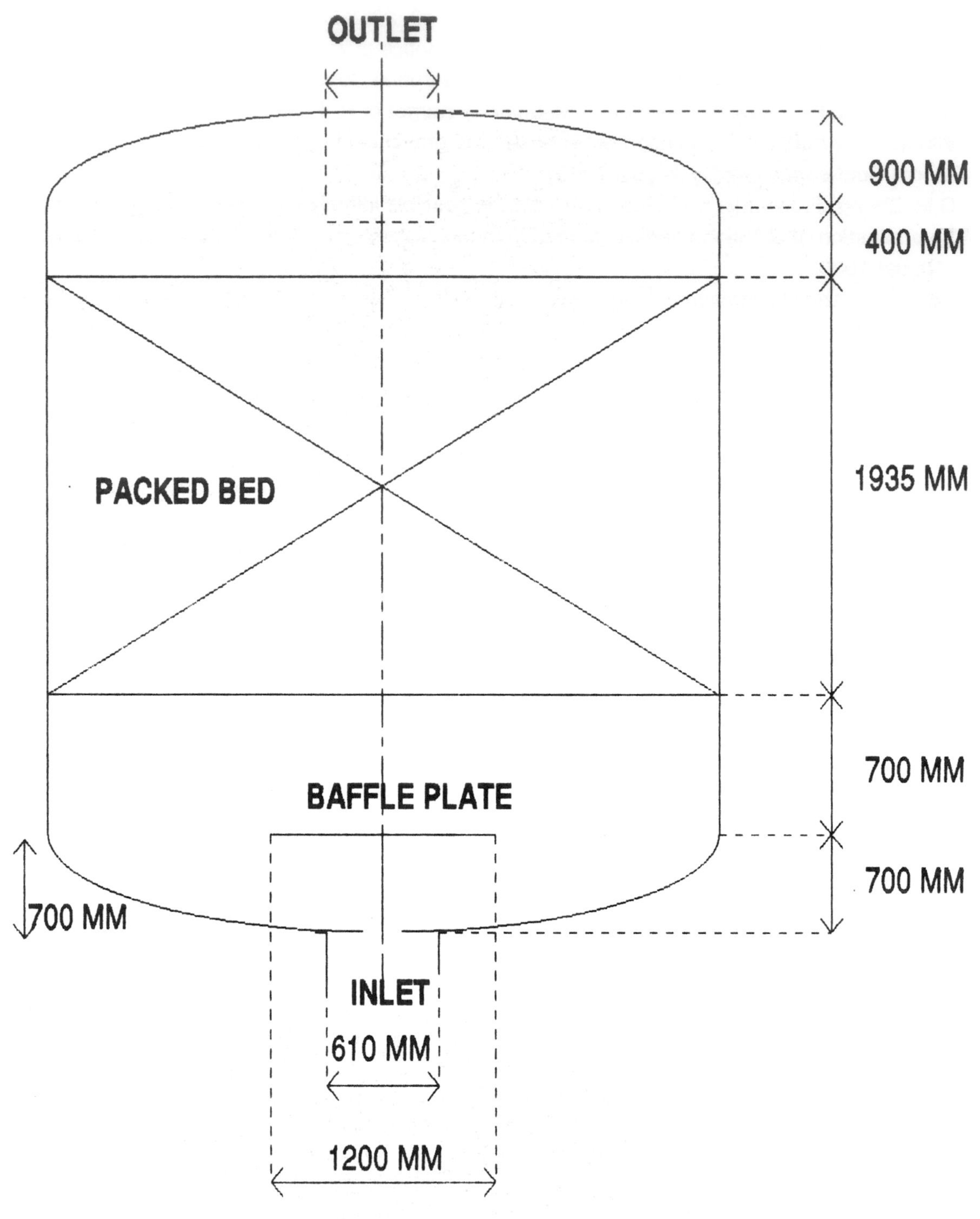

FIGURE 1. GEOMETRY OF THE PACKED BED AND ITS VESSEL

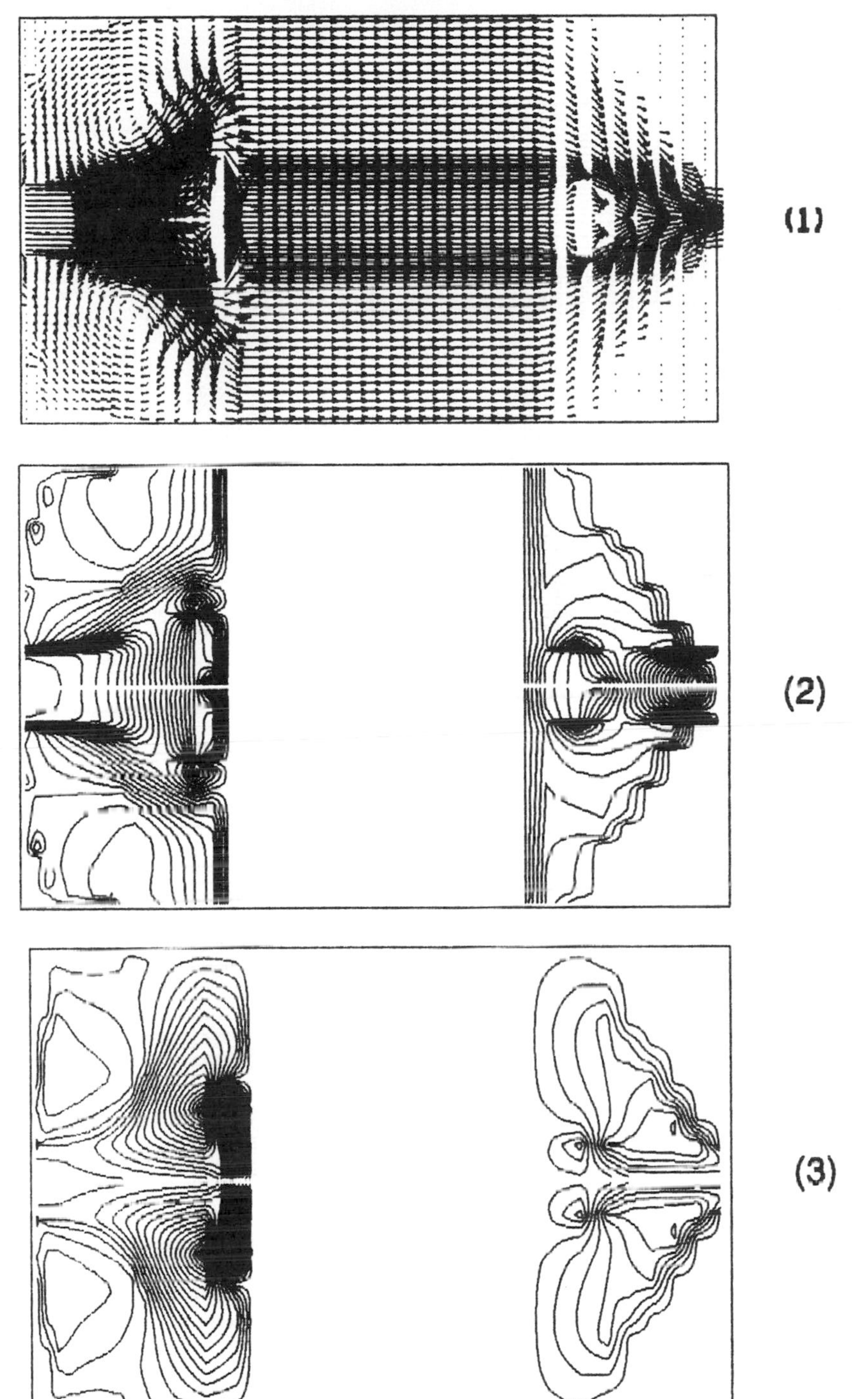

FIGURE 2. 1. VELOCITY VECTORS FROM THE STEADY-STATE ADSORPTION CALCULATION BAFFLE HEIGHT 1200 mm

2. VELOCITY W1 CONTOURS FOR THE STEADY-STATE ADSORPTION CALCULATION.. BAFFLE PLATE 1200mm

3. VELOCITY V1 CONTOURS FOR THE STEADY-STATE ADSORPTION CALCULATION. BAFFLE HEIGHT 1200

PACKED BED. NO MASS TRANSFER

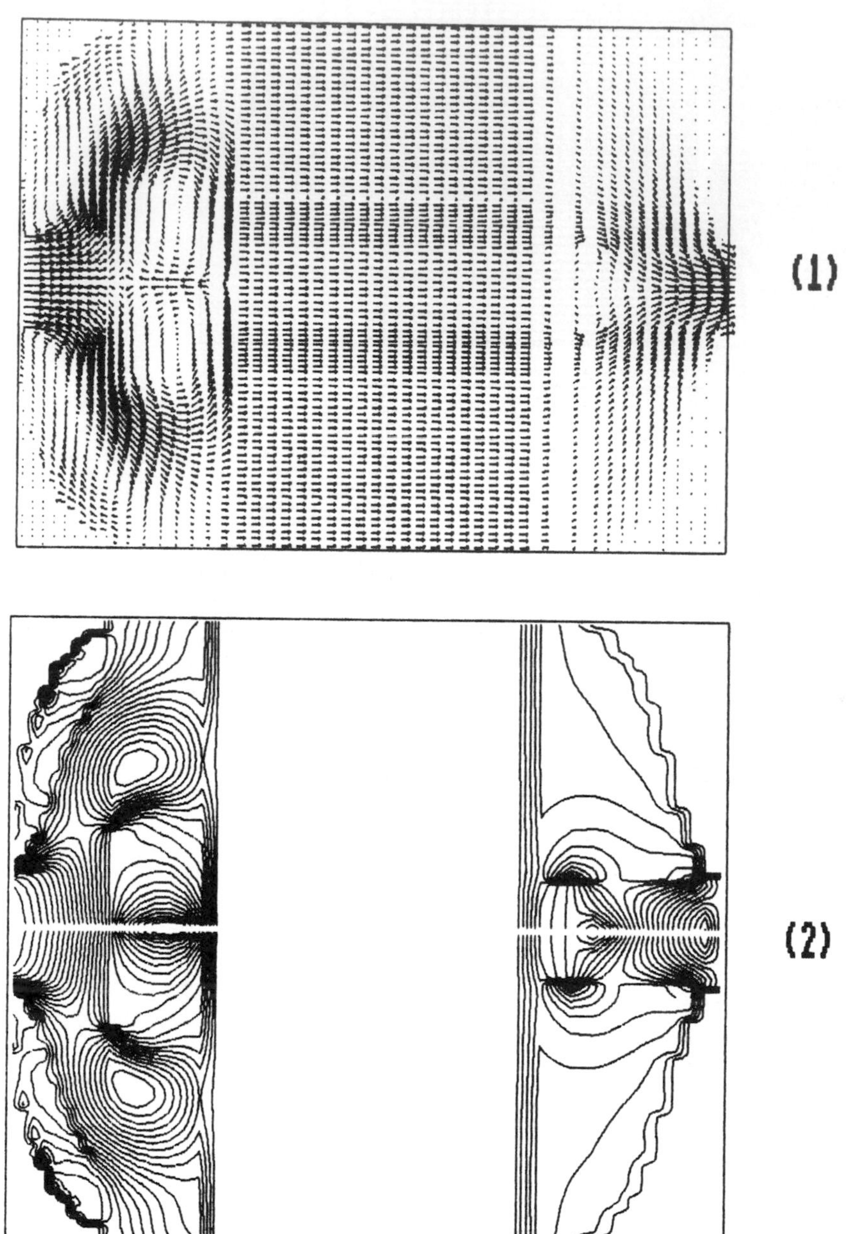

FIGURE 3. 1. VELOCITY VECTORS FROM THE STEADY-STATE ADSORPTION CALCULATION. BAFFLE HEIGHT 700 mm

2. VELOCITY W1 CONTURS FOR THE STEADY-STATE ADSORPTION CALCULATION. BAFFLE HEIGHT 700 mm.

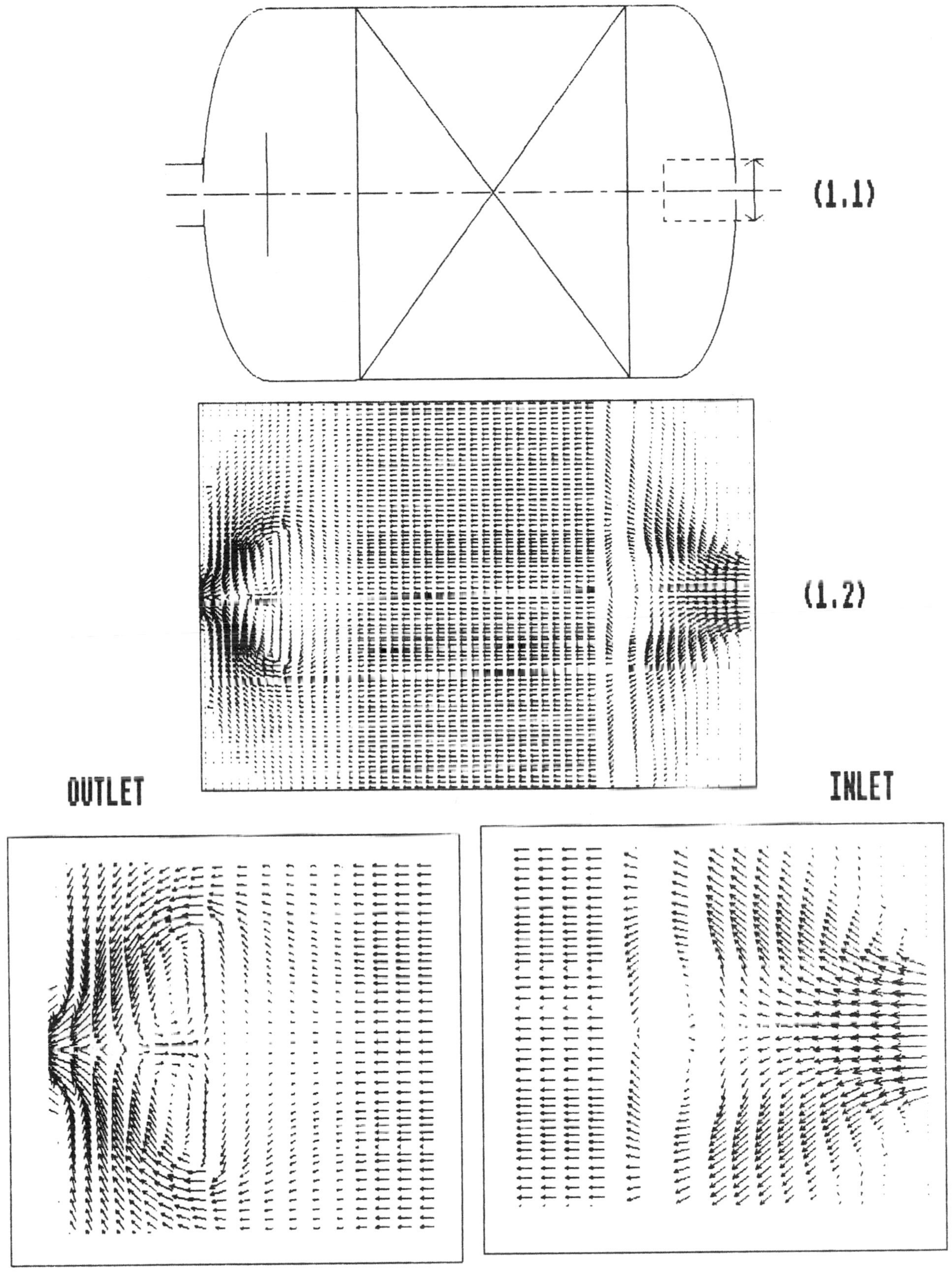

FIGURE 4. 1.1 GEOMETRY OF THE PACKED BED AND ITS VESSEL
1.2 VELOCITY VECTORS INTO THE REGENERATION CYCLE. DISTRIBUTOR HEIGHT 900 M M

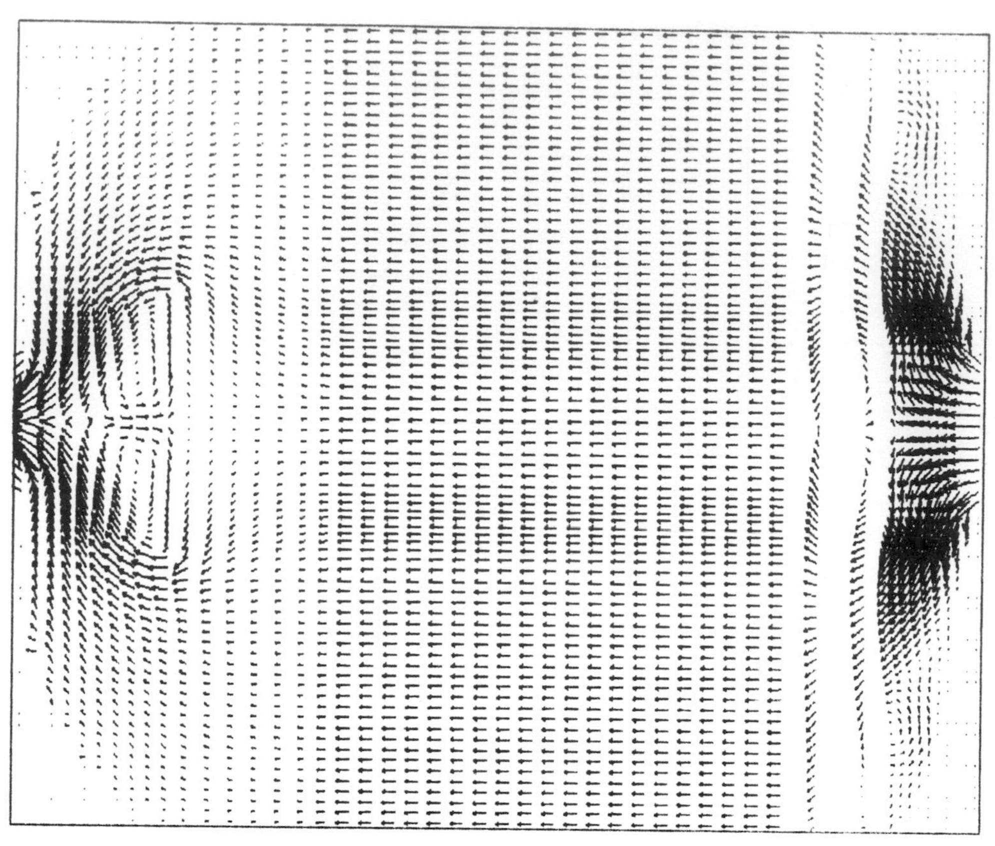

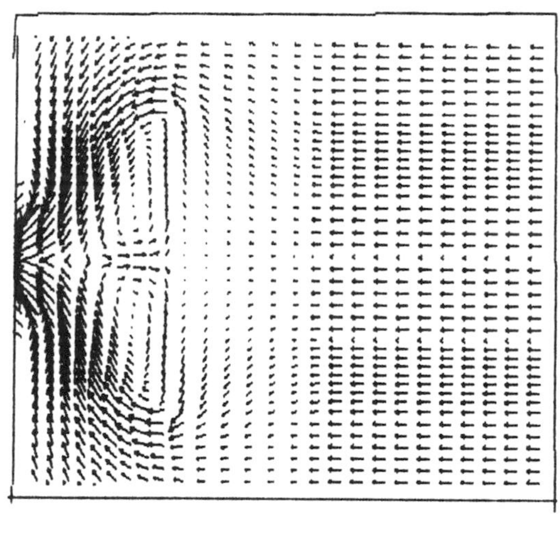

OUTLET

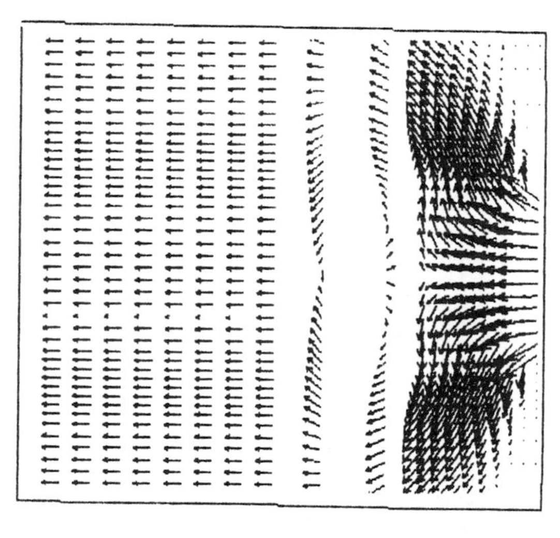

INLET.

VELOCITY VECTORS INTO THE REGENERATION CYCLE.DISTRIBUTOR HEIGHT 400 MM.

FIGURE 5.

REPLACEMENT OF R12 IN REFRIGERATION SYSTEMS

Prof. J.T. McMullan Dr. N.E. Murphy
University of Ulster at Coleraine
Northern Ireland
Contract JOUE-0055-C (EDB)

PARTICIPANTS

T.N.O. — Dr. P. Vermeulen
University of Hannover — Dr.-Ing. C. Elle
C.N.R. Istituto per la Technica del Freddo — Dr. R. Camporese
I.C.I. Chemicals and Polymers Ltd. — Dr. A. Lindley
AKZO Chemicals B.V. — Dr.-Ing. R.S. Koene

SUMMARY

This project will investigate possible routes for the replacement of refrigerant R12 in commercial and industrial refrigeration systems. The problems associated with R134a will be examined, and a search will be made for suitable binary mixtures. Attention will be paid to thermodynamic properties, lubrication problems, and the search for suitable lubricants (which still remain a significant problem area). Theoretical analysis will be carried out and backed up by experimental measurements.

INTRODUCTION

The recent concern over possible damage to stratospheric ozone by the chlorofluorocarbons has caused a rush to find suitable replacements for those currently in use as refrigerants. Refrigeration manufacturers are looking for a simple drop-in replacement which can be retro-fitted to existing systems without requiring any major modifications.

Two approaches are being adopted in the present contract. The first is to investigate the behaviour of one candidate single fluid, together with its lubrication problems; the second is to search for suitable pairs of refrigerants to use in more complex systems.

The single fluid work at the University of Ulster is the most advanced, and will form the bulk of this article. The status of the two fluid work will be reported in another article.

The refrigerant most commonly used today is R12, (CF_2Cl_2), used for medium temperature cooling. The most promising potential replacement developed so far is known as R134a. R134a, ($C_2H_2F_4$), is a close match for the thermodynamic properties of R12 in most respects, but is completely immiscible with standard refrigeration oils whereas R12 is completely miscible with oil under all conditions.

Refrigerant-oil miscibility in conventional systems aids the transfer of oil around the system, lubricating the service and expansion valves, before returning the oil to the compressor via the suction line. If an immiscible oil-refrigerant pair is used in a conventional system, oil escaping from the compressor may become trapped in the condenser or evaporator, leading to oil logging of these devices, and to the compressor running short of lubricant.

The refrigerant producers and refrigeration manufacturers are therefore eager to find alternatives to the conventional refrigeration oils which are miscible with R134a. Several types of synthetic oil have been suggested, however problems exist with regard to materials compatibility and purity. (Some of the suggested oils are hygroscopic which can lead to acid formation in the system.)

In a previous contract we have shown that the performance of a refrigeration or heat pump system was impaired by the use of a miscible oil-refrigerant pair. It may therefore be preferable to operate a system with an immiscible oil and make other arrangements to ensure sufficient lubrication in the compressor.

In any case, research is needed into the effect of the choice of refrigerant-lubricant pair on the thermodynamic and structural performance of refrigeration and heat pump systems using R134a, as no obvious lubricant has yet been identified and difficulties are being experienced with some of the possible candidates.

OBJECTIVES

The objective of this work is to identify replacements for R12 which can be used in commercial refrigeration systems. This involves both single fluids and binary fluid mixtures, and will include investigation of both physical and thermodynamic properties, including the problem of lubrication.

TASKS OF PARTICIPANTS

University of Ulster

The Centre for Energy Research at the University will design and construct two refrigeration test rigs, with R134a as a working fluid, to cover a range of evaporating temperatures from -20°C to +10°C and condensing temperatures from +35°C to +45°C.

We will examine the performance of these test rigs with measured amounts, up to 20%, of a range of lubricants, circulating through the evaporator and condenser.

University of Hannover

The University will be working on several aspects of the non-azeotropic mixtures section of the project. These may be summarised as follows :-

A. Fluid Properties.

1 The identification of candidate fluids for mixture cascade applications. A mixture cascade is a one stage system (using only one compressor) for use with large temperature differences between the evaporator and condenser, using the special behaviour of a non-azeotropic mixture.

2 The development of an equation of state for one candidate mixture.

3 The estimation of the behaviour of non-azeotropic mixtures with mineral and synthetic oils. The identification of not more than six promising oil-mixture combinations.

B. Cycle Simulation.

Simulation of selected non-azeotropic mixtures for commercial application regimes.

C. Experimental Tests.

Performance (COP) and compatibility (material interactions, corrosion, ageing, etc.) measurements on a system using a selected mixture. The tests will be carried out over a range of evaporation temperatures from -40°C to -80°C.

D. Design Studies into Applications of Non-azeotropic Mixtures.

1 Investigation of possible fields of application. Comparison of the cost of utilisation of non-azeotropic mixtures with classical fluids.

2 Determination of the potential of using a mixture cascade system in place of a multiple stage conventional system.

C.N.R. Istituto per la Technica del Freddo

The work carried out will be concerned with binary pairs of refrigerants, and will consist of :-

A. Identification of candidate mixtures for commercial applications.
B. Thermodynamic modelling of selected binary pairs.
C. Cycle simulation in commercial refrigeration applications.
D. Modification of refrigeration display cases to suit binary mixture applications.

T.N.O.

This part of the project will also be concerned with binary pairs of refrigerants. The following tasks will be carried out :-

A. Identification of candidate mixtures for industrial applications.
B. Thermodynamic measurements on selected binary pair mixtures.
C. Flammability tests.

D. Cycle simulation for industrial applications.
E. Performance measurements using selected binary mixtures.

PRELIMINARY RESULTS

University of Ulster

To further develop our understanding of the properties of oil-refrigerant mixtures, we have continued our series of experiments on the existing R22-oil mixtures test rig. Additionally, we have used the data of Spauschus[1], to calculate an equation relating the temperature, pressure and oil fraction of an Refrigerant 22 -oil mixture. Figure 1 shows a plot of vapour pressure against temperature and oil fraction, taken from Spauchus's data; while Figure 2 shows a comparable plot from our equation. When solubility data is available for R134a and the prospective lubricating oils, similar equations will be developed.

We have now designed and commenced construction of the first of the two R134a test rigs. The test rigs are small in size (using a 1 hp reciprocating compressor) because R134a is still in relatively short supply. ICI are supplying the R134a and a range of lubricants for testing. The exact test program will be decided when the first of the test rigs has been completed.

Figure 3 shows the design of the R134a test rigs. The test heat pump consists of the primary compressor and oil separator, the primary condenser, subcooler, expansion valves and the evaporator. A separate subcooler is used as this allows us to use the condenser conditions to control the compressor discharge pressure, and to use the subcooler to control the expansion valve inlet conditions. Capacity control is provided to permit a range of refrigerant mass flows to be investigated.

The remainder of the equipment is used to inject and recover the test lubricant. There are two possible injection points, upstream of the primary condenser or before the expansion valve. This allows us to investigate the effects in either the condenser or the evaporator as desired.

The injected oil is pumped by a positive displacement gear pump from a high pressure reservoir. The pressure in this reservoir is controlled so that the gear pump is always operating over a constant pressure difference, thus helping to keep the injection rate constant.

The oil is extracted, along with a fraction of the refrigerant in solution, by an oil separator at the evaporator outlet. From here the mixture is passed to a separation vessel where the refrigerant component is distilled off by a combination of heating and low pressure. The distilled refrigerant is compressed by the secondary compressor and condensed before being returned to the main system. The oil in the separation vessel is pumped to the high pressure reservoir. A pressure relief valve controls the pressure in this reservoir, when the set pressure has been reached the valve opens allowing the excess oil to return to the separation vessel which also functions as a low pressure reservoir.

As with the previous contracts the test rig is controlled and data-logged by a micro-computer based system. The software which was constructed for the previous contract has been ported to an IBM compatible machine and is functioning correctly.

The new software has several advantages over that used on the previous R12 - R22 / oil test rig. Data can now be logged almost ten times faster, roughly once per second. Also the test rig can now be run without the mainframe computer. It provides a built-in graph of any four of the test rig parameters, and a much greater degree of numerical analysis of the data can be carried out on the micro. The mainframe is still used for subsequent analysis and plotting of the data, but data can be collected on the micro and transferred across after the experiment has finished.

TNO

In order to assess the possible impact of non-azeotropic mixtures on energy conservation TNO has started to determine the applications of industrial refrigeration, the types of systems used, and the average temperature differences for various application/system combinations. Preliminary results strongly suggest that the attention of the project should be focused on an attempt to produce a small saving over a large part of the market, rather than a large saving over a limited market area.

The main section of the project to be carried out by TNO will come later and depends on the results of the work from the University of Hannover and CNR Istituto per la Technica del Freddo.

University of Hannover

The work due to be carried out has been delayed.

C.N.R. Istituto per la Technica del Freddo

The literature survey on thermodynamic data of methane and ethane based refrigerant with low ozone depletion potential has begun, together with screening to identify binary mixtures for commercial refrigeration. Preliminary work has also begun on the construction of computer programs based on the Redlich-Kwong-Soave equation of state with the following purposes:

- calculation of the thermodynamic properties of low ozone depletion potential refrigerants,
- calculation of the binary interaction parameter,
- calculation of vapour-liquid equilibria,
- calculation of thermodynamic properties of binary mixtures.

GENERAL STATUS

The work programme is now under way and the next four months will be critical to determining the detail of future work. Only after the initial assessment phase has been completed will the practical (and analytical) parts of the binary mixtures work be fully definable.

On the single fluid side, emphasis will be placed on R134a, and effort will concentrate (a) on establishing equations to describe its thermodynamic behaviour, and (b) on evaluating, with ICI, the problems of lubrication and choice of lubricant.

This is an area which suffers seriously from a lack of understanding and of data. Despite bland statements to the contrary, there are, as yet, no real replacements for existing refrigerants, and no assurance that the outstanding technical problems are amenable to solution. The bulk of research and development is currently being carried out in the USA, and it has been difficult to awaken the European refrigeration industry to the scale of the problem.

FUTURE R&D

1. There is still a need for long term research on a range of replacement CFCs. As yet there are no replacements for R22/R502, and the only proposed replacement for R12, that is R134a, has unresolved problems. Comparing the conventional CFCs and the suggested replacements (Figure 4), we can see that large gaps exist in the range of boiling points. This problem also has an impact on the whole industrial solvents area.

2. Further investigation is needed into the lubrication and chemical stability problems associated with replacement refrigerants. For example, the use of PAG lubricants can result in side effects such as corrosion and metal transport (plating).

3. A related area is that of materials compatibility, for example, the selection of suitable elastomer seals and compressor gaskets for use with the replacement CFCs.

4. Research is also needed into system performance problems because R134a is thermodynamically less efficient than R12.

REFERENCES

1 H. O. Spauschus. Vapor pressures, volumes and miscibility limits of Refrigerant 22-oil solutions.
ASHRAE Transactions No. 1893, July 1964.

2 European Community haste to cut CFCs. P216 Chemistry in Britain. March 1990.

3 Less friendly CFC replacements. P217 Chemistry in Britain. March 1990.

4 R. Stevenson. CFCs RIP. P731-733 Chemistry in Britain. August 1990.

5 M. O. McLinden. Thermodynamic Properties of CFC Alternatives, A Survey of the Available Data. Proceedings, ASHRAE CFC Technology Conf. Sept. 27-28th 1989.

6 P. E. Hansen. R134a for Domestic Refrigeration. Manuscript for an oral presentation at the ASHRAE winter meeting, Atlanta, 13th Feb. 1990.

7 K.R. Den Braven, S.O. Troxel. Method for Predicting the Performance of Non-azeotropic Mixtures in Heat Pumps. ASHRAE Transactions No. 3336. (Preprint) 1990.

Figure 1. R22/Oil Solubility (Spauschus data, 1964)

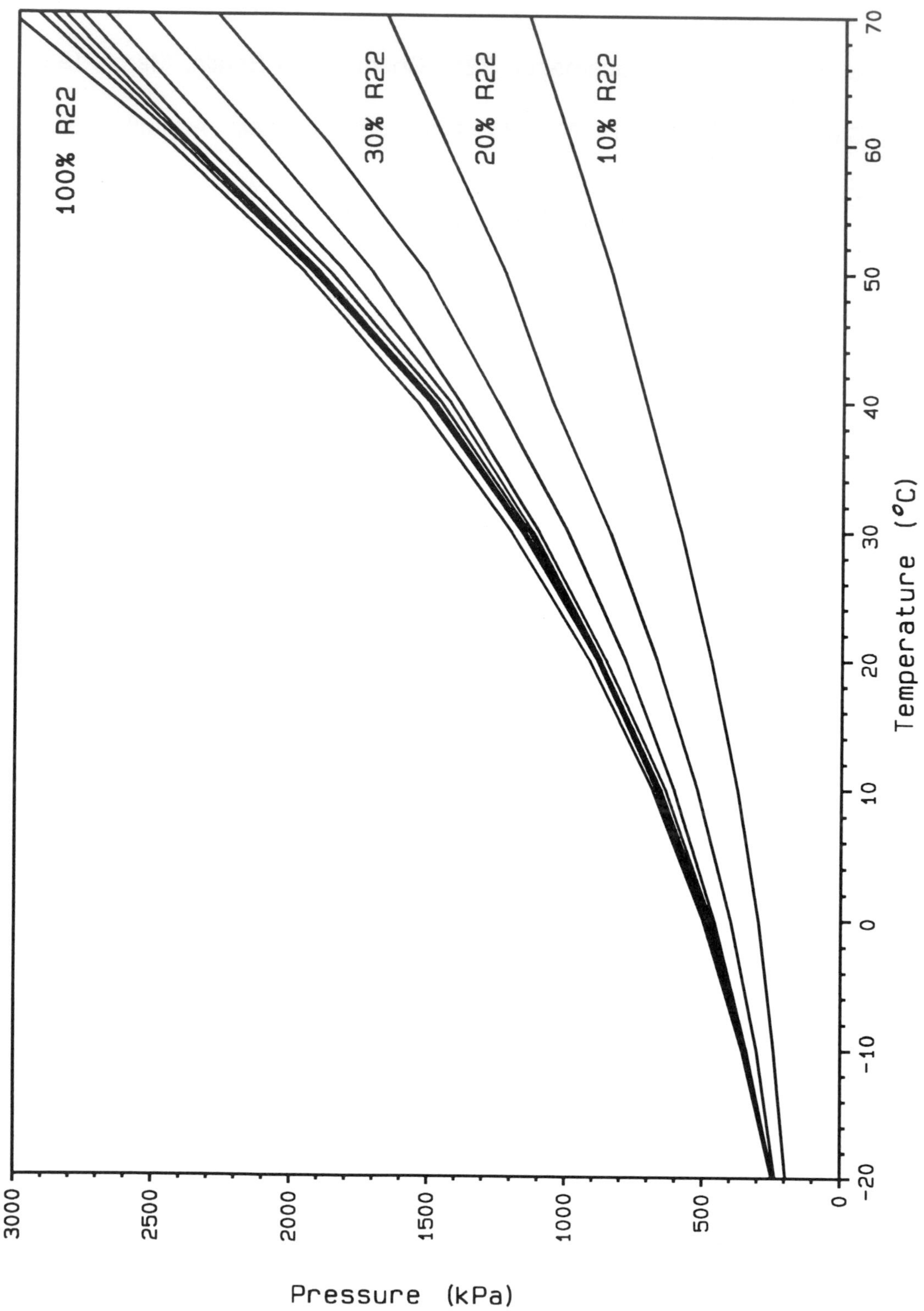

Figure 2. R22/Oil Solubility (Mathematically Derived)

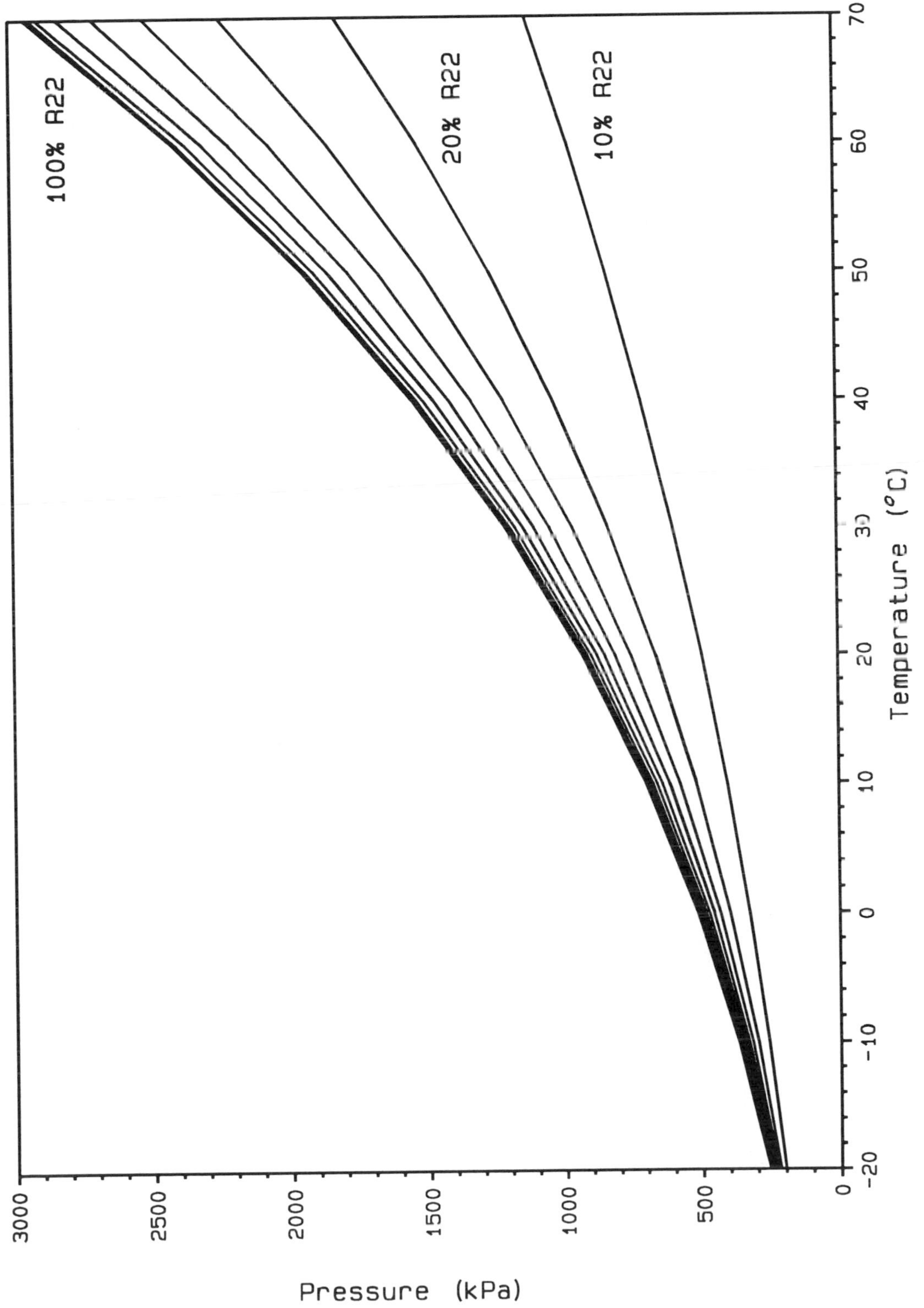

Figure 3. The R134a/Oil Test Facility.

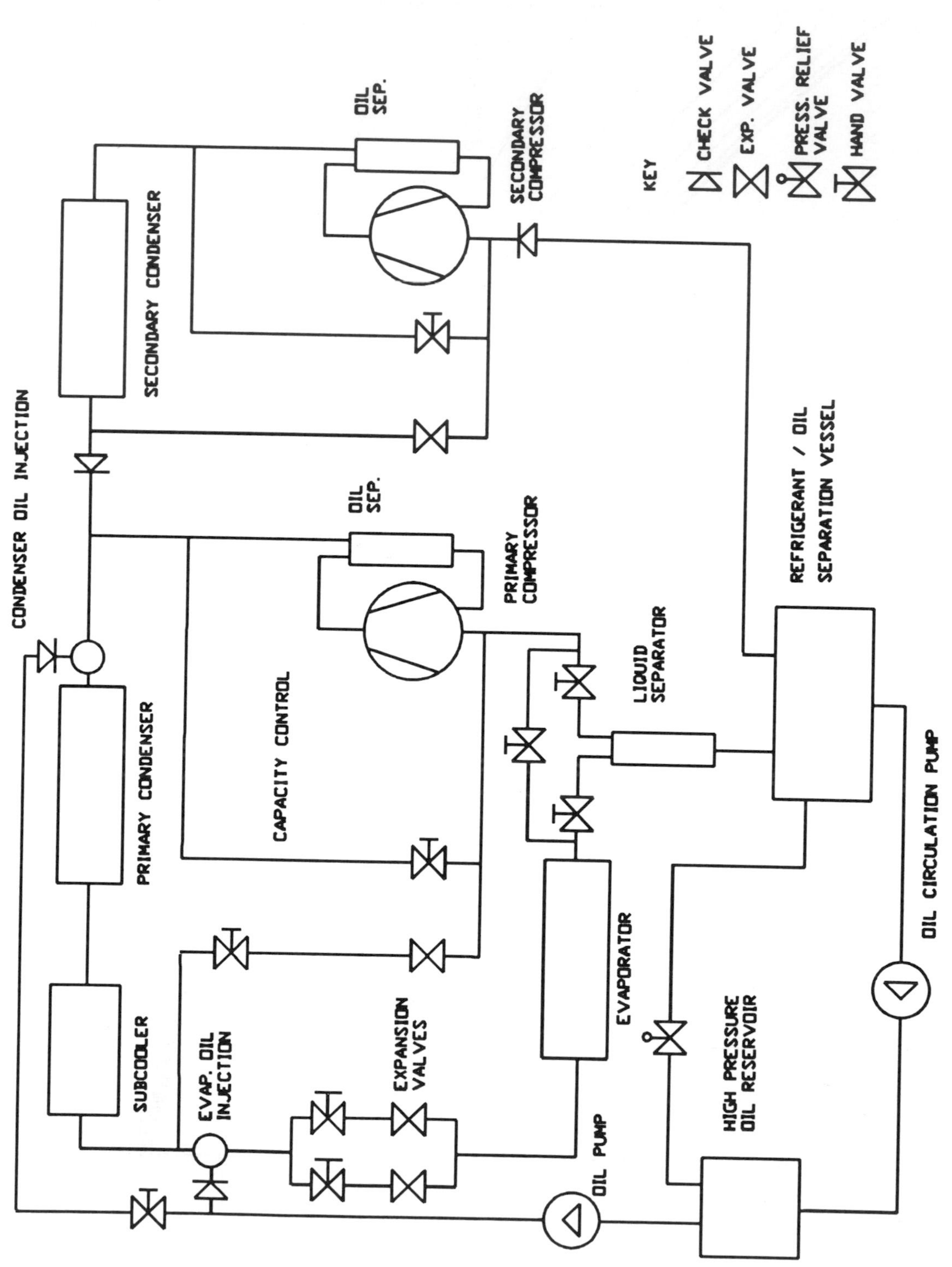

Figure 4 Current and Alternative Refrigeration Working Fluids

EXISTING FLUIDS (CFC's)		ALTERNATIVE FLUIDS	
NAME	BP (°C)	BP (°C)	NAME
R113	48		
R11	24		
		5	R143
R114	4		
		-27	R134a
R12	-30		
R22	-41		
R502	-45		
		-48	R125

ENERGY AND PROCESS SYSTEM MODELS

Chairman: Mr. R. Dumon

DESIGN AND OPERATION OF ENERGY EFFICICENT BATCH PROCESSES

E Kotjabasakis, P M M Brown and B Linnhoff

Linnhoff March Ltd
Knutsford WA16 OPL
U K

Contract : JOUE-0043-C

PARTICIPANTS

1.	Prof B Kalitventzeff Dr R Gosset	Belsim S A (Belgium)
2.	Prof L Puigjaner	Universitat Politecnica de Catalunya (UPC) (Spain)
3.	Dr N Murphy Prof A M de Paor	University College Dublin (UCD) (Eire)
4	Prof B Linnhoff Dr E Kotjabasakis	UMIST (UK)
5.	Mr I C Kemp	UK Atomic Energy Authority (UKAEA) (UK)
6.	Dr G Prokopakis	SPEC (Greece)

SUMMARY

The immediate outcome of the project will be new practical technology for the design and operation of energy efficient batch processes. The main focus of the work will be energy efficiency. However, we will also consider the interactions between energy and the other important factors of batch processes such as process yields, plant utilisation and product quality. We tackle these factors by bringing together experts in the areas of process integration, batch scheduling, multi-product and multi-purpose batch processes, process simulation and process control. Schedule control algorithms developed in this project will ensure that the energy savings identified in design can be fully realised in day-to-day plant operation. All the procedures developed will subsequently be brought together in a single computer software package. The results of case studies conducted using this package will then provide the impetus industry needs to apply it.

INTRODUCTION

This paper describes the research work which is currently performed for the "Design and Operation of Energy Efficient Batch Processes" under the finance from the EEC Joule Programme.

The integration of batch plants for energy saving is a rare practice. There are few known instances where plants have been designed in this way. This is unfortunate for it has resulted in batch plants having poor energy efficiencies. This is demonstrated by the process integration studies that have been conducted on this type of plant in recent years. All have shown high savings. In one instance, integration led to a saving of 70% of the process's energy consumption.

There are a number of factors that hinder the integration of batch plants:

1. A procedure for the integration of batch processes has only recently been developed (see references) and this only applies to plants manufacturing a single product. It is not applicable to multi-purpose or multi-product plants.

2. Plant operators are worried that integration will adversely affect process control, plant flexibility and operability.

3. Operators recognise that integration requires good schedule control. The operating information (or computer software) necessary to ensure this is not available.

4. Plant operators have not generally considered energy to be the most significant factor in their costs. Process yield, product quality and plant utilisation are all considered to be more important than energy consumption.

Recent work has demonstrated that the key to good integration, and through it good energy efficiency, is effective process scheduling. This is also the key to optimum process yields and high plant utilisation. Thus, the willingness of plant operators to live with poor energy efficiencies can be overcome by demonstrating the benefits integration has on these other factors.

OBJECTIVES

The overall objective of the project is the development of an industrially useful and accepted procedure for the design and operation of energy efficient batch processes.

The benefits of this project to the European Community are as follows:

1. Industry will be provided with the ability to identify potential energy savings through the integration of batch processes.

2. The current barrier to the use of process integration on batch plants (worries about subsequent plant operability) will be removed.

3. Industry will be provided with the tools necessary to realise these savings through design technology and through plant operating technology.

Experience with the integration of batch processes has shown that energy savings of 30 to 50% may accrue.

It is estimated that the present energy consumption of batch processes operating within the European Community is costing around 1350 million ECU/year. Little energy recovery is currently practised. The probable energy saving potential for such processes is 40%, or 540 million ECU/year.

TASKS OF PARTICIPANTS

The project is organised into four project areas:

1. Development of batch process synthesis technology.

2. Development of batch process simulation technology

3. Development of batch process control technology.

4. Validation of procedures using Case Studies.

Project Area 1. Development of Batch Process Synthesis Technology.

Four research groups will be working in this project area: UPC, UMIST, SPEC Ltd and UKAEA. UKAEA will be participating as consultants working with UMIST.

Batch plants can generally be divided into three categories: single purpose, multi-product and multi-purpose. Multi-product plants are those in which more than one batch of product is to be produced using several production stages which may have more than one piece of equipment operating in parallel (network flowshop). Multi-purpose plants are those in which processes are conducted in equipment as and when equipment becomes available through the completion of earlier batches without a common pattern for the movement of material (jobshop).

This project will examine the synthesis of both multi-product and multi-purpose processes. The work on multi-product processes will be led by UPC. The work on multi-purpose processes will be led by SPEC.

The UPC work programme is as follows:

1.1.1 Definition of the standards to be used in the production of the software. Specification of command structure, Data Base Management System, user interface detail and communication protocols.

1.1.2 Industrial cases will be examined in order to establish actual needs, true problem dimensions and how suited current procedures are in the solution of the real problem.

1.1.3 Standard benchmark problems will be developed for testing of the algorithms.

1.1.4 Multi-product network flowshop definition and specification.

1.1.5 Development of software for the design of new plants producing multiple products.

1.1.6 Collaboration with SPEC and UMIST in the development of process synthesis procedures. Development of procedures which properly consider the rational use of intermediate storage (depending on temperature) for heat recovery. Rational use of parallel equipment.

1.1.7 Scheduling and Production Planning Studies in Multi-product Plants.

(a) Optimisation of scheduling and production planning in existing multiproduct plants.

(b) Energy Integration considerations on existing plants

(c) Design optimisation procedures to improve energy use.

1.1.8 Collaboration with SPEC in the study of how uncertainty affects design and how it can be catered for at the design stage. The specific uncertainties considered here are possible long and short term variations in product demand, the possible incidence of batch failure and the possible incidence of equipment failure.

1.1.9 Application of developed software to capacity expansion and retrofitting of existing plants

The UMIST work programme is as follows:

1.2.1 There are currently two thermodynamic tools available for the energy analysis of batch plants. The 'time cascade model' and the 'time average/event combination model'. UMIST will examine, refine, compare and appraise both of these approaches for the energy analysis of batch processes.

1.2.2 Development of a computer program which utilises these models for the energy analysis of batch processes.

1.2.3 Testing of both algorithms and program on the standard integration problems

(a) Retrofit of a single purpose plant
(b) Retrofit of a multi-purpose plant
(c) Grassroots design of a single-purpose plant
(d) Grassroots design of a multi-purpose plant

1.2.4 Development of process synthesis procedure for batch processes (see task 1.1.6).

1.2.5 Systematisation of an energy saving retrofit technology for batch plants based on process integration.

1.2.6 Systematisation of an integration procedure for grassroots design

The SPEC work programme is as follows.

As stated above SPEC will work on the synthesis of multi-purpose plants (as opposed to multi product plants).

1.3.1 Collaboration with UPC and UMIST in the development of software standards.

1.3.2 Examination of industrial problems (in a task analogous to 1.1.2). This will be followed by a critical analysis of existing procedures.

1.3.3 Collaboration with UPC and UMIST in the development of standard benchmark problems.

1.3.4 In collaboration with UMIST two potential industrial case studies will be identified for the testing of the procedures.

1.3.5 Development of software for scheduling and sequencing in multi-purpose plants

(a) Problem formulation
(b) Development of methodology for the identification of scheduling conflicts among products/intermediates
(c) Scheduling and sequencing algorithm development
(d) Programming
(e) Case studies (dealt with in 4.5.1)

1.3.6 Sensitivity of Scheduling and Sequencing in Multi-purpose Plants

(a) Effect on schedules of batch network size and connectivity; effect of due dates distribution
(b) effect on schedules of different objective functions, minimise tardiness, minimise makespan, maximise utilisation of processor etc.
(c) effect of uncertainty

1.3.7 Alternate Routings and Pathways in Multi-purpose Batch Plants

(a) Alternate routings in product scheduling

(b) Alternate reaction pathways in product scheduling

Project Area 2 : Development of Batch Process Simulation Technology

The work conducted in this area will primarily be done by Belsim S.A. UPC will provide the linkage between this sub-task and the work conducted in other areas.

The result of the work conducted in area 1 will be a synthesis procedure which will provide information on process structure, schedule and integrated heat balance. In order to determine equipment sizes simulation calculations will be needed. Although specific programs have demonstrated the usefulness of simulation at the scale of restricted units, general computer programs for these functions do not currently exist. They will be developed in this sub-task.

Belsim S.A. has the experience of large scale, general purpose process simulation programs. Specific subroutines for typical unit operations can be assembled to form the simulation program for a production process (note: the current BELSIM simulation package deals solely with steady state processes).

The models developed will be general and flexible. For instance, the batch reactor forms a key element of a batch process. The models produced in this project will have the flexibility to handle many different types of reaction in a wide range of specified geometries.

In addition to the development of numerical algorithms the work will involve the study of how to correctly state the simulation problem, how to define the initial conditions and an examination of problem stiffness.

The software produced in this sub-task will be interfaced with that developed in Project Area 1.

The Belsim work programme is as follows:

2.1.1 Data Base Management System and 4th Generation Language Select the most relevant relational data base software and train staff in its use.

2.1.2 Modelling of reactors. A reactor model which allows for differing reaction streams will be developed for the most common reactor configurations used in batch processes.

2.1.3 Modelling of batch distillation. Experience in solving the problem of transients in continuous distillation columns will bring this to bear in the development of a batch distillation model.

2.1.4 Modelling of heat exchangers.

2.1.5 Modelling of evaporators. What happens when hold-up varies and modelling of the effects of liquid concentration on vapour and liquid temperatures.

2.1.6 Modelling of crystallizers. Modelling of crystal nucleation rates and crystal growth.

2.1.7 Simulation of linked unit operations. The different unit operations are to be simulated together.

2.1.8 Transfer of information to other collaborators and linkage into common data base system.

The UPC work programme will involve:

2.2.1 Development of common data base structure - in particular, linkage between simulation and synthesis software.

Project Area 3: Development of Batch Process Control Technology.

The work conducted in this area will primarily be done by UMIST, Belsim S.A. and UCD. Again UPC will provide the linkage between this Project Area and the work conducted in other areas.

The UMIST work programme is as follows:

3.1.1 Standard benchmark problem for a batch schedule control will be developed. The purpose of this problem is the introduction and maintainance of industrial reality in the research.

3.1.2 Development of procedures for determining required compensating adjustments in the scheduling of integrated batch plants forced by processsing delays in other parts of the plant.

3.1.3 Testing of procedures developed.

3.1.4 Development of procedures for the prediction of the effects of processing delays and unexpected changes in operating conditions on utility demand.

3.1.5 Development of procedures for the synthesis of schedule control and safety schemes for energy integrated batch processes.

The Belsim S A work programme is as follows:

3.2.1 Development of procedures for the scheduling of control events. Determine how to introduce the schedule and what types of test are to be implemented.

3.2.2 Examination of interactive control decision making. Through user interactions the engineer can test different perturbations and control measures.

The UCD work programme is as follows:

It is common in the process industries engaged in batch processing to employ a number of heat transfer fluids to span the temperature range required for processing. It is also common practice to put each utility through the jacket of the same reaction vessel in order to obtain the temperature changes required by the process. This methodology has severe drawbacks. These include dangerous cross contamination of utilities, poor control, non-availability of utility at certain points in the cycle, and poor cycle times.

One means of overcoming these problems is the use of a single heat transfer medium that will span the full temperature range required by a process. Currently there are no design procedures for such utility systems. UCD will examine the possibility of using single medium utility systems and will develop the design procedures necessary for their use.

The work will consist of the following tasks:

3.3.1 Study of the heat transfer characteristics, safety characteristics and corrosivity of currently available heat transfer fluids.

3.3.2 Development of Process & Instrumentation Diagrams for a single fluid utility system associated with a batch reactor.

3.3.3 Dynamic modelling of the plant developed under task 3.3.2

The utility is supplied to the plant at a 'high' and 'low' temperature. In a conventional control scheme the set point is the temperature of the vessel contents. The way in which the set point is adjusted can lead to overshoots. These overshoots can have severe consequences.

The routines developed in this task will provide the real time element of control necessary for the implementation of the schedule control algorithms developed in task 3.1.2.

UPC's work programme is:

3.4.1 Incorporation of software developed under the Area 3 into the common data base structure.

Project Area 4: Validation through Case Studies.

The work conducted in this area will be done by Linnhoff March Ltd, Belsim S A, UPC, UCD and SPEC.

The Linnhoff March work will involve the testing of appropriate technologies produced in this project on industrial projects. Their work programme is as follows:

4.1.1 Identification of industrial case studies. Three case studies will be undertaken. These will be taken from the food and drink industry and from the chemical industry.

4.1.2 Plant data collection and reconciliation

4.1.3 Process Integration, appropriate analyses and validation of procedures.

4.1.4 Feedback to researchers

The Belsim S A work will be:

4.2.1. Validation of batch process simulation package

4.2.2 Participation in Case Studies. The batch simulation program will be used in case studies. Feedback from these studies will be used for the subsequent adaptation of the program.

4.3.1 The UPC work will be undertaken as an integral part of the work in project area 1. Initially two industrial case studies will be considered: one relating to synthetic fibre manufacture, the other with latex products. Other case studies which may subsequently be undertaken include one on cosmetic production and one on pigment manufacture.

4.4.1 The UCD work will involve the testing of their single utility procedures on an industrial case study associated with fine chemicals manufacture.

4.5.1 The SPEC work will also be undertaken as an integral part of the work in project area 1.3 and will involve the case studies identified in task 1.3.4.

PRELIMINARY RESULTS

The project work has only started very recently. So, despite the fact that all participants had informal communications between them and had considerable progress, we cannot report at this moment any results in a structured form.

FUTURE R & D

This work is concerned with the development of algorithms, methodologies and procedures for the systematic design of energy efficient batch processes. The various techniques are combined in a preliminary data base which will require considerable development to permit industry to use it in day to day operation. This development will involve the refinement and expansion of the algorithms, more research into the relationships of yield and reaction kinetics to energy consumption, and the improvement of the interface between different sections of the programme and between the user and the software to make it user friendly.

The operational aspects of batch processes are much more complex than for continuous ones. The present programme covers off line techniques for schedule optimisation and debottlenecking, to improve specific energy consumption. Future R & D is required to develop techniques for real time on line control to maximize plant efficiency. This would include algorithms and techniques for control with daily, hourly and by minute time horizons. Distributed control techniques linked with a main control computer system would be utilized. The system would be tested on both simulated and real plants.

The utility plant for batch processes cycles as the process requirements change. Experience on continuous plants shows real energy savings at zero capital expenditure by on line optimisation of utility systems. With batch plants the dynamics of the system are much more complex, with large swings in usage. Considerable development is needed to extend the techniques to the batch industries where the savings in primary energy should be significantly greater than in continuous processes.

Models for the most common batch processes are being developed in area 2 of the present study. To be universally useful in the batch environment, models for several more unit operations must be developed. In addition, the application of MVR or thermal heat pumps have not been considered in time/temperature variable mode. Development of algorithms for these energy saving devices needs to be undertaken so that they can be handled in the batch process design.

Due to the nature of batch processes, effluents are generated at varying intervals and these may interact with one another complicating the waste handling. In any event the gaseous and liquid effluents must be treated and these usually incur an energy penalty. R & D is required to study the way effluents are produced and disposed of in the batch process industry. Procedures must be formulated for integration of the waste treatment facilities with the process in order to reduce the quantities of waste to be treated and to maximize the recovery of energy. The issues are complex but preliminary research indicates that techniques can be evolved for reducing effluent, capital and energy in batch plants simultaneously. Considerable further R & D is required.

The batch industry traditionally uses standard equipment which is often costly to produce in energy terms and wasteful of energy when in operation. The development of an expert system for the selection of the optimum equipment which minimizes energy consumption for the process duty required, would benefit the industry and improve its competitiveness in world markets.

REFERENCES

1. "The Cascade Analysis for Energy and Process Integration of Batch Processes", I C Kemp and A W Deakin, ChERD, Vol 67, September 1989.

2. "On Pinch Technology Based Procedures for the Design of Batch Processes", E D A Obeng and G J Ashton, ChERD, Vol 66, May 1988.

3. "Process Integration of Batch Processes", Paper No 92, AIChE Annual Meeting, New York, November 1987.

SIMULATION AND CONTROL OF FAST TRANSIENTS IN PROCESS AND UTILITY SYSTEMS

Professor P Hutchinson &
School of Mechanical Engineering
Cranfield Institute of Technology
Cranfield
Bedford United Kingdom

Dr M E Gill
W S Atkins Engineering Sciences Ltd
Woodcote Grove
Ashley Road
EPSOM Surrey KT18 5BW

CONTRACT JOUE - 0047 - C

PARTICIPANTS

Professor P Hutchinson, Cranfield Institute of Technology, UK
Professor B Kalitventzeff, Université de Liège, Belgium
D Marchio, Ecole des Mines de Paris, France
F Macke, Thomassen International, Netherlands
M E Gill, W S Atkins, UK

SUMMARY

The objective of the project is to develop models to simulate fast transients in process elements and utility networks, including controls, and to integrate them into a flow sheeting package of a form compatible with such dynamic simulation codes as SPEEDUP or CHEDYN. This will allow the management of process plant in a more optimally energy efficient way and thus lead to substantial energy savings.

The project will bring together three complementary areas of expertise - dynamic flow sheeting, individual component dynamic representation and control simulation. These techniques will be integrated through technology exchange. The outcome will be a broader range of the application of dynamic simulation for process and utility plant in the areas of energy efficiency, control and safety. The project involves work for the process industry.

The objectives will be achieved by developing fluid dynamic models for individual plant elements, control algorithims applicable to particular plant designs, and a general systems simulator. The new developments will be assessed by testing them using data obtained from real process plants.

INTRODUCTION

ENERGY SAVING

There is a significant potential for improving the energy efficiency of process systems if their behaviour can be adequately modelled and such models used to provide a basis for optimal control. This would assist efficient management and operation of the plant and has a strong potential for energy saving.

Process systems can only operate in a satisfactory manner if supplied with utilities, such as electricity, steam or compressed air. Utilities are usually distributed through a network, where several potential suppliers can be selected according to required duties, economical or technical considerations.

Optimal energy usage is achieved by occasionally switching or reconfiguring the utility supplies, and the transients resulting from this action will perturb the working point of the process.

Since the network material inventory is low with respect to instantaneous demand, the perturbation will rapidly affect many items of process equipment linked to the network. Hence, to develop effective control strategies, and achieve efficient energy usage while maintaining safety margin, it is essential to have a well founded understanding of transients in the complete system and their interaction. This demonstrates the importance of studying fast transients in this context.

The process plant designer and operator have available to them various tools to aid in specification and operation of the plant while maintaining safety and efficiency, namely flow sheet analyses, controller software and some detailed knowledge of how components in the system operate in isolation. The operation of the whole process may be described by using these methods in combination.

Each of these topics has been demonstrated to be useful to the process industry but often the areas of applicability are limited. Also, the inadequate integration of these tools leads to the necessity to over design in some areas of applicability.

Current dynamic process simulators (such as the Imperial College programme SPEEDUP or the Université de Liège program CHEDYN) are mainly developed to study the transient behaviour of processes which usually exhibit a rather slow response to external perturbations. This is due to the nature of most continuous production processes, which are composed of a sequence of devices, each containing a substantial material hold up. Perturbations are usually smoothed out when transferred from one equipment to the next with some time delay.

These models do not, therefore, include the detailed fluid dynamic models which are needed to study fast transients. The numerical algorithms used in such process simulations are optimised for this type of problem, but as a result individual items of equipment, for example turbomachinery or controls, are modelled quite simplistically.

When fast acting transients occur in the system the simple representation will no longer give an account of the correct response. Fast transients might be caused by trip or by compressor surge, (a self-induced instability which occurs at low mass flow rate, and may actually result from a much slower process transient). In these situations, the system response can only be correctly modelled by including a detailed representation of the equipment and its interaction with the rest of the system or process.

Models which take account of the fluid dynamic interaction have been developed and validated for simulation of fast transients in some particular process elements such as compressors. The scope of this project will be to develop further these models for additional process elements and integrate them into a dynamic flowsheeting package in a form compatible with such industry standard packages as SPEEDUP or CHEDYN.

The treatment of controllers is one of the weakest points in the software dealing with thermal devices, and complex control models are not available in the general purpose simulators. For the description of the process plant, the model will need to define the logic of the plant operation. Also the controller parameters will have to be selected or adjusted for actual plant. This adjustment generally requires empirical or semiempirical techniques. This situation has led to the implementation of adaptive controllers, whose parameter synthesis is made on-line during the system evolution, on the basis of an estimated model and given criteria.

Adaptive controllers can simplify the simulation of the thermal plants control system, but since they are based on an assumption of linear system behaviour, they may not function correctly where significant non-linearities are induced by the plant.

Identification of the best approach to be used in the control model, and interaction with the simulation of the system will form a major part of this aspect of the project.

OBJECTIVES

The project aims to develop new capabilities for the benefit of operators of process and utility systems within Europe. The particular area at which this project is aimed is in the operation, control and layout design of utility systems. The outcome will be improved simulation of the overall process, and integration with the latest control philosophies.

Specific objectives by which this will be achieved are as follows:

- Integration of improved models into a flowsheeting simulator.
- Validation of existing and new models against industrial test cases.
- Comparison and exchange of the methodology of component simulators (explicit) with process flowsheet simulators (implicit) and optimisation of the dynamic simulator.

Since the project is aimed at developing techniques, at a pre-competitive level, the results will be available for exploitation in all areas of the community in process and utility plant.

TASKS OF PARTICIPANTS

The project will concentrate on the following areas:-

(i) Existing fluid dynamic models will be extended to simulate transients occurring in plant components such as condensers and reboilers, compressors and turbines. They will be interfaced with the network models through the distribution of physical variables such as temperature.

(ii) Models for classic and self tuning controllers adapted to the dynamic behaviour of the system will be developed.

(iii) A systems simulator will be developed and applied to describe cogeneration cycles (where both turbines and heaters are active and steam is produced both in process dependent waste heat boilers and in conventional boilers), and compressors in gas handling systems.

(iv) Examples related to real industrial problems will be used to test the applicability of the methods to rating and design studies.

Developments in each of these areas will be carried out, initially as developments to existing modules, then integrated together to form a pre-competitive software package for dynamic simulation of general process system. The interface between the modules will be defined by input and output of boundary conditions to process sub-systems. This modular approach, relying on specification of input and output conditions for each module will provide a form which is compatible with or easily adaptable to process dynamic simulation packages such as Imperial College SPEEDUP or University of Liège CHEDYN. The applicability of the methods will be evaluated by carrying out case studies in the utilities industry.

Two test cases will be provided by one of the associated industrial partners (Thomassen International of the Netherlands) and have been selected to test the individual element models.

The first case study is a gas turbine heat and power plant (cogeneration plant). The requirement is to simulate gas-turbine drivers, together with a model for the heat recovery boiler and control system. The time history of the steam and power output will be simulated during transients caused by trip or change in power requirements.

The second case study will be of an integrated rotating equipment system for the distribution network of an ethylene production plant. Hence the process simulation will consider steam turbines driving the process gas compressors. The effect of changes in gas composition on the compressors will be simulated, and optimal control strategies developed. Refrigeration elements will also be considered in this test case.

The breakdown of the project by technology area, (and for contributing partner) is given in the following sections.

Partner 1 - Cranfield Institute of Technology

Within many industries, from process to aerospace, it is necessary to transport and compress gases, and centrifugal and axial flow compressors are efficient components for achieving this aim. A knowledge of the transient operation of compressors in these applications is important, in defining control strategy and ensuring stable and efficient operation of the plant. The transient operation of a compressor in a system depends on the fluid dynamic interaction of the compressor with the rest of the system, and on its interaction with controls. Cranfield Institute of Technology have been working for many years on mathematical models to simulate compressor transient operations with applications in the aeroegine and process industries.

The modelling approach that has been used is based on a dynamic representation of the fluid flows within the compressor itself and the system of which the compressor is a part. The model uses the dynamic forms of the conservation equations of mass, momentum and energy, which applied to a general element may be written.

Momentum

$$\int_V \frac{\partial}{\partial t}(\rho_s d\overline{c})\, dV = -\int_S P_s d\overline{s} - \int_S \rho_s \overline{c}(c \,.\, d\overline{s}) + F_{NET} \qquad .. (1)$$

Continuity

$$\int_V \frac{\partial \rho_s}{\partial t}\, dV = -\int_S \rho_s \overline{c} \,.\, d\overline{s} \qquad .. (2)$$

Energy

$$\int_V \frac{\partial}{\partial T} [\rho_s (U_i + KE)] \, dV = - \int_S (h + KE) \rho_s \bar{c} \cdot d\bar{s} + E_{NET}$$

.. (3)

Where

ρ_s = density

$\bar{c}$ = velocity
V = volume
P_s = static pressure

$\bar{s}$ = surface vector
U_i = internal energy
KE = Kinetic energy
h = specific enthalpy
F_{NET} = force input
E_{NET} = energy input

From these general equations, and an appropriate discretisation of the system, a dynamic model of the fluid system can be derived. The ability to deal with different gases and mixtures built into the model by the use of the polytropic analysis of Schultz, was chosen for its flexibility and general applicability, although alternative analyses could be used.

An important feature of the approach is in the definition of the force and energy input terms which appear in the governing equations. These terms can be evaluated for any element of the system (compressor, duct, valve etc) from a knowledge of the pressure rise or loss, and energy input or loss associated with that element. Hence, data input to the model consists of performance characteristics (derived from steady state performance) for the components of the system, plus geometric parameters.

The Cranfield model has been programmed into a FORTRAN code, using a Runge Kutta explicit integration, and has been used extensively on compression systems, and gas turbines, to predict transient performance, stability limits (compressor surge) and post instability performance. Details of those applications can be found in the bibliography. The model has been demonstrated to contain the required physical physical representation to simulate fast fluid dynamic transients in compression systems. The general formulation can be adapted for other components of process and utility systems, to provide the fast transient capability which is not covered by existing process models.

The tasks to be undertaken by partner 1, Cranfield Institute of Technology are as follows:-

Plant Elements - Extension of Models

The first task to be addressed by the project is to consider existing modelling capabilities for plant elements, (compressors, steam and gas turbines, condensors and reboilers) and compare and exchange the technologies used in the different applications. The existing models will need to be extended to be capable of simulating phenomena of different time scales. Traditionally, simulation of many plant elements is handled in a very crude manner, using algebraic balance equations, which is adequate when studying long timescale variations in processes.

Partner 1 will have responsibility for extending existing models which have been used on compressors to other components of the system. This task will involve close association with partner 2 (Université de Liège), who have experience in the modelling of other process elements. In addition the need to interface the models which use an explicit integration with existing flowsheet simulators which use implicit schemes will be addressed.
This will be carried out in association with the industrial partner 5 (W S Atkins), who have experience in dynamic simulation in process plant.

The approach to be taken in this task is as follows:-

(i) Determination of appropriate discrete elements to which the fluid dynamic equations can be applied.

(ii) Derivation of the physical relationships decribing the processes existing within the element, and the data set which will form the input to the model.

(iii) Application of the model elements alone, in a small system and as part of a complex system.

Plant elements to be considered by partner 1 are compressors, and turbines, (for process and utility plant).

Existing fluid dynamics models will be tuned and configured to interface with the complex system of the plant network.

Gas Turbine Drivers

Many processes use gas turbines to supply the power for other items of machinery, and exhaust gases for waste heat recovery. Relatively simple models of these components are used, which disguise the complexities of the component and their effect on the dynamic response of associated equipment. Mechanical and fluid dynamic processes are closely integrated as well as complex control systems. During this task the capability of existing models will be assessed and improvements developed based on the outcome of tasks 1.1 and 3.1 (described below). Task 1.2 will be the responsibility of Partner 1, and consists of the following items:

(i) Assessment of existing simple models and to suggest areas where increased complexity will improve the representation of the system, including the effect on associated components.

(ii) Consideration of the interaction between the fluid dynamic, mechanical and control processes which exist, and how they should be embodied in the simulation.

(iii) Development of the physical and mathematical models for the processes in the gas turbine, based on tasks 1.1 and 1.3.

(iv) Testing and validation of the model, and integration into a complex system, eg, a waste heat recovery steam generator.

Dynamic Simulator

Having defined in Task 1 the physical and mathematical representation of the plant items, Task 3 addresses the implementation of those models into the dynamic simulator. The dynamic model must be able to simulate the fast acting transients associated with the turbomachinery, and the coupling with the slower response time of the process.

Process simulators have traditionally employed implicit integrators, while simulations of fast acting transients in rotating machinery have used explicit integrators. This task will compare explicit and implicit integration algorithms to develop an efficient dynamic simulator. the task will involve Partner 1 for explicit techniques and Partner 2 for implicit techniques.

Partner 2 - University of Liège,

The Laboratory for Analysis and Synthesis of Chemical Systems (LASSC) of the University of Liège is active in research and development of computer aided process engineering software. Software which have already been developed includes EPIC (physical and thermodynamic property data bank). BELSIM-VALI (plant data analysis and reconciliation), SYNEP (energy integration and utility management, and CHEDYN (dynamic process simulation).

The tasks to be undertaken by partner 2 are described in the following sections. The emphasis will be in development of existing component representations to allow them to simulate fast transients which may be imposed by changing conditions elsewhere in the network. Optimisation of the numerical solution algorithms to satisfy the requirements of the process simulation and to allow it to interface with models developed by partner 1 will be a major task. Finally, in collaboration with partners 1 and 3, the component and control models will be integrated into a dynamic simulator of a process or utility network.

Plant Elements - Condenser Boilers

Some equipment is traditionally described in a very crude way when studying long term variations in processes, and the models are then limited to algebraic balance quations. In order to study phenomena at shorter time scales, more complete models of some equipment must be developed and embedded in the simulator.

Candidates for such a development are:

- **condensers:** classical models are usually lumped parameter models assuming that thermodynamic equilibrium is achieved. A more detailed model could take into account temperature distribution and mass transfer limitations.

- **reboilers:** again, classical models are usually lumped parameter models assuming that thermodynamic equilibrium is achieved. More detailed models could take into account temperature distribution, departure from equilibrium, and various boiling regimes. Classical control schemes should also be introduced in the model.

Network Component Models

Some instabilities in equipment, such as that including rotating machines, may be induced by the layout or sizing of network components, for example, too small a pipe diameter can cause a pressure drop such that a turbine is unable to respond to a sudden increase in power demand. Thus, it is important to include in the simulator detailed models of network components, taking account of all significant geometric factors. Particular items of equipment to be considered are:-

(i) Pipework elements - size, material and geometry will determine the pressure drop and dynamic response of these elements.

(ii) Valves - typical valve characteristics will be embedded in the model.

(iii) Headers - these require a particular model, since the direction and importance of flow can vary with time as a function of demand and suppply in all connected equipment.

Numerical Integration Techniques

Dynamic models of process plant are usually intended for study of long time scale response of the process, of the order of minutes, hours or days. Thus fast acting phenomena are usually assumed to remain at their equilibrium value. The resulting simulation is a combination of algebraic and ordinary differential equations which is best solved by an implicit integration method. These methods are dictated by the stiffness of the differential equations (widely different time constants) and the need to solve the combination of algebraic and ordinary differential equations. This approach presents difficulties in systems where the equation set itself can change with time, for example due to a change in the nature of a phonomena such as a phase transition, or saturation of a controller, or switching on or off of equipment. For these cases, explicit integrators eg Runge-Kutta, Newton-Raphson, may be the better choice. The task is aimed at developing the above issues by the following steps:-

(i) Exchanging of methodology between process (implicit) and fluid dynamic (explicit) approaches.

(ii) Comparison of integration algorithms and their tuning strategies.

(iii) Derivation of an efficient integration for fast acting (rotating machinery) or discontinuous changes (phase transition, controller saturation) with implicit integration for numerical stability.

Partner 3 - Ecole des Mines de Paris

The treatment of controllers is currently one of the weakest points in the software dealing with thermal devices. The objectives of the tasks defined by Partner 3 (Ecole des Mines de Paris) will be to address the problem of how best to include a representative controller model in the dynamic simulator of the process or utility plant. Having defined the approach to be used, appropriate languages and interfaces between the thermo-fluid dynamic models and, the controller model will be tested on simulations of real plant operation.

In actual plant, classical controllers have often to be adjusted on site and parameters are not those specified by the manufacturer. This adjustment requires generally empirical or semi-empirical techniques. The problem of parameters selection in a simulation model, is in practice equivalent to the one encountered by the engineer who installs an actual plant. This tuning requires a sufficient knowledge of controlled system's open or closed loop response (inertia, response time, gain, etc.) as well as expertise. It is supposed that such qualities are rare among code users.

Adaptative controllers, whose parameter synthesis is made on-line during the system evolution, on the basis of an estimated model and a given criterion of adaptation can overcome this difficulty. Such controllers can simplify the simulation of the thermal plant's control systems, but most are based on the hypothesis of linear system behaviour and may, therefore, not function properly if faced with significant non-linearities. Moreover, all adaptive controllers require an initial selection of a certain number of parameters.

Thus, development of adaptative controllers models must be in the most simplified form (ie initial parameters, taking into account default values in most).

Controllers - Tuning and Adaptive Control

The trend in process control is to increase the complexity of control strategies, in order to be able to simulate the behaviour of complex control systems. Therefore, a facility to add specific modules to the simulator will be provided.

Simplified Models of Numerical Controllers

A representation of adaptive and self-tuning controllers will be developed in simplified form.

Adaptive controllers are particularly useful when system dynamics may change or very variable perturbations may be encountered. Parameters for the controller are synthesised on-line during the evolution of the system, using an estimated model for the system and a given adaptive criterion. The development of these controllers to include in the simulation will necessarily be in a simplified form, using limited choices of initial parameters and default values. Exchange of information between the partners will be necessary to define these parameters. Two types of identification algorithms will be built:-

(i) Off-line identification for classical controllers and systems with non-varying dynamics, in this case pseudo-random sequences of perturbations must be generated.

(ii) On-line identification for adaptive controllers with forgetting procedure.

Finally, implementation of the pole placement procedure for the controller synthesis will be carried out.

Schematic of Network Operation

Networks are made up of physical components (gas turbines, boilers, pipes, etc) as well as the control components. The modeller must consider two levels to define logics of the plant operation:-.

(i) Local loops; where each physical component is defined by the functions to be guaranteed, the quantities to be controlled, and the control components (devices, control mode, sensors).

(ii) The logic of the global management of the system is described by defining the data necesary for control decisions, system and subsystems concerned and the local network linking the states.

A usable description for each part of the network will be developed by Partner 3 by considering the following:-

(i) Level one; the use of language - formalised description, rules, relay-sheets, setpoint definition.

(ii) Level two; rules, summary table of states/actions, relay-sheets, sequential diagrams, state transition

Adaptation of Computing Timestep During the Simulation

In a typical plant, different control loops have different dynamic responses, varying from those with time constants of a few tens of seconds to the slowest with time constants of hours or days. The feasibility of carrying out a variable time step controller simulation, and implementation of this into the dynamic simulator will be carried out by partner 3.

Integration of the models into a common frame work and validation using plant data

Dynamic Simulator - Coding Dynamic Models

Having defined the appropriate physical models, and integration algorithms for all elements of the system, these must be coded and incorporated into the dynamic simulator by **all partners.** Each partner will be responsible for coding, testing and running benchmarks for the individual models, and documenting the programs.

Dynamic Simulator - Integration into a common Framework

The models for all process items will interact and should be integrated simultaneously. They should be interfaced into a common set of mathematical tools to solve and integrate the governing equations. A decision as to a common language, simulation or high level language, and hardware will be made. A preliminary user guide to the program may be produced. This will involve **all partners.**

Test Cases

The research program is pre-competitive and will result in a product which will require considerable expertise for application to a large industrial system. The validity of the approach will be tested on two case studies to be provided by an associated partner, Thomassen International of the Netherlands. Comparison of the predictions of the model with real plant data will be carried out.

The first study is of a gas turbine heat and power plant (co-generation plant). Requirements will be to simulate gas-turbine drivers, with a controls model, and a simple model for the heat recovery boiler.

The second case study will be of integrated rotating equipment systems for the steam and process gas distribution network of an ethylene production plant. Here the process simulation will consider steam turbines, and gas turbines, driving the process and utility gas compressors. The effect of changes in gas composition on the compressors will be simulated, and optimal control strategies developed. Refrigeration elements will also be considered in this test case.

All partners will participate in the gathering of the modules developed and tested under Tasks 1 to 3 to create the software package able to treat the test studies.

Partner 1 will concentrate on the models for the rotating machinery.

Partner 2 will deal with the network configuration, valves, pipework and the interaction with the equipment.

Partner 3 will particularly focus on the comparison between off-line adjusted PID controller and an adaptive controller.

Associated Industrial Partner 1 Thomassen International, will provide data for the test cases. This will be the configuration of the plant, characteristic data for the equipment, and operational data from the plant as available.

Associated Industrial Partner 2 W S Atkins Engineering Sciences Limited, will provide additional expertise in definition and collection of data for the test cases. They will also assist in the development of the dynamic models for plant element and integration into the dynamic simulator.

CONCLUSIONS

We have defined a collaborative project which will bring together expertise in process simulation, dynamic modelling of process elements, and controls modelling, with the objective of producing an efficient dynamic simulator for fast transients and control of process and utility plant.

The project will develop models of process elements (compressors, turbines, condensors and reboilers) and integrate these into a flowsheet simulator.

Different numerical integration techniques are currently offered in simulation models, where implicit and explicit methods are both available. The advantages of each of the methods will be assessed. The optimisation of the integration in the simulator, with variable time step, will be a major task of the project.

New representations of control algorithms will be developed and included in a form which can interact with the fast, non-linear transients which will occur in a simulation of a process or utility plant. The methodology will be validated using real plant data supplied by industrial partners.

The project involves three laboratories and two industrial partners from four European countries.

The resultant package should be able to simulate and test control strategies for process and utility plants and thus allow their more optimal energy management. When applied in industry, it will thus offer the possibility of significant energy savings arising from the improved operation of such plants.

FUTURE R & D

There are substantial possibilities for future R & D in this field. The first consideration should be to extend the range of process and utility systems for which the methodology has been developed and tested, especially with test cases based on data from full-scale industrial plant. As such experience accrues it will be possible to develop improved control algorithms and to incorporate fault detection into the simulation system.

The approach as presently constructed will require substantial computer time when applied to real systems which are generally large and complex. However, it may be possible to alleviate this requirement by developing systems based around parallel computors.

There are uncertainties in the detector information supplied to the controller and it will be important to understand the implications of this for operation of the plant.

A further interesting development would be to extend the optimisation of the control strategy to cover demand and cost considerations in, for example, water and electricity distribution.

Finally the present approach takes no account of pinch technology. An extension of dynamic optimal control and simulation of plant operations to include a pinch analysis could open up further new avenues for energy conservation.

REFERENCES

1 Elder, R. L., Gill, M. E. and Razk, A. M. Y.
Validation of a Compressor Model.
Transactions of the Institute of Measurement and Control.
Vol. 8, No. 4, Oct. 1986, p 171-181.

2 Elder, R. L., Gill, M. E. and Razak, A. M. Y.
Simulation of the Transient Performance of a Compressor in a Natural Gas Pumping Station.
"Fluid Machinery for the Oil, Petrochemical and Related Industries".
Institution of Mechanical Engineers Conference 1987-4, Paper C116/87.

3 B. Kalitventzeff, F. Marechal
SYNEP1: A methodology for Energy Analysis and Optimal Heat Exchanger Network Synthesis
CHEMDATA 88: XIX Conference The Use of Computers in Chemical Engineering - June 13 - 15, 1988, Götenborg (Sweden).

4 B. Kalitventzeff, F. Marechal
The Management of a Utility Network
PSE 88 Symposium, Sydney, Australia, Aug. 28 - Sept 2nd, 1988.

5 P. Bacot, R. Bonfils, D. Marchio
Programme SYSTHERN pour le Calcul de Systèmes Thermiques Quelconques Revue Générale de Thermique n° 70, Janvier 1984.

6 M. Ouederni, D. Marchio
Modèlisation et Simulation des Régulations pour Systèmes Thermiques sur SYSTHERM
Rapport AFME, EMP, Février 1989.

20.14

ENERGY SYNTHESIS IN INDUSTRIAL PROCESSES

Professor B. Kalitventzeff,
Institut de Chimie Bât. B 6
Sart Tilman - B-4000 LIEGE

Contract JOUE-0009-BE

PARTICIPANTS

- Laboratoire d'Analyse et de Synthèse des Systèmes Chimiques (B) :
F. Maréchal, M. Hanquet, E. Lejeune, A. Kontopoulos;
- Lindsey Oil Refinery (UK) : B. Goublomme
- Motor Oil (Greece) : P. Tzannetakis
- Fina Research (B) : B. Vrielynck

SUMMARY

This communication presents the objectives and the results of the contract JOUE-0009-BE. Integrate available and developed technology for rational use of energy in the processing industry, into a set of software ; strengthen the techniques and promote technology transfer through industrial case studies : these are the goals of the R/D project.

The developed computer tools are SYNEP and EMS. SYNEP concerns the design of energy efficient plants and the retrofit of existing ones. EMS is a help for the optimal management of energy utility networks.

Several industrial case studies have been performed in chemical processes, refineries, powerhouses, in different European countries ; substantial energy savings have been demonstrated. New capabilities have been implemented in the software tools as a consequence of these case studies.

INTRODUCTION

The recent international situation has stressed, if it was necessary, the need for a generalized policy of rational use of energy. In the processing industry, this means energy efficiency in the design of the production plants and therefore retrofit of existing plants to meet this objective. This means as well energy minded management of the production plants. The CEC is aware that such goals can only be obtained by research and development of new technologies, and by the developments of state of the art computer tools.

The "SYNEP Plus" research project (JOUE-0009-BE) is the continuation of the SYNEP research program supported by the Commission of the European Communities (project SYNEP : EN3E-0136-B). Within the first project, the energy synthesis of industrial processes was considered under two aspects : engineering and management. Computer tools were developed as a help for the engineer. The engineering tool for energy integration of chemical processes concerns the design of energy efficient chemical plants as well as the retrofit of existing plants. The management tool leads to a day to day optimal use of the existing energy utility network. At the end of this first project, industrial partners have shown the need for complementary developments in order that the technology better meets the industry requirement. This has initiated the new project named SYNEP Plus. It has two "orientations" : the strengthening of the new techniques by solving industrial case studies and the development of new capabilities to better solve the industrial problems.

OBJECTIVES

As the rational use of energy is an important concern of the industry, the objectives of the present contract were identified by confrontation with industrial partners. They gave us precise information about their needs, what they were waiting for, and what capabilities they asked from energy synthesis computer tools.

The main demand has been the integration of the new computer tools into an existing software package. They already have computer tools for simulation, data reconciliation, measurements collection, ... and they want to exploit these data with the computer tools.

New capabilities were identified for the two computer tools : they concern the problem definition (new simulation models), the ease of use (userfriendliness of the programs) as well as new functionalities (adequacy to solve specific problems such as retrofit) or help for numerical problem analysis ("what if ?").

The robustness and the suitability of the methods to solve real problems had to be tested in cooperation with european industrial partners that had to provide real test cases. Among the European partners in the test case studies, we will mention Motor Oil (Greece), Lindsey Oil Refinery (England) and Petrofina (Belgium).

TASKS OF THE PARTICIPANTS

We think that it would be irrelevant to describe here the tasks and the results of the present contract, without explaining shortly the scientific background of each part of the project, because it is, as already mentioned, the continuation of another project.

The research concerns two aspects of the energy synthesis of industrial processes : engineering and management. We will focus here on what has been achieved, and what process engineer's tasks can be tackled and computer aided by the developed methods.

SYNEP : energy synthesis of industrial processes

Energy synthesis of industrial processes concerns the engineering department. It consists in achieving the best use of energy by changing the structure of the installation and/or its operating conditions. The challenge of energy integration is to solve the trade-off between energy savings and the capital investment.

We aimed at implementing most of the features of existing methods and refinements that we did develop in a set of softwares for process analysis.

Since 1970, a lot of scientific publications deal with energy savings. Numerous scientific methods have been proposed. Among them, the most important is the "Pinch technology" proposed by Linnhoff (1982). In the beginning, this method has been developed for hand solving. The use of the computer allows to extend the principles of this method and to integrate other methods into a software. We have analysed and criticized the existing methods, then we developed a suitable mathematical formulation and implemented it into a computer code. In this approach, we use the powerful mathematics of optimization codes and develop specific algorithms.

Another characteristic of the SYNEP software is its imbedding in a general methodology for process analysis. Industrial problems usually concern existing plants. The process data reconciliation and/or the process simulation are thus complementary tasks of the energy synthesis. SYNEP is able to use the data of other already existing computer tools designed to perform the other tasks of the methodology. Although the SYNEP approach is best suited for existing plants (retrofit problems), the software is also suitable for grassroot problems.

Industrial managers define the optimality as the minimum cost solution that satisfy a number of objective or subjective criteria. Among them, we can mention the flexibility of the installation, the safety, the layout, the fouling, etc. This requires the possibility of testing these criteria. In the SYNEP approach, the computer tools are integrated in a computer toolbox. The data transfer between these tools or with spreadsheet tools facilitates the process analysis .

As in other energy synthesis approaches, the problem is solved in two steps. The targeting step sets the targets that have to be achieved in the synthesis step.

Targeting

The targeting defines the minimum energy requirement (MER) according to the "temperature difference approach" (DTmin); this parameter can be seen as a measure of the Energy -Capital trade-off.

The data are collected in the flowsheets or from the control computer. Data reconciliation and simulation softwares will be of great help in defining a coherent set of data. The enthalpy-temperature composite curves indicate opportunities for energy recovery. For retrofit problems the targeting allows to identify the advisability of the study prior to any process modification calculation.

The analysis of the composite curves obtained allows also to identify process modifications and the utilities to be used. Two important facts were considered : high number of possibilities and minimum cost criteria instead of minimum of energy . For example, process modifications can be mechanical vapour recompression or pressure change in distillation columns. The utilities can be steam at different temperature and pressure levels, gas turbines, refrigeration cycles, etc.

For solving this targeting problem, SYNEP adopts the following strategy : the engineer proposes as many alternatives as he wants, and introduces them in SYNEP ; SYNEP makes the optimal choice. A MILP (mixed integer linear programming) formulation is used to choose the best alternative(s) and to calculate their optimal integration on a cost basis. The use of simulation software allows to simulate precisely the alternatives, especially when they concern existing units, before introducing the corresponding data into the SYNEP software. Figure 1 illustrates this feature.

When solving industrial problems it was pointed out that there is restricted matches that can lead to energy penalty. This is especially the case in retrofit problems where the layout is a limiting factor, or more generally, when safety or corrosion problems can occur

The restricted or forbidden matches are coded into specific equations in the optimization approach. All the restricted matches are taken simultaneously into account. When the utilities is considered together with the process, the program gives the less costly penalty satisfying the match restrictions. In this case, utilities such as Rankine cycles, or "hot belts" can be used as intermediate streams that will permit again the exchange and remove part of the restricted match energy penalty.

Analysis of the composite curves points out the key units of the process. Restricting precise calculation of these units only accelerates the obtaining of a precise enough result.

Applications

The targeting part of SYNEP has been applied in two processes. The first of them in a collaboration with Motor Oil (Greece). Motor Oil collected all the data and gave us the necessary information concerning a visbreaking unit and a vacuum distillation unit. The first question to be answered was : is it profitable to interconnect the two units in the energy integration or is there only a marginal loss in energy savings by not doing this ? We concluded that the two units could be kept independant with respect to energy integration; this allows more flexibility.

We also applied the targeting procedure to an ethylene production plant, battery limits excluding the cracker furnace. Two process alternatives and not less than six refrigeration cycles have been proposed to the SYNEP program, restricting the number of alternatives to be selected to one and the number of refrigeration cycles to maximum two or three in different trials. The very interesting results obtained have been published in ComChem '90 European Symposium, Kontopoulos at all (1990).

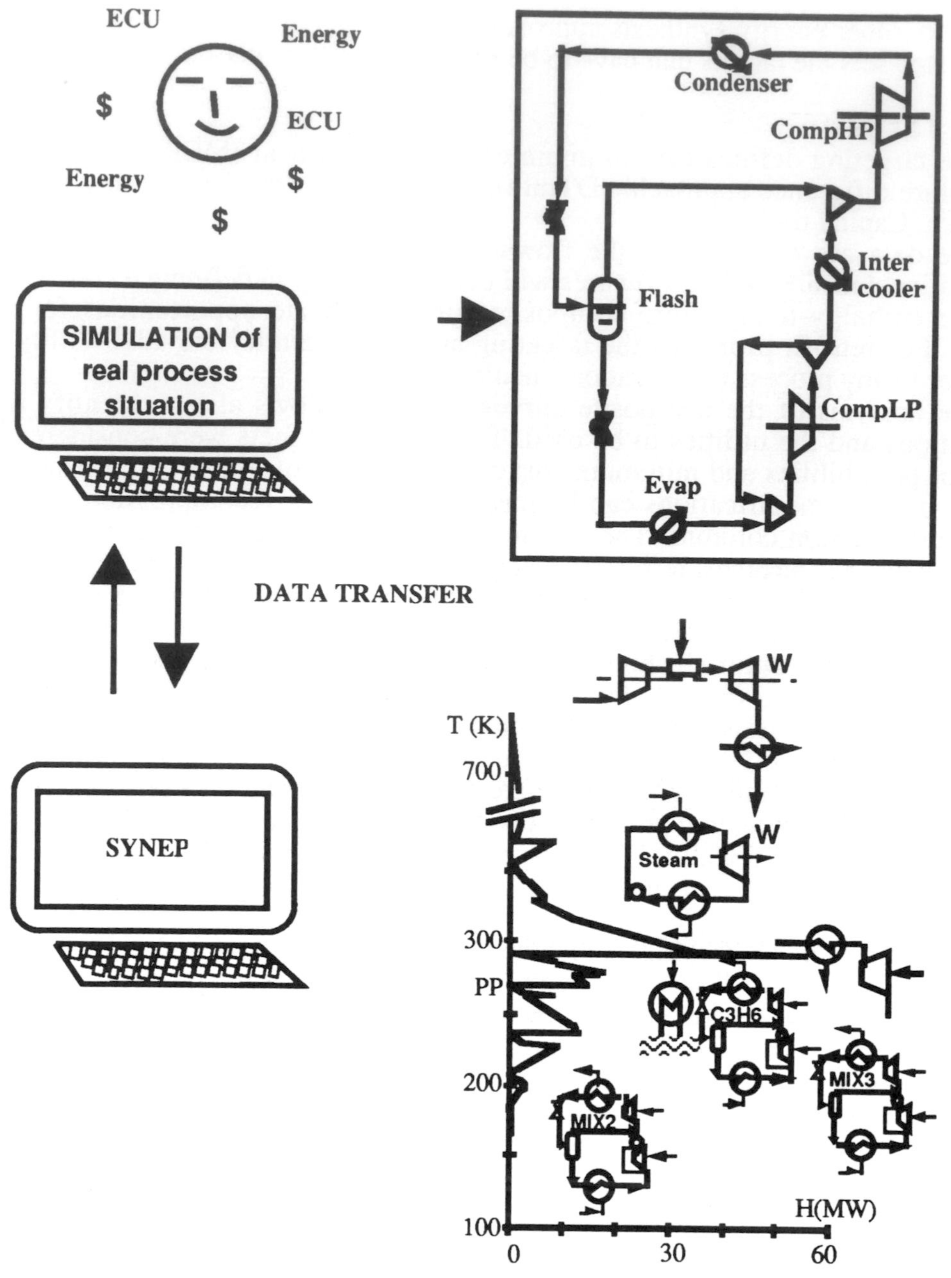

Figure 1. - Links between detailed refrigeration cycle simulation and the targeting step of the energy integration.

Synthesis

If the literature is rather abundant for targeting, information about synthesis is less abundant and it is rather scarce about the retrofit of existing plants.

We do not believe that this type of problem can efficiently be solved with a pencil and a sheet of paper, although we highly recommend the exercise : driving force plots etc. are of some help, but the combinatorial problem is such that sorting all the feasible heat exchanger load distributions, which satisfy the MER (Minimum Energy Requirement) is a valuable contribution that we performed. These feasible heat exchanger load distributions will generate HEN that will be examined for flexibility, controlability, and other criteria. Only some of the feasible MER networks will than be optimized for minimum total cost. When selecting some of the load distributions, the software makes use of heuristics based on the pinch technology or gives at will priority to the user's wishes : as shown in figure 2, one easy interacts with the program. The user can also give specifications such as matches to impose, or to favour, or to avoid ; the forbidden matches have been decided in the targeting step. Figure 2 shows also that the program is a help to the user ; for such problems, it is unrealistic to dream of a "press the button" software.

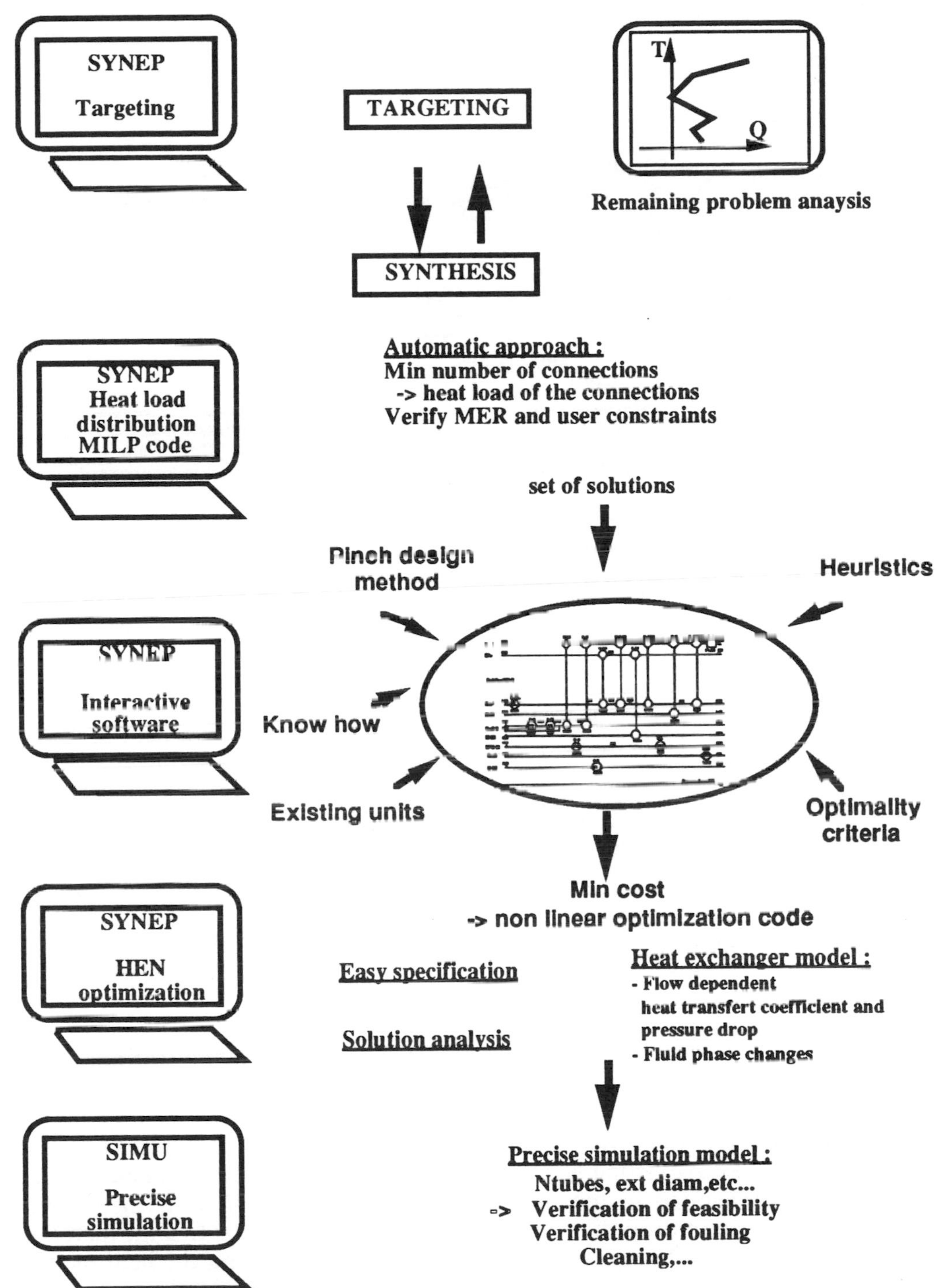

Figure 2. - Interactions between user and software.

The links with other softwares : data reconciliation and simulation, make that it is possible to tune the models and refine the analysis when the HEN has to be designed or retrofitted. Rating simulation is to be performed, taking into account real actual equipment performances : existing accurate models can be used, they are available. Data reconciliation is a must for obtaining consistent preformance data.

We will not report here about the selection of the optimization methods : MILP methods and MINLP methods also have been tested. For the NLP steps, we successfully used SQP (Sequential Quadratic Programming).

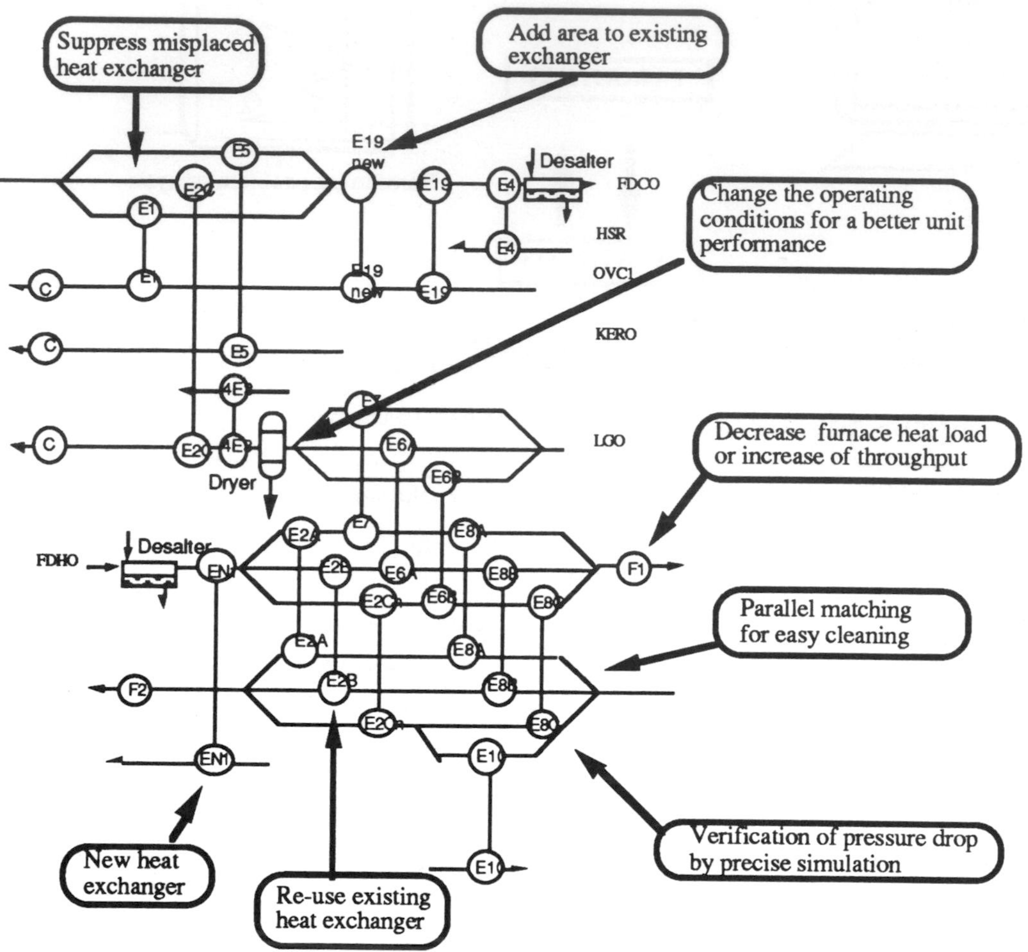

Figure 3. - Retrofit of a crude oil topping preheat train.

Applications

The energy synthesis part of SYNEP has been used in two applications : the one concerns a butyl rubber plant and the other concerns a preheat train of a crude topping unit. The last one has been performed in collaboration with Fina Research (B). As shown in figure 3, this case study did propose several plant modifications : suppress misplaced heat exchanger, add area to existing heat exchanger, re-use misplaced heat exchanger, all actions that have been cited in the literature. Let us quote also : change operating conditions, check pressure drop distributions before and after retrofitting, increase the number of parallel heat exchangers, where fouling is real, allowing for heat exchanger cleaning between two unit shutdowns. When reduction in furnace loads is converted in capacity increase, we never will enough stress the necessity of precise simulation of selected alternatives : pressure drops can severily be modified and therefore flowrates and heat transfer coefficients (performances). Our tools allow the state of the art engineer to interact here also with the program, to better assess the feasibility and the profitability of his inventive ideas.

Thanks to this Fina Research application, we did better evaluate the needs of the industry and prove that plant specialists can efficiently use our sotfware package.

EMS : optimal management of utility networks

The second part of the SYNEP Plus project concerns the optimal management of utility networks. The name of the tool developed is EMS : energy management system. Two areas were developed : simulation models and optimization facilities. When calculating utility networks, the simulation models have to represent as well as possible, the behaviour of the existing installation. But, on the other hand, they have to allow easy optimization. The main part of the development was to realize the trade-off between the precision of the models and the optimization procedure.

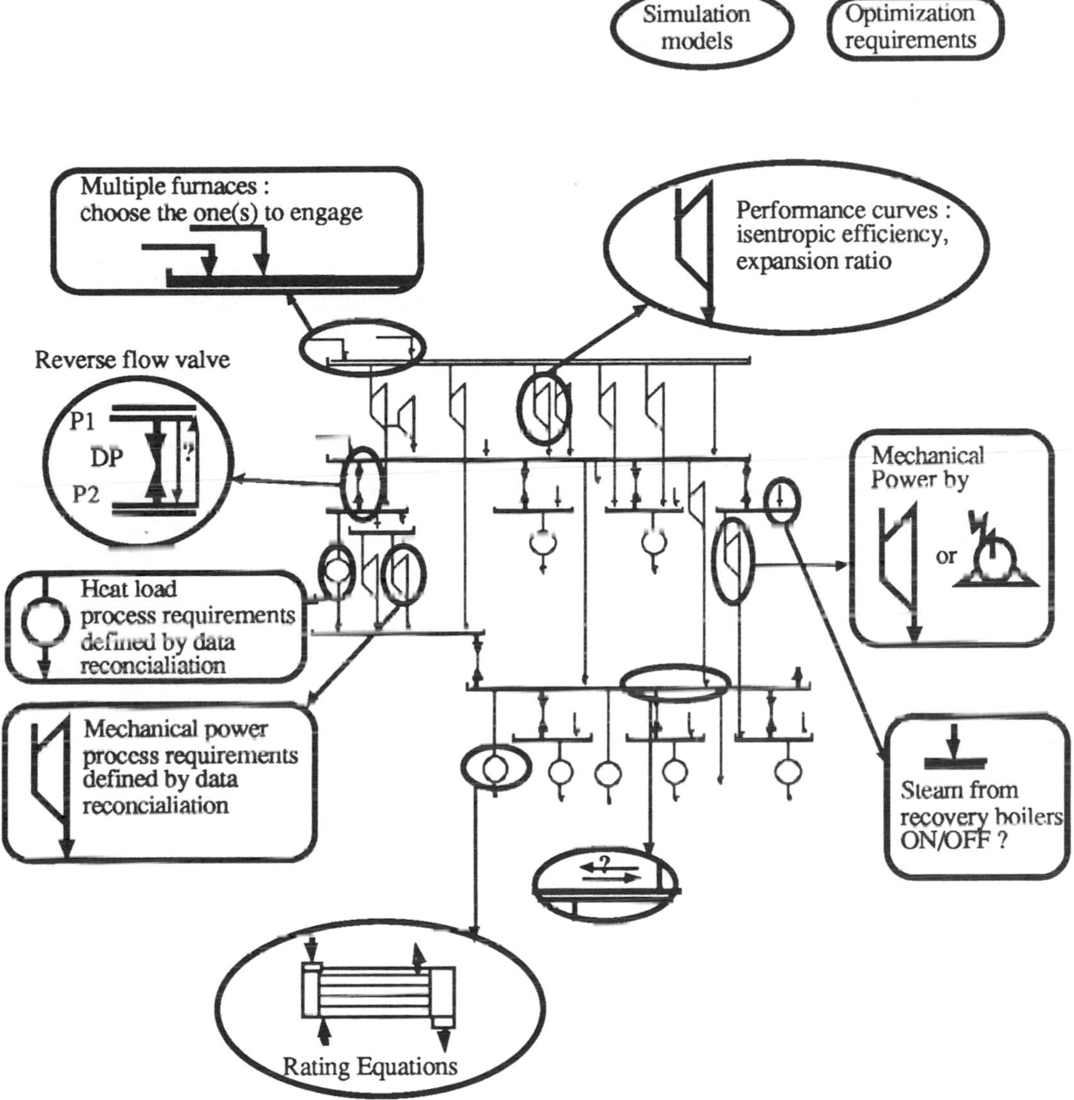

Figure 4. - EMS application to an industrial utility network.

Out of the two common approaches in simulation : sequential modular and equation solver, we did choose the second one. It allows to make easy specifications and is particularly well suited to optimization formulation. In the advantages, we will mention the easy handling of inequality constraints and the automatic numerical problem analysis before computation. In this approach, the unit simulation models have been arranged to be simultaneously worked out.

We can describe here certain characteristics of the developed models. They are illustrated in the utility network example described on figure 4. The expander model includes the performance curves : isentropic efficiency and expansion ratio can be expressed as a function of volumetric flowrate, temperature, pressure. The simulation model of the heat exchangers takes into account the fluid phase changes. Performance curves express pressure drops and film heat transfert coefficients as a function of the flowrate.

Performance curves are obtained from parameter identification. This is performed using the data resulting from the data reconciliation tool that has to transfer data with EMS. The process demands, heat loads and mechanical power, that have to be produced by the utility system comes also from the data reconciliation tool.

Specific models have been developed to simulate the headers. In such units, the flow direction can change according to the utility network production. Furthermore, the headers are interconnected by two directional links in which the flow direction depends on the pressures of the interconnected headers. In this case, the pressure drop depends on the flowrate and on its direction. The model used is fitted to avoid the discontinuities that may hinder the optimization procedure to converge to a numerical solution.

The optimal management consists in definig the value of the control variables that define the minimum operating cost. Two types of degrees of freedom characterize the optimal management : one corresponds to yes/no decisions, for example what are the furnaces to engage, is it profitable to produce the mechanical power requirement by electrical motors or by steam turbines; the second concerns the level decisions : the steam flowrates, the flowrates in refrigeration cycles, the operating temperatures or pressures of given units.

In EMS, the problem is coded as a mixed integer non linear programming optimization problem. The resolution of this type of problem is only possible by using a decomposition strategy that leads to successive non linear programming and mixed integer linear programming problems for which specific algorithms exist. We have chosen what we think is the most suitable problem decomposition method and compared the different optimization programs that we did have available.

During the discussion with the industrial operators, they did focus on the statement that initialization is very important, especially in equation solver approach. We have developed an initialization procedure. It uses the interactive mode to perform efficient initialization by simulating the stand alone units in given conditions. The process knowledge helps the engineer to use the best initialization scheme for each unit and to test interactively the behaviour of a given unit.

Applications

Three real plant size applications of EMS have been performed, only one being supported by the SYNEP Plus project. This one concerns the electricity production line of the Baudour powerhouse in Belgium (115 MW). A. Kontopoulos did use EMS to optimize the rather complex refrigeration system of a butyl rubber production line : changes in recirculating flowrates are caused by the in turn cleaning operation of the polymerisation reactors. The refrigeration system is to be optimized for different numbers of reactors in operation. The third application concerns an application of EMS to the optimal management of a large part of the utility network of one of the big refineries of UK : Lindsey Oil Refinery. A simplified flowsheet of the system coded into EMS is given in figure 4 ; some features of EMS mentioned hereabove are also illustrated there.

GENERAL RESULTS

Although the "Synep Plus" project is still in progress, it is already possible to draw some conclusions. The participation of industrial operators has significantly influenced the achievements even if the developers have a rather good experience in computer tools for process analysis and in execution of real plant case studies. We are pleased to thank them all for their active collaboration. This participation of industrial operators was a must for the CEC project manager : it is clear that he was right when imposing it.

It is not possible to mention all the items that we implemented to meet the process industry requirements, let us mention some of them. The forbidden matches is a more fruitfull and more flexible concept than the remaining problem analysis (the latter is still available) : it is also difficult to develop the correct formulation of this restriction. The two directional links between headers is also a difficult to formulate concept :it introduces severe non linearities and may hamper convergence of the calculations ; we recall that we use an "equation solver" approach instead of a "sequential modular" algorithm that is irrelevant for utility network computation.

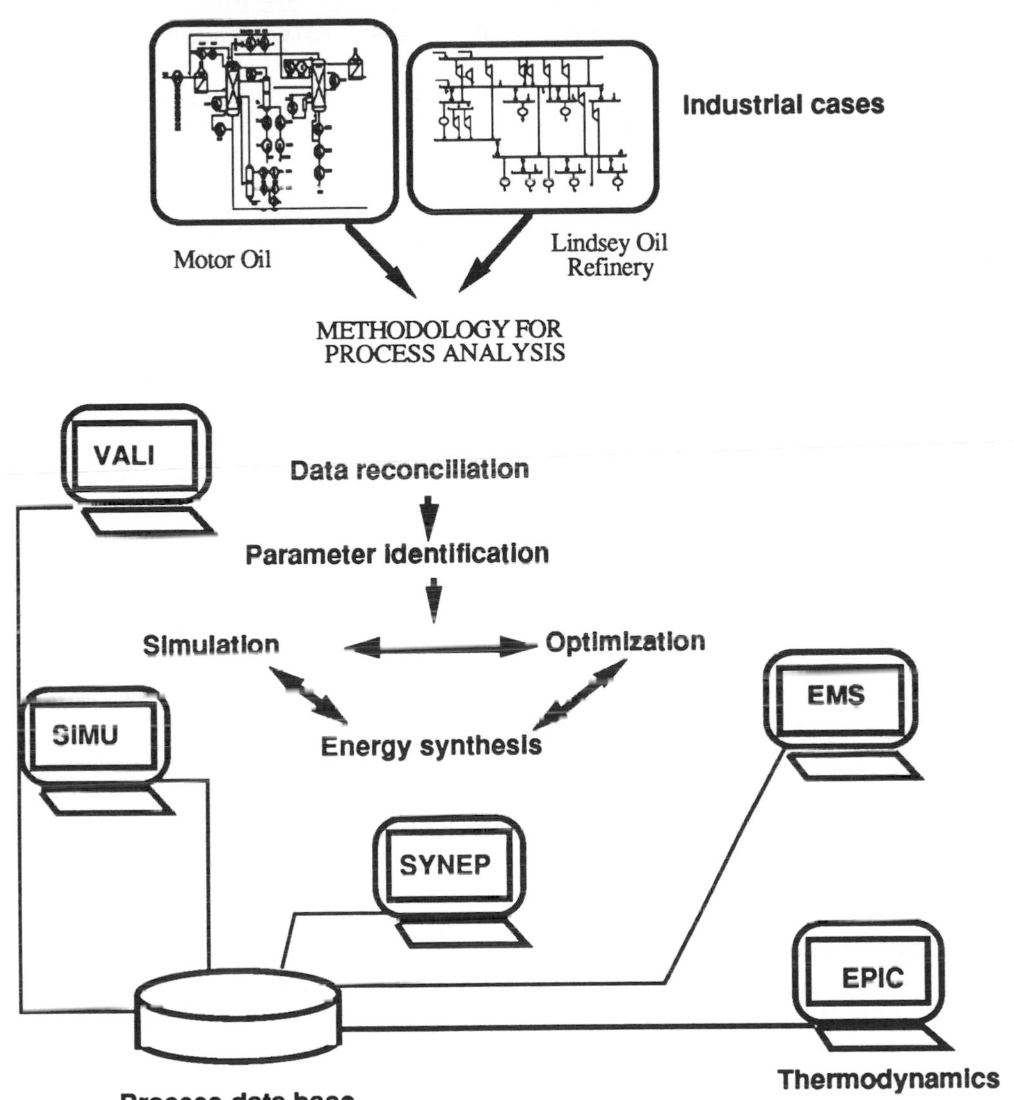

Figure 5. - EMS application to an industrial utility network.

Industrial operators urged at developing the automatic links between SYNEP and EMS softwares and other computer aided process analysis tools : validation and simulation tools of the BELSIM package. Nevertheless SYNEP and EMS are also stand alone programs and could be linked to other simulation packages. In this respect, figure 5 illustrates the methodology for process analysis that we developed since more than a decade, and which is progressively applied in the industry : we claim that it is the best way to follow for plant retrofit or to achieve peak performance. Start with data reconciliation to develop a sound coherent base of information (how could a manager decide without proper information ?). Evaluate performance parameters as such, for plant follow-up, but also because these appear in the mathematical models of unit operations which make up the plant. This than allows full plant rating simulation, assessment of operating specifications for profit optimization, evaluation of process alternatives, energy synthesis, management of utility network, retrofit studies. All the data are collected in a unique data base, output results of a given step of the methodology can be a part of the input list of another one. All the calculations are based on the same thermodynamics throughout the computation for plant management (optimum operation or retrofit/revamp); the EPIC software contains all state of the art thermodynamic models. As can be seen in figure 5, all the steps of the methodology are interrelated and there exists an appropriate software for each step ; these software can also be used independently of each other.

We are sure that CEC has made a good decision in supporting the developments we have reported upon.

FUTURE R & D.

This R/D project concerns a precompetitive research work. It remains to furbish the userfriendliness of the program and to promote the technology transfer. Pinch technology for instance is a marvelous set of concepts, but it is not yet enough known, and many of those who did use it are convinced that it gives processes that lack flexibility, and that are therefore difficult to control or to adapt to variations of production rate. More is to be done to convince engineers that those drawbacks can be avoided, for instance with the SYNEP methodology.

Technology transfer can be promoted by supporting industrial case studies, by supporting the training of engineers, by supporting the introduction of the developed softwares in technical colleges of European universities.

We support the idea that the complete methodology can still be refined and that it should be possible at European level to rewrite the whole softwares using the new technologies now available or soon available : fourth generation languages, new tools for graphic interfaces, recent robust optimalization algorithms, etc. The goal being to arrive in the late nineties at automatic scientific optimization of production plants, tools being available ON LINE : computer integrated processing (C.I.P.) has to become a reality. Goals to be achieved being maximum profit, plant flexibility, safety but within more severe environment constraints. This C.I.P. technology is the technology of the next years, it has been announced by the American H.P.I. (Hydrocarbon Processing Industry). Will Europe wait for it or compete and develop this technology intra muros ?

ACKNOWLEDGMENTS

Thanks are addressed to the CEC from all the partenrs of this SYNEP Plus R/D project. Special thanks also to François Maréchal who did lead the development team in the LASSC. Without him, Jenny Roppe and Georges Heyen, this communication would not have been written in due time, I sincerely thank them.

REFERENCES

FLOUDAS C.A., CIRIC A.R.
Global optimum issues on heat exchanger network synthesis
Proceedings of the PSE'88 symposium. Sydney Australia (1988)

GROSSMANN I.E., KOCIS G.R.
Computational experience in solving MINLP problems with DICOPT.
Proceedings of the PSE'88 symposium. Sydney Australia (1988)

MARECHAL F., KALITVENTZEFF B.
SYNEP1 : a methodology for energy integration and optimal heat exchanger network synthesis.
Proceedings of the CHEMDATA '88. Göteborg Sweden. 13-15 June (1988).
Computer and Chemical Engineering., Vol. 13, n°4/5, (1989).

KONTOPOULOS A., MARECHAL F., KALITVENTZEFF B.
Simulation and energy integration of an ethylene production plant.
Simo'88 colloquium Toulouse, France, 14-15 September (1988)

MARECHAL F., KALITVENTZEFF B.
The optimal management of a utility network.
Proceedings of the PSE'88 symposium Sydney Australia (1988b)
à paraître dans Computer and Chemical Engineering.

KALITVENTZEFF B., MARECHAL F., GOSSET R.
Process simulation and optimization : links between methodology and software. Application to optimal utility network management.
ACHEMA'88, communication presented at the conferences and symposia held by DECHEMA. Frankfurt 7th june (1988c).

KALITVENTZEFF B., MARECHAL F., TAQUET B.
Synep1 : a methodology for energy integration and optimal heat exchanger network synthesis.
Synop2 : a methodology for optimal management of a utility network.
Contractors meeting, energy efficiency in industrial processes. Proceedings, Bruxelles, 29 june (1988).

AHMAD S.
Heat exchanger networks, cost tradeoffs in energy and capital.
Ph. D. Thesis UMIST (1985)

LINNHOFF B.
User guide on process integration for the efficient use of energy.
The institution of chemical engineers (1982)

GEOFFRION M.A..
Generalized Benders decomposition.
Journal of Optimization Theory and applications. Vol. 10, n°4, (1972).

DURAN M.A., GROSSMAN I.E.
A mixed integer nonlinear programming algorithm for process systems synthesis.
A.I.CHE. Journal - Vol 32 n°4. (1986).

GROSSMANN I.E., FLOUDAS C.A., CIRIC A.R.
Automatic synthesis of optimum heat exchanger network configuration.
AIChE Journal, Vol 32, n° 2 (1986)

KALITVENTZEFF B.
Mixed Integer non lnear programming and its aplication to the management of utility networks.
Mathematical Programming : a tool for engineers - Second Conference on Mathematics for Engineers organized by the Faculté Polytechnique de Mons - Mons, 17-19 May (1989).

KALITVENTZEFF B.
Synthèse énergétique optimale dans les procédés industriels dans l'industrie.
Proceedings of S.R.B.I.I. - Journée d'études "Utilisation optimale de l'Energie dans l'industrie" - Bruxelles 15 mars 1990.

KONTOPOULOS A.J., MARECHAL F. , KALITVENTZEFF B.
Simulation and Optimization of an Ethylene Production Plant.
European Symposium on Computer Applications in Chemical Engineering
ComChem '90 - The Hague (NL), 7-9 May (1990).

SENSORS AND INSTRUMENTATION

Chairman: Mr. R. Dumon

DEVELOPMENT OF ADVANCED SENSORS

Franz Durst
Institute of Fluid Mechanics (LSTM-Erlangen)
University of Erlangen-Nürnberg
Cauerstr. 4, D-8520 Erlangen, FRG

JOULE-0056-C (MB)

PARTICIPANTS

J.H. Whitelaw
Imperial College of Science and Technology, UK

J.L. Baptista
University of Aveiro
Portugal

J.-P. Martin
Laboratoire E.M2.C. du CNRS
Ecole Centrale des Arts et Manufactures, France

G. Dimaczek
Applikations- und Technikzentrum (ATZ-EVUS), FRG

U. Führer
AMA Arbeitsgemeinschaft
Meßwertaufnehmer, FRG

SUMMARY

The present paper summarizes work to be carried out on the development of advanced sensors and their application to processes that are known to have high energy consumption but offer the possibility of energy savings when operated under controlled conditions. The need for sensors is apparent in processes in the steel industry and in the chemical industry, and the present research and its results can be transfered readily to equipment in other industries where control can result in energy savings. Effective control require measurements of the essential quantities of the processes in question in order to ensure that the reduction in energy consumption does not result in a poorer product. A summary of the state of the work carried out by the various partners is given and future work is outlined.

INTRODUCTION

This research proposal was based on the recognition that many processes in industry with high rates of energy consumption will not become energy-efficient unless on-line sensor technology is introduced. Through these sensors, information about the ongoing processes may be obtained continuously, and be employed to introduce control of energy consumption. The aim of the proposed research and development work is to contribute to on-line sensor technology for the above purpose.

To prepare the present proposal, a study was carried out to determine the most urgent needs for development of sensors and these were found to be in the following fields:

- o Mass and volume flow rate measurements using instruments applicable to single-phase and two-phase flows.
- o Humidity measurements in harsh environments.

- Local measurements of temperature distributions using infra-red detectors.
- In-situ sensor systems to measure particle concentrations, particle size and particle velocity distributions.
- In-situ sensor systems to measure local temperature and concentration of chemical species.
- Diagnostic instruments to study flow models.

The needs for developments in the above fields were expressed by industry at a meeting to prepare the present project for the Joule-Programme of the Commission of the European Communities.

OBJECTIVES

The general objective of the present project is based on the recognition that many processes in industry with high rates of energy consumption will not become energy-efficient unless on-line sensor technology is introduced. Sensors allow information about the ongoing processes to be obtained continuously and employed to control with the aim of reducing energy consumption. More scientific objectives are:

1. In-situ sensor systems will be developed to measure particle concentration, particle size and particle velocity distributions. Optical sensors will be employed and will incorporate semiconductor lasers and detectors to yield small instruments. Verification experiments will be performed.
2. Humidity measuring sensors will be developed and measurements carried out under conditions typical to ovens, kilns and furnaces.
3. In-situ sensor systems will be developed to measure local temperatures and concentrations of chemical species and measurements will be carried out in gaseous combustion.
4. Mass and volume flow rate measurements using instruments applicable to single-phase and two-phase flows, will be developed and applied in liquid and gaseous particulate two-phase flows.
5. Emphasis will also be placed on the transfer of the results to the various European companies that are members of AMA (Arbeitsgemeinschaft Meßwertaufnehmer). These companies will be part of a steering committee to guide the present research project and will ensure that the knowledge is transferred to sensor companies all over Europe.

These objectives will be achieved by close collaboration of LSTM-Erlangen with the various partners of the project.

TASKS OF THE PARTICIPANTS

1. LSTM-Erlangen, University of Erlangen-Nürnberg (FRG)

In this section the tasks of the participants are summarized. LSTM-Erlangen will coordinate the programme and carry out research work on advanced sensors as described below:

- Development of small phase-Doppler anemometers using semi-conductor lasers and photodetectors with glass fibre probes

- Phase-Doppler anemometers will be developed for detailed particle size measurements providing maximum, minimum and average size, size distribution, etc.. Particle velocity and particle concentration measurements in particulate two-phase flows in chemical reactors (gas-solid particle flows, liquid-gas bubble flows) will be carried out. Applications will be performed in oil burner sprays employed in process industries.

- Developments and applications of mass and volume flow rate measurements will be performed combining the new instruments with those already available for single-phase and two-phase flows. Coriolis flow meters will here be a particular emphasis. Applications will include the liquid and gaseous particulate flows of the process industries.

- Together with partner 3, applications of humidity sensors in harsh environments will be carried out after tests of the sensors under laboratory and less severe industrial conditions. Flows in ovens and furnaces will be typical examples.

2. Collaboration with Imperial College, London (U.K.)

New developments at LSTM-Erlangen have resulted in new ways to arrange and construct optical systems. At Imperial College, new counter systems have been developed which dramatically improve data rates and identify particle size (maximum, minimum, average size, size distribution). Development has shown that the data rate can be tremendously improved with the new counter system which, in preliminary measurements, has proved to be accurate and convenient to use.

Combining the optical developments of LSTM-Erlangen and the electronics developments at Imperial College will permit a new generation of laser-Doppler anemometers to be designed and built. The objectives for this combined development work mainly concentrate in the fields of:

- Development of new signal processing systems for phase-Doppler anemometers.

- Combinations of electronics and optics to yield instruments that are applicable in industrial environments.

- Application of phase-Doppler anemometers in various particulate two-phase flows. Measuring efforts will concentrate on gas-solid and gas-liquid flows as used by LSTM-Erlangen for chemical reactors and sprays.

3. Collaboration with University of Aveiro (P)

The control of humidity is important in many industrial applications, e.g. for the drying of materials in fabrication procedures, where humidity and temperature information is required. On-line control of humidity is necessary to process industrial products and to reduce the amount of energy needed, thus carrying out the drying under the most economical conditions.

- Some previous work at the University of Aveiro suggests that acceptable performance may be obtained with a humidity sensor based on doped ZnO ceramics. In preliminary studies, a promising system based on Lithium doping, has been investigated and will be developed during this project.

- The concentration of the doppant, the evolution of microstructure of the ZnO ceramic during sintering and the electrical response to relative humidity at several temperatures will be subjects of the investigation in order to determine the best conditions for the use of the material as an on-line humidity sensor.

- Spray pyrolysis deposition over non-conducting substrates will be investigated as an alternative approach to the development of humidity sensors based on the same materials.

- Besides the conductivity variation with relative humidity of the materials under development, other characteristics of importance in industrial applications will be a major concern of this project, such as long term stability, hysteresis, response and recovery time, all of them important to the on-line system.

- The sensor applicability will be tested at realistic pressures and temperatures.

4. Collaboration with Ecole Centrale, Paris (F)

In many industrial processes, information is needed on reaction kinetics of gaseous chemical species and on local temperature. Measurements need to be carried out with sensors that allow in-situ measurements in a time and space-resolved manner so that variations of global kinetics and temperature can be studied and optical sensors are appropriate for those requirements. Combustion is a field where measurements of this kind are needed and LSTM-Erlangen and Laboratoire E.M2.C of the C.N.R.S. of Ecole Centrale have collaborated in the past to use optical techniques for combustion research. It will be the aim of the collaboration within this project to continue this development to yield sensor systems that can be employed in practical flow fields with combusting gas heated systems.

- The laser deviation technique has been used to measure density in one-dimensional combustion flows and also for spectral analysis of turbulence. For axisymmetric flows, the laser beam deviation will be associated to an Abel inversion calculation to obtain the local density and its gradients. Knowing the local concentration profile of gaseous chemical species the method will be developed for temperature measurements along a laser beam trajectory in the flame.

- Rayleigh scattering from molecules will be analized to get temperature or density information. Comparisons with CARS will be made.

- Another objective is the determination of global reaction kinetics for several fuels and stoichiometric conditions in a flat counter flow diffusion flame. By measuring the radial velocity gradient (strain rate) in the flame sheet by means of an LDV-system near extinction global reaction kinetics will be deduced. With further information of the temperature field at the extinction limit, it is possible to evaluate the activation energy and the pre-exponential factor of an Arrhenius type reaction equation.

- A flat flame burner will be used to determine the chemical kinetics of the combustion reaction. Information will be obtained on the efficiency of combustion and NO_x- and SO_2-reactions examined.

5. Collaboration with ATZ-EVUS Sulzbach-Rosenberg (D)

This part of the research and development work will be concerned with the application of Coriolis and inductive flow meters in liquid-solid and liquid-gas flows to yield measurements of the instantaneous mass flow rates of both phases. The collaboration between LSTM-Erlangen and ATZ-EVUS Sulzbach-Rosenberg will aim at an integrated instrument that can be employed in industry, i.e. to measure the flow rates of both phases in slurries, sewage water, hydraulic conveyance, industrial muds, etc..

The work at ATZ-EVUS at Sulzbach-Rosenberg will be based on instruments previously developed for coal supply systems and will require redesigning to be applicable to the coal flow rates of furnaces and kilns. The turbine in the Coriolis flow meter needs to be reduced with more sensitive sensors and the electronics redesigned.

o For gas-solid flows, the development work will involve Coriolis flow meters to measure the total mass flow under conditions of heavy particle loading for which the mass flow of the gas is negligible and hence, the Coriolis flow meter measures only the mass flow of the particles. To yield applications of Coriolis flow meters in various gas-solid flows, they must still be redesigned and rebuilt to allow problem-free operation without clogging.

o When these Coriolis flow meters are applied to the measurement of heavy particles, questions arise regarding the linear dependence of the measurement signal on the instantaneous flow rate. The questions require careful consideration and a reevaluation of the theory of Coriolis flow meters.

o LSTM-Erlangen will be involved in theoretical studies of the effect of density of the flowing material on the measurements and results of these theoretical studies will influence the development work at FI-Sulzbach-Rosenberg.

6. Collaboration with AMA, München (D)

AMA is an organisation that embraces 160 small and medium size companies effectively working in sensor design, development, manufacturing and distribution. For the present project AMA will form a steering committee of six members which is responsible for the work of the present project. All the information gathered in the project will be made available for AMA which will analyse it and provide feedback for further work. Through this advice, guidance will be given to all partners.

Free of charge, AMA brings out every three months a technical bulletin providing information to all its member firms. This bulletin will be available to the project to provide information on the state of the project, new results, completion of instrumentation developments, etc.. In this way, the results will become available to firms in Germany that are interested in sensor developments. AMA is a member of the European Sensor Committee which will make the results available to European firms active in the field of sensor technology. AMA is involved in the preparation of SENSOR 91, a conference and exhibition on sensor technology, and will ensure that results are presented there.

PRELIMINARY RESULTS

Work at LSTM-Erlangen started out with the development of small anemometers using semi-conductor lasers. A test unit was set up as shown in Figure 1, consisting of a semi-conductor laser, a beam splitter unit, a double Bragg-cell and coupling devices for glass fibers. The front part of the optics is a glass fiber probe for LDA-measurements. For further details see Ref. 1.

The LDA-system shown in Figure 1 has the advantage that it does not employ large gas lasers as used in conventional LDA-systems.

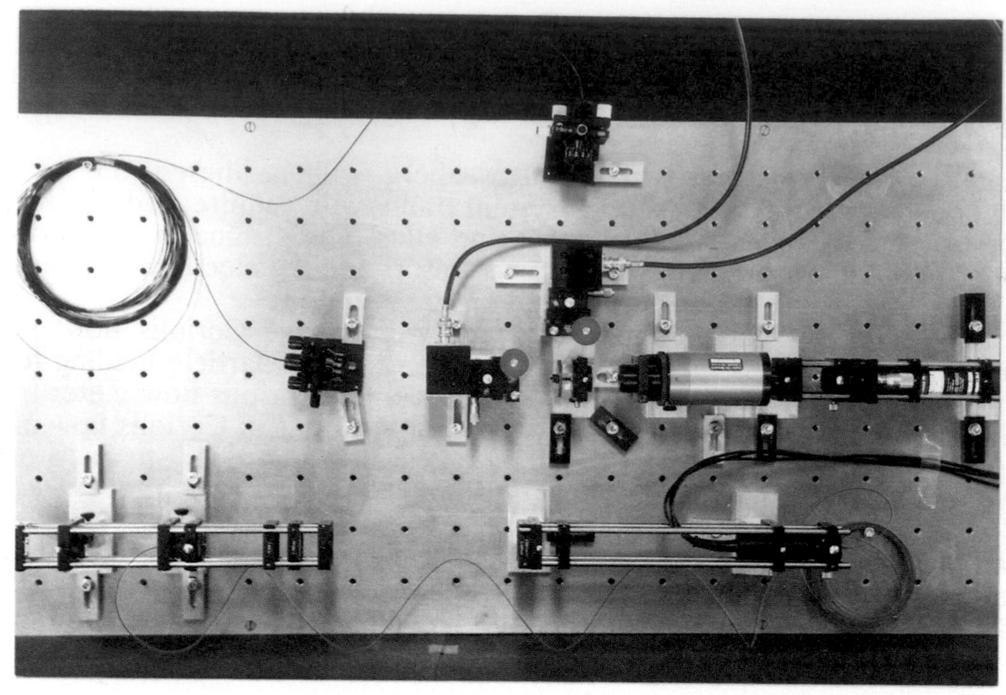

Fig. 1: LDA-system based on semi-conductor laser and using glass fiber probe

The employment of semi-conductor lasers and semi-conductor photo-detectors allows a small unit to be build that utilizes low electrical energy. The size of the front probe also makes it easy to use and permits measurements in industrial environments.

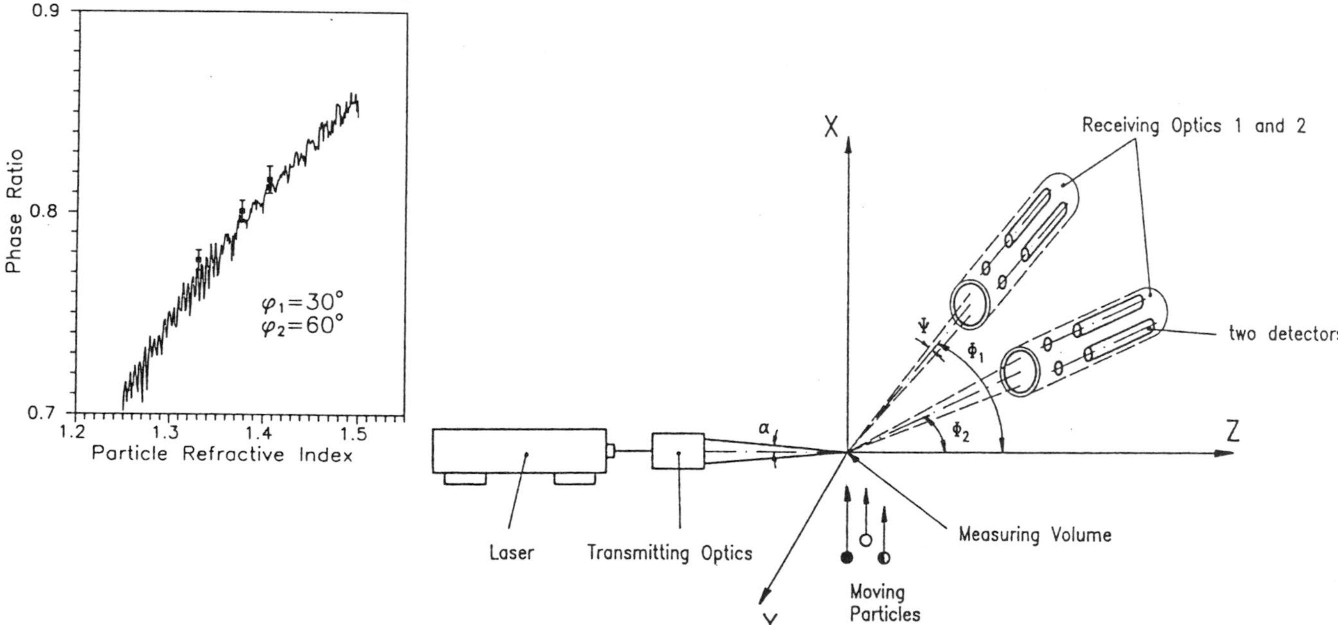

Fig. 2: Extended PDA-system for multi-phase flow measurements

First results are also available on the extension of phase-Doppler anemometry to multi-phase flows. Conventional phase-Doppler anemometry permits particle measurements without recognizing the particle material. It has been shown at LSTM-Erlangen that the addition of a second pair of photo-detectors also permits the refractive index of the particle material to be recognized and, hence, particle size and velocity measurements are possible with discrimination of the particle material. This will allow the phase-

Doppler technique to be used in multi-phase flows. The principle is shown in Fig. 2 and further details are provided in Ref. 2.

The work at Imperial College has so far concentrated on the completion of a counter signal processor for phase-Doppler measurements. Verification experiments have shown that the counter works satisfactorily and can be used as the electronic part of the phase-Doppler system developed at LSTM-Erlangen. The counter can also be used for LDA-signal processing only and, hence, is a good extension of the work on minituarized LDA-system performed at LSTM-Erlangen. Complete systems will be put together and will be made available for experimental studies at Imperial College and at LSTM-Erlangen. Measurements will include swirling, combusting flows of direct relevance to industrial burners and gasoline and Diesel sprays of immediate importance to internal combustion engines. It is anticipated that a short investigation of the flow in a kerosene fuelled gas turbine combustor will also be carried out. Applications in two-phase and particulate flows are planned and first test-rig constructions have started.

At the Laboratoire E.M2.C du CNRS at Ecole Centrale in Paris, measurements of density and temperature by laser beam deviation have been started. They are based on the finding that, if the refractive index of a medium is not constant, the optical path of a ray of light, i.e. by a laser beam, is a straight line and the beam deviates no longer towards the high refractive index region. If an axisymmetric medium is employed, calculations show that the deviation of the laser beam can be related to the local refractive index by an Abel-inversion. In this way, the local density can be calculated. Figure 3 shows the density profile across a supersonic free jet, and that the spatial resolution is good enough to detect the shock structure caused by the interaction of the supersonic jet and the surrounding gas. In a flame, characterized by a constant pressure and a high dilution of the reacting species in nitrogen, the density can be related to the temperature. Figure 4 shows the temperature in the vicinity of a flat diffusion flame produced between two opposed jets.

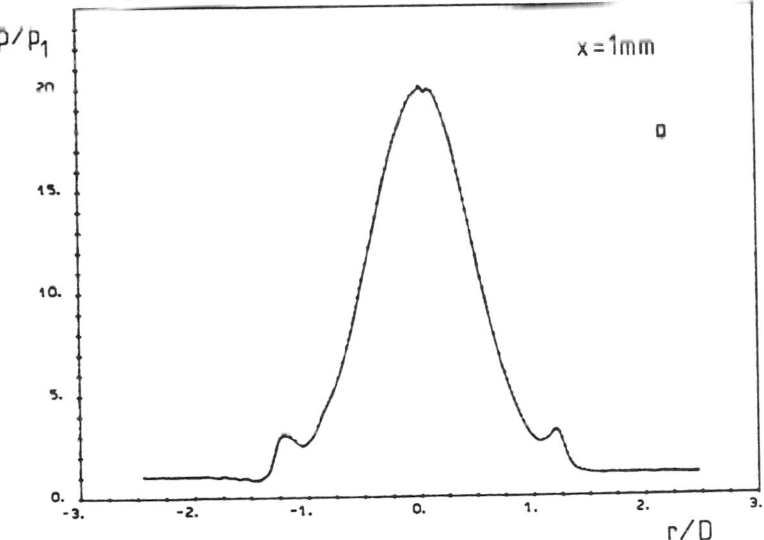

Fig. 3: Density map of a supersonic free jet, showing a disturbed interaction zone between the jet and the surrounding gas.

If the flow is not axisymmetric, e.g. in the interaction zone between two parallel free jets for example, the Abel-inversion is not useful and a more general technique needs to be developed. The experimental set-up is similar to the former one but two measurements are required for each measuring distance from the nozzle exit at different angles. A tomography algorithm needs to be devised to reconstruct the density known as the back projections of a filtered projection algorithm.

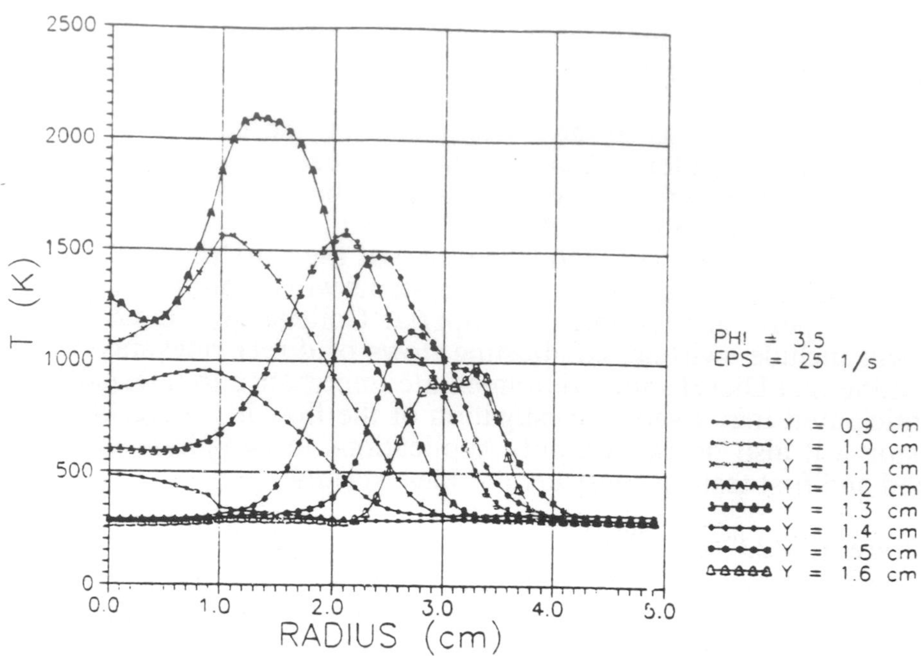

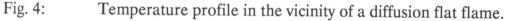

Fig. 4: Temperature profile in the vicinity of a diffusion flat flame.

Figure 5 shows the results of such measurements in a supersonic free jet with a non-axisymmetric shock structure due to a very strong interaction of the jet with the surrounding gas. Figure 6 presents the interaction region between two parallel free jets. It clearly shows the creation of the secondary jet between the two initial jets.

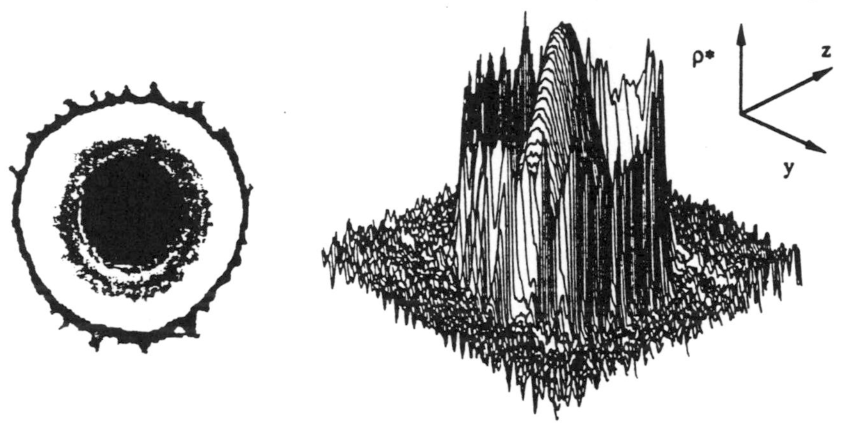

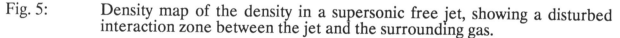

Fig. 5: Density map of the density in a supersonic free jet, showing a disturbed interaction zone between the jet and the surrounding gas.

At the University of Aveiro, a humidity sensor is being developed to withstand harsh environments. Ceramics are employed because they are inherently more stable in their humidity sensitive properties than other materials. The work includes comparison of various materials in order to assess their potential advantages.

Preliminary work carried out at the University of Aveiro on Lithium-doped ZnO ceramics has already shown this material to have good potential for humidity sensing. As an example, Fig. 7 shows the response to relative humidity for sintered samples of ZnO and Li-doped ZnO. The electrical conductivity of the doped sample changed by two orders of magnitude upon varying relative humidity from 2 to 95%. The sensitivity to water vapour and response time are strongly dependent on microstructure as well as doping levels; pore size distribution and the type of defects generated by Li incorporation in the ZnO lattice are expected to dictate sensor behaviour. A three-variable optimization method is currently being used, to find the best combination of sintering and composition parameters, see also Ref. 3.

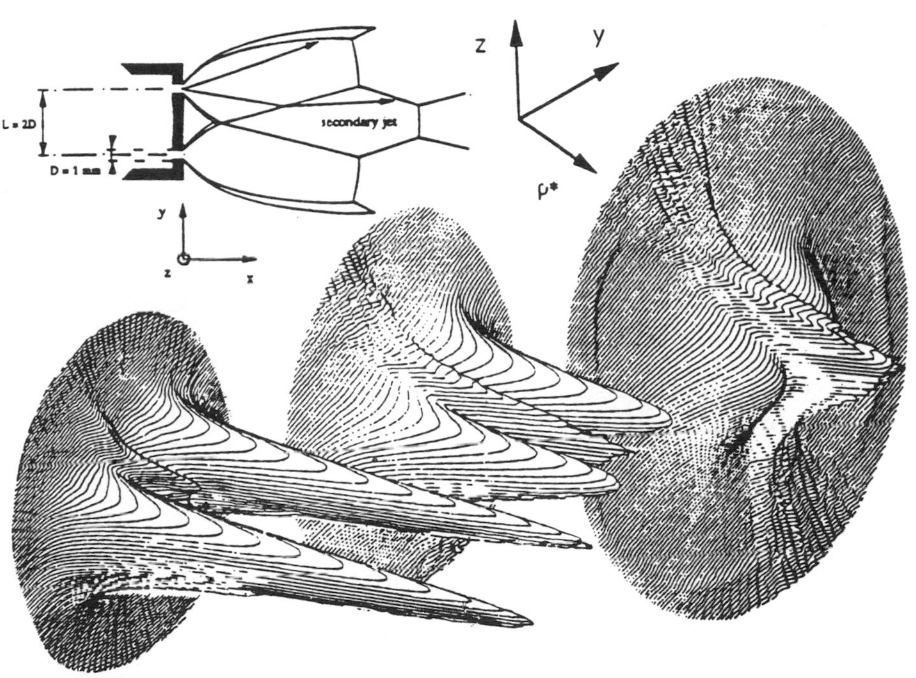

Fig. 6: Density maps at three different distances from the nozzle, measured in the interaction zone between two supersonic jets.

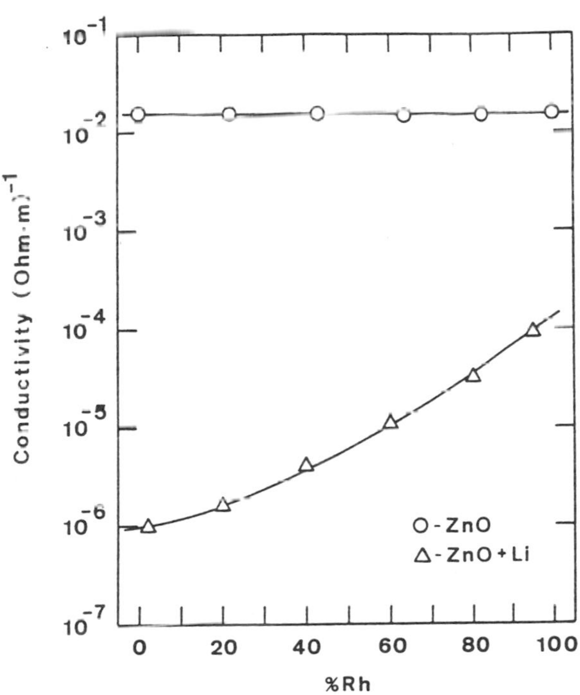

Fig. 7: Change of conductivity with relative humidity for ZnO and Li-doped ZnO.

Alternative shaping methods to prepare the sensing elements, namely thin or thick films, will be tried in addition to the pressing of pellets and is expected to influence response time favourably. Long term stability, selectivity and operating range are also important characterisitics of the sensors and will be tested at high temperatures and pressures. This part of the work will be done in collaboration with LSTM-Erlangen.

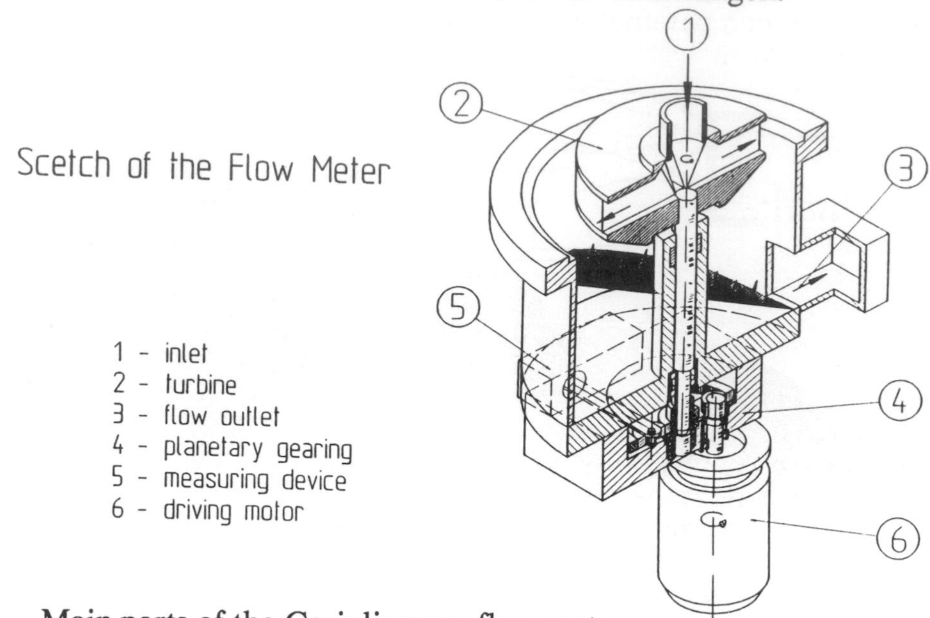

Fig. 8: Main parts of the Coriolis mass flow meter.

The work at ATZ-EVUS has concentrated on the modification of a Coriolis-mass flow meter developed by this institute. The meter requires modification in order to be used with mass flow rates typical for a wide range of applications in industry. Modifications are necessary in the turbine drive and the actual measuring device requiring a fourth sensor that allows low flow rates of coal particles to be monitored.

Figure 8 shows the mass flow meter as it is presently constructed for first measurements in a test loop made available by ATZ-EVUS. This test loop is shown in Figure 9.

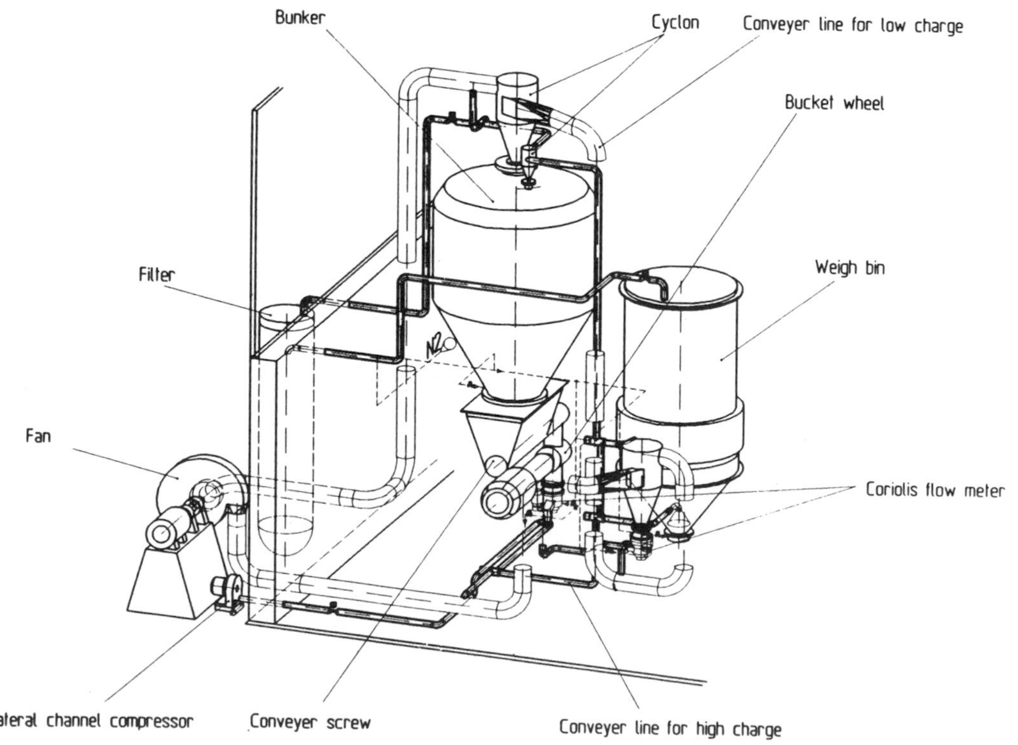

Fig. 9: Test plant for Coriolis flow meter

The results gathered in this project will be made available to industry through AMA (Arbeitsgemeinschaft Meßwertaufnehmer) and the European Sensor Committee. Special seminars and presentations in conferences will be arranged by AMA to distribute the results of the present work.

FUTURE RESEARCH AND DEVELOPMENT WORK

In the process industry, single phase and multi phase fluids are transported and to control processes it is essential, that their mass and/or volume flow rates are known accurately. In addition, the properties of the single phase and multi phase fluids have to be known. This readily suggests that continuous efforts in sensor developments are needed to advance mass and volume flow rate measurements in the process industry. Sensors to measure fluid properties, especially in the presence of more than one phases are also an aim of advanced sensor developments that will require attention of R&D work in the future. In order to ensure that such sensors can also be employed in harsh environments, a special program on sensor packaging is needed so that sensors become available that can easily be handled in high temperature, high pressure environments possessing highly corrosive fluids.

There are also sensors available that can nowadays readily be used for process controls. Increased attention will therefore be given to the application of sensors to control processes. These should yield improved products and/or result in energy reductions. Laboratory studies should be carried out and the results transfered to applications in industry.

REFERENCES

/1/ J. Domnick, F. Durst, R. Müller and A. Naqwi; Improved optical systems for velocimetry and particle sizing using semiconductor lasers and detectors; 5th Int. Symp. on Applications of Laser Anemometry to Fluid Mechanics, Lisbon (1990).

/2/ A. Naqwi, F. Durst, X.Z. Liu; An extended phase-Doppler system for characterization of multiphase flows; Particle and Particle Systems Characterization, 1990.

/3/ E. Joanni and J.L. Baptista; Lithium-Doped Zinc Oxide Humidity Sensors; Paper to be presented at SENSOR 91, Nuremberg, May 1991

DISCUSSION

Present R & D Activities, (Day 1).

1. Paper By Prof. M. Groll.

Dr. C.J. Bates, University of Wales: How do you measure the heat transfer coefficient close to the surface ? Are they refined thermocouples ? Are you measuring turbulence enhancement ?

Prof. Groll: We are investigating pool boiling and flow boiling. The temperature in the bulk fluid is being measured, as well as close to the surface. We are not looking at the turbulence structure.

Prof. P. Le Goff, Nancy: Are you investigating non-boiling situations in thin films ?

Prof. Groll: No. This is not a falling film investigation. Films may be examined on the rotating disc experiments, however.

Questioner from DSM, The Netherlands: Are you targeting cost reductions for heat exchangers ?

Prof. Groll: All the enhanced concepts are more complicated than the common types, but a better heat transfer coefficient can lead to more compact and thus cheaper units. The four industrial partners will feed in experience on cost-effectiveness.

Prof. U. Hesse, University of Hannover: Improving heat transfer can lead to compact units; but one has to handle (large) mass flows. Therefore, it is necessary to consider the mechanics of the heat exchanger and factors such as tube vibrations.

Prof. Groll: I agree.

2. Paper by Dr. J. Hesselgreaves.

Dr. K. Cornwell, Heriot-Watt University: With increased longitudinal flow, could you not reach the case of having no baffles at all and a P/D ratio of 1 ?

Dr. Hesselgreaves: It is difficult to see then how one could introduce the fluid into the heat exchanger. Some manufacturers have put in a means of introducing the fluid all around the circumference, but this is not easy.

Dr. Cornwell: The fluid could be introduced longitudinally.

Dr. L.E. Haseler, HTFS, AEA Technology: With regard to the flow distribution in an axial flow heat exchanger, there may be problems in getting the flow into the bundle. I have two questions. Firstly, are you taking any precautions to avoid maldistribution in the heat exchanger, or to measure it ? Secondly, are you simulating the feedback between heat transfer, viscosity and flow resistance using computational fluid dynamics (CFD) ?

Dr. Hesselgreaves: With regard to your first question, yes. Both GRETh and NEL are examining the practical distribution at inlet and outlet by flow visualisation and the CFD package 'TRIO'. Concerning the second query, the simulations are not isothermal.

Prof. N.C. Markatos, NTU, Athens: The application of CFD in two-phase flows needs particular skills.

3. Paper by Dr. E.K. MacDonald.

Dr. R. Reimert, Lurgi GmbH: Could you elaborate on the types of adsorbants to be studied ?

Dr. MacDonald: We will be studying zeolites supplied by Rhone Poulenc and possibly activated carbons.

4. Paper By Dr. J.G. Arkenbout, TNO-Division of Energy for Society.

Prof. L.L. van Dierendonck, DSM Research: What is the difference between this technology and the Sulzer technique ?

Dr. Arkenbout: This is well-proven technology based on the layer growth technique. One needs to apply a large growth rate, of the order of 10^{-6} m/sec. At a recent conference it was concluded that it would be useful to look further at continuous processes.

Mr. W.E. Whitman, Leatherhead Food RA: Have you collaborated with the food industry, such as sugar processors ?

Dr. Arkenbout: Yes. Both salt and sugar has been investigated. In the latter case the crystals are isolated by centrifuge.

5. Paper by Prof. G. Froment, Rijksuniversiteit van Gent.

Chairman, (M. Dumon, CEC expert): What is the temperature range of the catalyst ?

Prof. Froment: We are checking the long term life of the catalyst under a variety of conditions by cycling etc.

6. Paper by Dr. Heijkoop, VEG Gasinstituut.

Dr. R. Reimert, Lurgi GmbH: Firstly, how do yo ensure good contact of the sinter structure with the vessel wall ? Secondly, when do you apply the catalyst, before or after insertion of the sinter structure into the reactor ?

Dr. Heijkoop: The 60 bar steam pressure ensures good contact. Also, the sintermetal expands thermally against the wall. With regard to your second query, so far we have constructed only laboratory reactors. The catalyst was applied after sintering the support structure in the tube. In the future we may regenerate the catalyst, and it would be applied by putting an emulsion containing the catalyst particles through the sinter structure.

7. Paper by Prof. S. Yanniotis, Hellas Energy.

Prof. N.C. Markatos: How did the team design the system ? Was it based on experiments, scaled up, or computationally ?

Prof. Yanniotis: It was designed computationally, using classical rate equations, not a sophisticated computer model. The evaporator worked to design, but the regenerator had a lower evaporation rate than expected.

Prof. P. Le Goff: Just a comment. The system is an open cycle absorption heat pump. Therefore one designs the falling film evaporator as for a heat pump.

8. Paper by Prof. M.G. Carvalho, Instituto Superior Tecnico.

Dr. T.M. Lowes, Blue Circle Industries: As a major energy user (4 billion ECU/annum cost), I am very interested in this work. The use of mathematical modelling was of most use if one could have a superior model of the heat transfer mixing in the bed. Also, the overall efficiency was a function of heat exchange in the prepeater tower, and it was therefore necessary to model this. Only 40-80% of the energy burnt in the kiln. A range of types of fuel is being used, and this leads to a range of situations with regard to burner modification to reduce NOx, without giving problems of poor clinker quality.

In the future, I recommend close consultation with the cement industry so that the work was relevant to their needs.

Prof. Carvalho: I agree that only a proportion of the energy is used in the kiln. We are looking at other types of kiln, and not only in the region of the flame. The bed (in cement kilns) is very complex.

Mr. J. Gilbert, British Glass Manufacturers Research Association:
I support both points of view. With regard to glass melting furnaces one should not be concerned just with the flame. Are you investigating the variation in temperature caused in regenerators ?

Prof. Carvalho: Yes. We are also working closely with the glass industry.

9. Paper by Prof. N.C. Markatos, NTU, Athens.

Dr. T.M. Lowes: I support the work you are doing on mathematical modelling. The work could be extended to the preheater system of cement kilns. However, with regard to the overall approach of industry, one would need massive funding if CFD is to successful and widely applied. The cement Research Consortium has been supporting such work with the IFRC on flame research.

10. Paper by Prof. J. McMullan, University of Ulster.

Prof. E. Macchi, Politecnico di Milano: Are there any compressor manufacturers in the group (for this project) ?

Prof. McMullan: Industry has not yet fully appreciated that it has a problem.

Prof. Macchi: I act as a consultant to an Italian company which would be interested in collaboration.

Prof. McMullan: Not all of industry is informed about the problems it is facing. It is essentially an industry composed of SMEs.

Unkonwn Questioner: Does the group think that R22 is dangerous ?

Prof. McMullan: It is important that Germany is banning R22, therefore every manufacturer will be unable to use this working fluid.

11. Paper by Prof. B. Kalitventzeff, University of Liege.

Dr. G.J. Prokopakis, SPEC: I am interested in the way different methodologies are being used. Does this program offer the design of heat exchanger networks, or tackle problem difficult for existing methodologies ?

Prof. Kalitventzeff: I do not believe in 'press button' software. The number of possibilities is such that it is difficult to find the solution. First one needs to go to the application of targeting procedures and at each step of the energy synthesis methodology, the user can interact with the program. One can go to the Grand Composite Curve analysis and also vary some process features and study the new composite curve.

Prof. P. Le Goff: There are three types of equation: mass balance, energy balance etc. One can also have a concept of 'value balance' which takes into account ecology, 2nd law analyses and economy. How do you include these in your model ?

Prof. Kalitventzeff: The equations are written into it automatically. For example, the cost function can be in a standard form, or other forms with an interactive mode. One can also make minimum energy analyses. We do not yet cater for environmental aspects.

12. Paper by Prof. F. Durst, University of Erlangen-Nurnberg.

Mr. W.E. Whitman: What is the potential for coal firing ? How low (flow rate measurement) can one get ?

Prof. Durst: Down to rates of grams/minute.

******

Future R&D Requirements - Workshop (Day 2).

Group 4. Heat Exchanger Fouling. Rapporteur: Mr. R. Vidil, GRETh.

Mr. W.E. Whitman, Leatherhead Food RA: An observation: The food industry has specific problems. If one has intensified heat transfer surfaces, how does one clean them. Thus intensified heat exchangers may be undesirable in the food industry.

Group 5. Gas Adsorption. Rapporteur: Prof. D. Tondeur, ENSIC, Nancy.

Dr. M.J. Tierney, Harwell Laboratory: There are two adsorber-type projects in the current JOULE programme. BOC has a current interest in shallow bed adsorbers. Temperature swing adsorption gives heat transfer problems, so one needs CFD solutions to some aspects of the process.

Prof. Tondeur: We are not proposing to develop a new CFD tool in this project. However, it might be possible to include data arising out of the project in (other) CFD tools.

Group 7. Glass Making Furnaces, Cement Kilns and Baking Ovens. Prof. H.L.J. Meunier, Faculté Polytechnique de Mons.

Mr. W.C. Dobie, ERDC: There was no mention of electric technologies in your presentation. These include plasma technologies for glass making and dielectric heating in bakeries.

Prof. Meunier: It is difficult to comment, as these were not discussed in the group.

Group 8. Dryers. Prof. D. Mewes, Institut für Verfahrenstechnik, Hannover.

Dr. G.J. Prokopakis, SPEC: The food industry consumes large amounts of energy (in drying), and therefore control of dryers is important.

Prof. Mewes: I will send our summary (of the discussion) to you, and add this comment.

Mr. W.E. Whitman: In the case of spray dryers, if one could use more concentrated liquids, one could save energy. Also there is a need for better modelling of and measurements in spray dryers. In particular the starting operation needs control.

A comment from the Floor: If one is looking at increased liquid concentration, atomiser research may be needed.

Group 9. Refrigeration (Replacement of CFCs). Ir. P.E.J. Vermeulen, MT-TNO Heat & Refrigeration Technology Dept.

Prof. F. Meunier, LIMSI-CNRS: What kind of results are you anticipating for the new fluids ?

Ir. Vermeulen: We should not look at R134a, but at other fluids and blends.

Groupe 10. Energy and Environmental Process Integration. Prof. R.W.K. Allen, Harwell Laboratory.

Dr. T.M. Lowes, Blue Circle: In the next 5 years it is necessary to get plant emissions down to levels specified by the UK government.

Prof. Allen: It would be helpful if one had, or could identify, a range of ways of producing the end product, (to optimise on minimum emissions).

Dr. J. Hesselgreaves, NEL: One should include social aspects under environmental aspects. For example decentralisation and a reduction in support for growth in the transport industry, particularly with respect to the motor industry and petroleum products.

Prof. Allen: It is important to include this aspect, but at a later stage or in a multidisciplinary activity related to clean technologies.

Group 11. Advanced Sensors for Process Control in the Process Industries. Prof. J.M. Ferreira de Jesus, INTERG.

W.E. Whitman: The food industry is particularly interested in pH measurement. At present the sensors are made of glass and we do not like using them. An alternative method would be of great interest.

FUTURE R&D REQUIREMENTS

Improved Energy Efficiency in the Process Industries

24 October 1990

THE NEW CEC PROGRAMME ON NON-NUCLEAR ENERGY

JOULE II (1991-1995)

P. ZEGERS

Commission of the European Communities

Before discussing the JOULE programme on Non-Nuclear Energy R&D, I first would like to say a few words about the CEC and how JOULE fits in the CEC structure.

The Commission of the European Communities has 17 Members or Commissioners who are in charge of 23 Directorate Generals which are very similar to Departments or Ministries in Member States. Directorate General XII is responsible for Science, Research and Development. CEC research is brought together in a Five Year Framework Programme, which contains all the important R&D programmes of the Commission: ESPRIT, BRITE, JOULE, etc. The total budget of the ongoing Framework Programme (1987-1991) is 5,400 MECU. Research on "Rational Use of Energy in Industry" is carried out in the JOULE programme (1989-1991). For this ongoing three year JOULE programme 122 MECU have been allocated.

In 1990, a new Third Framework Programme was approved for the period 1990-1995 with an overall budget of 5,700 MECU. This will include a JOULE II programme (1991-1995) for which 157 MECU have been allocated. A detailed JOULE II programme is expected to be approved by the end of 1991 by the Council of Ministers and the European Parliament. It consists of the following sub-programmes:

Models for energy and environment

Rational use of energy: Energy conservation in industry and buildings, combustion, fuel cells, advanced battery and fuel cell driven electrical vehicles.

Renewable energies: wind, solar energy, biomass and geothermal energy.

Energy from fossil sources: hydrocarbons and solid fuels.

Research on Rational Use of Energy in Industry is carried out in the Rational Use of Energy sub-programme. The objective of this programme is to develop technologies and techniques for energy use and production sectors which will lead to major improvements in energy efficiency and pollution abatement.

There is still much scope for reducing primary energy demand through energy conservation in end-use sectors as well as for the improvement of energy supply and storage. Energy savings of a few percent result in the saving of billions of ECU as well as reductions in pollutant emissions. Moreover, the search for a more rational use of energy may lead to technological advances which may help the situation of EC industry in relation to its worldwide competitors.

(*) 1 MECU = 10^6 ECU (European Currency Unit)

Projects carried out in the framework of the JOULE programme should satisfy the following profile:

- targeted research with clear (mostly long term) objectives;

- collaborative projects in which industry, universities, public and private research organizations participate;

- industry has an important role to play in setting the goals;

- the collaborative projects can serve as a focus for information exchange into which information from the US and Japan can also be fed.

The CEC will contribute to the cost of the research projects in the following ways:

- Universities and colleges of higher education:
  Contribution up to 100% of the actual marginal costs incurred as additional expenditure of the R&D project.

- Other organizations:
  Contribution up to 50% of the actual full economic cost of the R&D project.

After approval of the JOULE programme, a call for proposals will be published in the Official Journal of the European Communities, probably towards the end of 1991. The duration of this call for proposals is generally 3-4 months. After the closing date, the selection and drafting of the contracts will require 5-6 months. The first contracts can therefore be expected in the second half of 1992.

ORGANISATION OF THE WORKSHOP

P. A. PILAVACHI

Commission of the European Communities

Participants in the Workshop were asked:

- To propose provisional topics for the forthcoming Programme in 1991. (Note that these may be in the form of tentative project proposals).
- To assess where possible the potential energy benefits of the recommended technologies, and their replication.

In considering proposals, they were advised to bear in mind that the Commission prefers collaboration between at least three Community countries, involving typically 5 to 7 participating organisations. Large projects are preferred, and the subject areas should cover precompetitive research for process industry applications.

The following Working Groups were organised:

- Chemical Reactors
- Heat Exchanger Intensification
- Process Plant Intensification
- Heat Exchanger Fouling
- Gas Adsorption
- Melt Crystallisation
- Glass Making and Ceramic Furnaces, Cement Kilns and Baking Ovens
- Dryers
- Refrigeration (Replacement of CFCs)
- Energy and Environmental Process Integration
  (Chemical process & paper production process)
- Advanced Sensors for Process Control in the Process Industries
- Catalytic Combustion
- Efficient Use of Electricity

The Commission intends to submit the project topics recommended at the Workshop to the appropriate Industrial Federations, so that their members may be given an opportunity to participate.

REPORTS ON WORKING GROUPS

Chairman: Prof. N. Peters

WORKING GROUP ON "CHEMICAL REACTORS"

A framework for further studies has been established. The main objective being the saving of energy and material, the improvement of chemical reactors should be obtained by an increase of the yields and selectivities.

An increase of the selectivity of a chemical reaction will have several beneficial effects:

- reduction of the amount of feedstock required,
- reduction of the energy needed for ensuring the separation of the products of the reaction,
- reduction of the amount of by-products and wastes.

In order to achieve these goals, several approaches may be adopted:

- a generic approach based on the detailed modelisation of the chemical reactors, or

- a more technological approach considering new types of equipment which could provide specific advantages for a given class of chemical systems (for example extractive reaction, reactive distillation, membrane reactors, etc...).

It is known that Residence Time Distribution (RTD) inside a chemical reactor has generally a marked effect on the selectivity of chemical reactions. One way of predicting RTD is to use Computational Fluid Dynamic (CFD) techniques for modelling chemical reactors. For single phase systems, the basic knowledge appears sufficient for dealing directly with a practical example. For multiphase systems, additional experiments would be required for getting the necessary data for the modelling step.

It will also be important to check the model predictions by comparing them to industrial equipment data.

Different types of reactor could be investigated, as for example:

1. a stirred tank reactor used for performing polymerisations; in that case the design of the stirrer is particularly difficult as a consequence of the important variation of viscosity due to the reaction. The quality of the polymer is on the other hand linked to the residence time distribution, which is largely dependent on the stirrer efficiency.

2. a bubble column reactor (with or without recirculation) often used for oxidation reactions. In that case of a two-phase system (gas and liquid), specially designed experiments at laboratory scale should be performed in order to get data relative to the interactions between gas bubbles and the liquid phase.

3. three-phase system reactors should, however, be preferentially considered. Among these systems the following are of special practical importance:

- the three-phase stirred tank reactor, the phases being gas, liquid and solid (catalyst or product of the reaction) maintained into suspension by a mechanical stirrer. Industrial applications of this type of reactor are numerous: hydrogenations, oxidations (e.g. terephthalic acid manufacture),

- the catalytic packed bed with two phase flow (gas and liquid), often called "Trickle Bed" and widely used in the oil and petrochemical industry.

Research projects corresponding to more precisely defined processes, requiring a new type of reactor, could also be considered.

<u>Participants</u>

P. Trambouze (Coordinator)	IFP-CEDI
A. J. P. Bongers	DSM-Research
G. Heijkoop	VEG-Gasinstitut
P. Neumann	Krebsöge
R. Nijsing	JRC-Ispra
G. Oliveri del Castillo	Montedipe
R. Liegeois	Solvay & Cie
F. C. Lockwood	Imperial College
N. Markatos	NTU-Athens
M. K. Patel	Thames Polytechnic
J. C. F. Pereira	IST-Lisboa
M. Sommerfeld	LSTM-Erlangen
M. Tierney	CFDS-Harwell

WORKING GROUP ON "HEAT EXCHANGERS INTENSIFICATION"

Introduction

It was generally agreed that, even if heat exchangers are a "mature" technology, there are still great opportunities for further improvements. Experimental and theoretical research activities should be directed at (i) gathering a better physical understanding of the complex phenomena taking place in heat exchangers, (ii) developing more accurate numerical modelization techniques of the thermo fluid-dynamic processes, as well as (iii) developing more advanced design methods and manufacturing procedures.

The enormous energy saving potential achievable by European process industry by means of better heat exchangers was universally recognized, owing to the wide diffusion of heat transfer equipment, to the huge amount of thermal power exchanged and to the high exergy losses currently present in these components. Substantial CEC funding in this subject area is therefore recommended.

Several participants put great emphasis on the importance of CFD (Computational Fluid Dynamics). Application of CFD models and experimental validation aimed at a greater understanding of single and two-phase flows within heat exchanger passages is seen as a priority in all research areas discussed below.

After some discussions, two subjects were identified as important research priorities: (i) Compact Heat Exchangers and (ii) Enhanced Heat Exchangers for "Dry" Heat rejections. The majority of the working group participants predicted that their organizations will be interested in exploring the possibility of cooperating in both areas within the framework of the EC Joule R&D Program. The rationale of the two proposals and tentative research topics are outlined in the followings.

Compact Heat Exchangers (CHE)

Two sorts of requirements were identified: the first related to improved modelling of Heat Transfer and Pressure Drop within the very small channels, which are characteristic of these exchangers. This could involve boiling or condensation or pressure drop measurements. It was noted that in small channels, convective, rather than nucleate boiling was likely to be dominant. Work on flow boiling in these channels could therefore be seen as a natural follow-on to the CEC work on enhanced pool boiling currently being coordinated by IKE Stuttgart. The benefit of generic work in small channels is twofold: 1) it can be applied to existing exchangers, where improved design methods could give engineers more confidence in using these novel exchangers, and 2) it could point to directions in which developments of new types of CHEs should take place.

Other topics which were regarded as important for CHEs were: (i) obtaining an understanding of flow distribution, (ii) flow modelling within heat exchanger passages, (iii) effect of metal surfaces on performance, (iv) development of manufacturing techniques and (v) new materials. It was not felt necessary to perform specific tests on the various fluids that might be used in CHEs in process industries since similarity parameters were assumed to be perfectly acceptable for fluid modelling.

There was some discussion of overall priorities, and it was agreed that developments relating to CHE, whether of established, or relatively novel types, should have priority over further developments of well-established Shell and Tube Heat Exchanger.

It was recognized that fouling was potentially an important issue for the development of CHEs, but it was noted that this topic was the subject of a separate Working Group.

Finally, a number of other topics relating to CHE were raised, including problems related to stability of their use and their linking with other processes, such as absorption, or fractionation.

Enhanced Dry Heat Rejection

Water scarcity makes "dry" heat rejection a very important topic in many applications, especially in hot regions, like Southern European countries. Heat exchangers presently adopted in the process industry are often characterized by relatively poor performance and operate under rather large temperature differences, if compared to the present state-of-the-art of other more advanced sectors, such as the automotive and air conditioning industry.

Topics to be investigated include heat transfer enhancement and flow modelling on both air and tube side (for either single and two phase flows), internal flow organization, new materials (including the use of plastic). The experimental activity should be directed at an optimization of complex heat transfer surface geometries such as fin turbulators and micro-grooves or inserts inside tubes. Detailed measurements of heat transfer coefficients, pressure drops, flow visualization are required.

Optimization techniques of heat transfer matrices and size based upon actual capital and operating costs should be assessed. The participation of manufacturers was seen as essential for the realization of this task. Monitoring existing heat exchangers was suggested by some working group participants as an important tool for providing a consistent data base.

Another topic which was felt important was the study of fluid-dynamic interaction between fans and heat exchangers, which also affects the noise generation related to heat rejection.

Ennio Macchi (coordinator)	Politecnico di Milano	Italy
André Bailly	Laboratoire CIAT	France
Colin Bates	University of Wales	U.K.
Knut Bauer	Hoechst AG	Germany
Leo Koot	TNO	Netherlands
Laurie Haseler	HTFS	U.K.
Manuel Heitor	IST (Univ. of Lisbon)	Portugal
J. E. Hesselgreaves	NEL	U.K.
Peter Hills	ICI Engineering	U.K.
M. Karagiorgas	Interclima Hellas	Greece
Fernand Lauro	GRETh	France
Christophe Marvillet	GRETh	France
Michel Messant	Trefimetaux	France
Stefan Roesler	IKE (Univ. of Stuttgart)	Germany
Stavros Yanniotis	Agr. Univ. of Athens	Greece

WORKING GROUP ON "PROCESS PLANT INTENSIFICATION"

Introduction

Process intensification (PI) is the strategy of making major reductions in the size of process equipment, in order to achieve very significant savings in the capital cost of processing systems. In order to be fully effective, the approach must cover all the process unit operations and also identify as many opportunities as possible for telescoping equipment functions - for example by performing heat exchange and distillation in one unit.

The energy saving potential of PI has several facets. The first and most obvious feature is that smaller equipment will involve less material and therefore less energy to make it. In addition a radical reduction in capital cost may allow alternative energy - saving process configurations to become economic. Finally, an improvement in heat and transfer coefficients is a vital factor in allowing individual unit operations to approach thermodynamically ideal operation. For example an intensified electrochemical cell will operate closer to the reversible voltage for the reaction involved, resulting in an obvious power saving.

Since PI is intended to effect orders of magnitude reduction in equipment volume, the approach must be radical rather than incremental. New equipment design will probably be involved and success is most likely if projects include collaborators with both manufacturing and processing skills. Advanced production engineering is expected to be an important factor in any successful development. The subject is clearly wide ranging and if effective EEC funding and project organisation is to be ensured, it is imperative that the 3 PI subject groups are considered together.

Framework proposals

A. The first project proposal centres on the need to assess the impact which process intensification may have on a whole plant, ie one comprising several different unit operations. Ideally a range of different processes should be examined but it is proposed that the study be limited to two.

One preferred candidate is the conversion of SO_2 to SO_3, which has reaction; absorption, heat transfer and environmental implications. Another could be a multi stage batch process (for a pharmaceutical?) which could be converted into a dedicated small continuous unit (see C below). Here the operations involved could well be crystallisation, phase disengagement, extraction/distillation and drying.

B. The benefits flowing from the development of a catalytic plate reactor are potentially extremely attractive, provided the catalyst kinetics are fast. Essentially the idea is to coat one side of an intensified heat exchanger (eg Heatric) with a process catalyst layer and provide the reaction endotherm/exotherm with a combustion catalyst or heat transfer fluid on the other side. This reactor configuration allows the reaction kinetics full rein by avoiding the heat and mass transfer limitations inherent in packed bed reactors.

Specifically it is suggested that a plate reactor be developed for the $SO_2 \rightarrow SO_3$ process such that this could be operated at pressure with pure oxygen. This could have major energy and environmental implications while demonstrating the plate reactor principle.

C. The operation of small scale (<1000 tpy) batch processes can involve a significant waste of energy, with relatively ineffective batch processors, since they must be designed for the peak of highly variable heat and mass transfer duties. Hence the development of intensified dedicated continuous equipment to process several cubic centimetres per second (The "desk top" processor) could be very attractive. Several such units, each with their microprocessor controller could replace a relatively large batch system.

D. The application of centrifugal fields to electrochemistry profoundly alters the fluid dynamic environment at and between the electrodes. Gas disengagement is facilitated and electrode mass transfer is enhanced dramatically. Thus the cell voltage is reduced and the selectivity of many electro organic synthesis is improved. Fully value - engineered cells designed to exploit centrifugal fields could save energy and widen the process applications for electrochemistry.

E. There are many highly exothermic gas - liquid reactions (chlorination/sulphonation/ oxidation) which are currently performed at dilute concentration in order to limit the exotherm. This not only wastes exergy but also increases the inventory of potentially hazardous material. A highly sheared liquid film on a rotating surface is known to exhibit excellent heat/mass transfer performance. Therefore an extension of the current JOULE spinning evaporator project to include multiphase reactors is recommended.

F. Liquid extraction and liquid membranes are two energy efficient separation techniques which are not widely used in bulk processing. Both are capable of very significant intensification in a centrifugal field using technology similar to that used in ICI's Higee vapour/liquid contactor. Development along these lines to improve the cost-effectiveness of these unit operations could encourage their more extensive application in large scale plants.

Participants

C. Ramshaw (Coordinator)	ICI, UK
A. Mercer	ETSU, UK
J. Jochems	DSM, NL
R. Nijsing	Ispra, I
Prof S. Yanniotis	Athens, GR
E. Petela	Linhoff March, UK
G. Prokapakis	Spec. Process Services, GR
Prof P. Le Goff	Nancy, F

WORKING GROUP ON "HEAT EXCHANGER FOULING"

Introduction

R&D needs in various industrial sectors were discussed. These covered fouling in cooling waters and the chemical and petrochemical industries as well as in the food processing industry. A considerable amount of work had been carried out on cooling water systems, but the results had only a limited range of application. Increasing pressure to conserve water and reduce the environmental impact of discharges were making it much more difficult to control fouling in cooling water systems. Existing data needed to be re-examined and extended in a generic way to address these new restrictions. Work on cooling waters would be important to most industrial sectors, while that on specific chemical or petrochemical systems would be less generally applicable. While the food industry was seen as an important area, it was recognised that the process fluids in it were very diverse in composition. It would therefore be a difficult area in which to apply generic R&D on fouling.

The influence of fouling on different exchanger configurations was also discussed. In particular it was felt that concern about fouling was a major reason for the low industrial investment in compact exchangers, and this should be addressed in future research.

It was noted that chemical removal of deposits involved the use and disposal of materials that represented hazards to personnel, process plant and the environment. While the choice of chemicals was a matter of commercial judgement, the lack of any generic model for the cleaning process meant that there was no means of maximising the effectiveness of the cleaning fluids and minimising the hazard.

Conclusions

1. There are clearly very wide-ranging needs in both gas- and liquid-side fouling.

2. The number of fouling environments to be considered cover a wide range. The most widely encountered problems are with cooling water, but the amount of information about fouling from process fluids in the chemical petrochemical and other process industries is much more limited, and some priority should be given to these areas, with emphasis on chemical and related sectors.

3. The general aims of the work should be to provide sets of data covering likely temperature and flow conditions for the chosen fluids in industrial process applications. The studies should aim to establish the mechanisms by which deposits are formed, and their rates of formation under a range of well-defined fluid flow and heat transfer conditions. They should provide information that can be used to provide fouling resistances for design purposes, guidance to minimise deposit formation during plant operation, and to aid the development of models that can be used to predict fouling rates.

4. The future R&D should therefore include studies on fouling from liquids under three headings: generic studies, in situ measurements, including monitoring and prevention and cleaning. Further work on gas-side fouling should also be undertaken.

RECOMMENDED WORK

"Liquid-side Fouling"

Generic studies

- Laboratory studies to establish the mechanisms of formation of deposits, and the effects of temperature, fluid flow and heat transfer on deposition rate, deposit structure and properties (including thermal fouling resistance) in well-defined systems. The results to be used to develop and validate a fouling model.

- Laboratory studies on cooling waters and process fluids representative of those in the chemical, petrochemical and some other process industries for comparison with the model developed for well-defined systems.

- Studies related to compact heat exchangers including the effects of small channels and surface extensions.

- Comparisons between measurements of fouling resistance, deposit amount and structure in heat exchangers in industrial plant and those made in the laboratory under similar conditions with the same fluids.

In situ Measurements

- The development of a fouling monitor that would provide an online, real time measurement of the amount of fouling deposit, using an appropriate physical technique. This should be distinguished from a fouling probe, which does not usually give any direct on-line measurement of fouling deposit, but which is designed to provide samples of deposit obtained under controlled conditions; depending on its design, a monitor may also be able to function as a probe.

- Measurement of thermal fouling resistance in different situations, and comparison with the generic studies.

Prevention and Cleaning

- Laboratory studies in a model system to produce a physical model for cleaning of deposits, taking into account deposit structure, fluid flow rate and residence time, and temperature.

"Gas-Side Fouling"

A number of items are put forward, some of which are aimed at maximising the benefit from existing data.

- Production of gas-side fouling data for a range of industrial processes. The aim would be to construct a data bank of sticking probability functions that could be used to predict fouling in important industrial processes such as glass production, coal and oil combustion, or others chosen to meet environmental or energy efficiency criteria. Use could be made of existing analytical techniques.

- Integration of fouling models with process integration computer programmes. The combination of fouling models with current or new methods for thermal process integration.

- Integration of process combustion modelling with the above fouling and process integration work. The aim would be to provide a tool for optimising a thermal energy system simultaneously for both energy and environmental criteria. This would allow, for example, the direct calculation of the economic consequences of emissions legislation on the design and operation of a specific energy system.

- Modifications and improvements to existing practical and modelling methodologies in the light of practical experience.

- Further development of the initial applications programmes, as indicated by the needs of potential users.

<u>Participants</u>

R. Vidil (Coordinator)	GRETh
R Dumon	CEC Expert
J D Isdale	NEL
A J Karabelas	CPERI
P Kew	H-W University
A M Pritchard	AEA Technology
B Ribier	AFME
B Valachis	CRES.

WORKING GROUP ON "ADSORPTION AS A LOW ENERGY SEPARATION AND PURIFICATION PROCESS"

Introduction

The process industries use more energy in separating and purifying products than in almost any other operation. This is particularly so when separating to high purity from dilute mixtures or where products are present with similar physical properties but widely different market values. Such separations, concentrations or purifications should be made to maximise yield and selectivity while minimising energy cost.

Examples of common energy intensive separation processes in use today are gas enrichment using cryogenic distillation, recovery of volatile organic components using cryogenic condensation, separation of isomers using fractional distillation, separation of azeotropic mixtures by extractive or azeotropic distillation.

In many such cases adsorption may be, and is considered as an interesting alternative from an energetic point of view, and also from a general technological and economical point of view. Adsorption has several distinctive features which allow potentially better energy efficiency than distillation or cryogenic separations.

- the selectivity, resulting from a choice of the adsorbing material and the operating conditions, is much more flexible (and usually much higher) than that resulting from the physical properties of the components to be separated;

- the "concentration power", i.e. the ability to condensate and concentrate a component even from a very dilute mixture, with a very low energetic cost, owing to the special microgeometry of porous adsorbents;

- the natural ability to operate at near ambient temperatures;

- the macrogeometry of adsorbent beds, which allow them to have many "theoretical plates", and thus to achieve separation of very close components.

In fact, the combination of these features make adsorption a potentially more reversible process than most other separations, which implies that the energy degradation is smaller.

On the other hand, this relative reversibility can be approached only at the cost of a good design of the process. The micro and macrogeometry of the material, the physico-chemical processes occurring in it, the non-linear transient behaviour of fixed beds, the complex multi-bed configurations, and the corresponding process control, are in general more complicated to design, operate and control than distillation, for example. Therefore, a good understanding of the mechanisms, good models and design tools are necessary.

In other words, energy saving through adsorption will be obtained at the cost of injecting more scientific knowledge in this process.

The proposed framework programme is inspired by these considerations. It could be built around four domains, each comprising a range of topics, the main lines of which are the following.

1. **Materials and properties**: new lines of research on ageing of adsorbents and methodology accounting for ageing.

2. **Modelling**: new lines of research on the connection of classical modelling with CFD modelling, and on energy analysis.

3. **Processes and configurations**: new lines of research on the combination of adsorption with other processes and on advanced flow sheets.

4. **Areas of applications**: new lines of research on adsorption from the liquid or supercritical phase, and on bulk gas separations.

MAIN LINES OF A FRAMEWORK PROGRAMME

1. Materials and properties

Generic methods and tests for:

- studying ageing of adsorbents
- studying the elementary processes influencing ageing
- evaluating new adsorbents.

These studies could include the development of accelerated tests for ageing, the physico-chemical characterisation of aged adsorbents, the effect of pretreatments, the effects on ageing of various regeneration techniques, the development of methods for monitoring column operations to account for ageing, the evaluation of new adsorbents (e.g. hydrophilic) for specific applications, the relation between structure and properties and the constitution of a data bank.

2. Modelling (theory, mathematics, computation)

Four aspects should be developed:

- **Knowledge models for elementary processes.**
  Special attention to intraparticle transfer and its coupling with "external"phenomena (multicomponent systems, non-isothermal effects, short-time phenomena; diffusions vs convection; theoretical analysis, experimental methodology).

- **Reduced models for process feasibility, predesign or control.**
  Evaluation of reduced models for adsorption from the liquid phase and from the supercritical phase and procedures for constructing them, with reference to knowledge models.

- **Connection with CFD modelling**
  Coupling and decoupling of "classical" adsorption models with detailed hydrodynamics, especially under "extreme" conditions (high pressure, large pressure drop, important friction effects and non-isothermal effects, rapid cycling, and multicomponent systems). Effects of 2 and 3-dimensional effects on adsorbent bed operations.

- **Energy and thermodynamic analysis.**
  Incorporate such aspects in modelling and software; develop methodology for analysis; this includes the energy saving aspects of adsorption, and the use of thermodynamic analysis for overall process improvement.

3. <u>Processes and configurations</u>

Study modelling, evaluation, experimentation of advanced processes and configurations. This comprises four main sub-directions:

- **Regeneration/desorption** is in most cases the key step for the energetics and economics of adsorption processes. The emphasis of the programme is put on non-classical regeneration or desorption methods: novel uses of classical energy for desorption (such as for example, the use of parametric pumping techniques in applying heat), or alternately, the use of forms of energy that are not conventional in desorption (for example, the direct application of electric current). Using the modelling and simulation tools, such desorption-regeneration processes should be analysed with respect to energy and materials economy.

- **Combined process**

  . Adsorption combined with chemical reactions, in order to enhance separation or to improve reaction selectivity and yield. Processes in which chemical reactions are coupled to separation and depend on some intensive variables, such as pressure or temperature (for example, reactive PSA).

  . Adsorption combined with diffusion processes: adsorptive membranes (membranes made of adsorbing material, or containing embedded adsorbing material); such membranes may be given a selectivity which conventional materials do not possess, but may require an operating mode similar to that of adsorbents (including regeneration cycles); conventional adsorption combined with a membrane process (the membrane process does the bulk separation and the adsorption does the final polishing); the pertinence and the watershed between combined and single process should be investigated. This requires experimentation, simulation and evaluation.

- **Advanced flow sheets**

  . Simulation and evaluation of multicomponent, continuous, semi-continuous or pseudo-continuous processes (e.g. simulated countercurrent processes).

  . Simulation of rapid cycles and kinetically governed processes.

- **Experimentation**

  . Bench-scale and pilot scale experiments should be used to validate the methodologies, models and simulation. This concerns in particular all processes in supercritical media, processes involving new materials, processes where ageing plays a role, and new process configurations (e.g. the combined processes mentioned above).

4. Areas of application

The areas privileged are those in which adsorption is most likely to be an alternative to other, energy intensive separation process, and in which energetic components are concerned.

Adsorption from the gas phase

- Bulk separation of gas mixtures: recovery of useful components from such mixtures as the gas associated to oil extraction, fuel-gas in refineries, cracking gas and other process gases; separation of isomeric hydrocarbons in the gas phase (octane number upgrading); recovery of rare gases from air.

- Concentration from relatively dilute mixtures: solvent recovery for example.

Adsorption from the liquid and from the supercritical phase:

- Separation of isomers (such as xylenes, or other substituted aromatics)
- Separation of azeotropic mixtures
- Adsorption in super-critical media; the energy economy of supercritical adsorption or regeneration versus conventional processes.

Participants

Universities

D. Tondeur (coordinator)	CNRS-ENSIC, Nancy
F. Meunier	CNRS-LIMSI, Orsay
A. Rodrigues	Universidade do Porto
G. Calleja	Universidad Complutense, Madrid
B. Crittenden	University of Bath
A. Mersmann	Tech. Universität München
G. Baron	Vrije Universiteit Brussels

Research Laboratories

E. McDonald	Harwell Laboratory
A. Deschamps	Institut Français du Pétrole
E. Garcin	Rhône-Poulenc Recherches
B. Ter Meulen	TNO

WORKING GROUP ON "MELT CRYSTALLIZATION"

Justification

All participants agreed that the need for ultrapure organic compounds like fine chemicals and intermediates is strongly increasing. The energy consumption is rather high, if ultrapurity should be achieved with common methods. The same is true for the separation of the chemical mass products, if e.g. the boiling points are close together. Melt crystallization is an energy and cost efficient unit operation which could solve many separation and purification problems. Melt crystallization has the advantages of

- low temperature level
- lower energy for the phase transitions compared to liquid-vapour processes (about 1/4 to 1/3)
- prevention of thermal decomposition
- high selectivities (reduction of necessary stages that means reduction of energy costs)
- smaller size of apparatus (less volume required for solids than for vapour phases)
- high environmental safety due to the absence of the vapour phase.

In Europe the solid layer type of melt crystallization processes dominate the market as far as the number of sold units is concerned. The solid layer technology features however, only a small interface between crystals and melt which leads to high driving forces in order to achieve the necessary yields.

A suspension type of melt crystallization process is in terms of sold units in Europe (and also in Japan there are almost no exceptions) only available in separate pieces of equipment for the crystallization, the washing and the separation (e.g. filtering or centrifuging) of the crystals from the remaining melt. The creation of one piece of equipment which can handle all operations in it could give the whole technique of melt crystallization a dramatic push forward.

Topic areas with further need of R&D

One important operation which has to be further investigated is ultrapurification or separation of organic compounds in one single crystallization operation (unit) which could be done with the suspension growth techniques. This technique features a very high solid-liquid interface for the mass transfer. There are already some demonstrations on a technical scale however in spite of all the theoretical advantages they are not compatible with the crystal layer type of apparatus or the suspension type of processes in a number of pieces of equipments for the different operations. The one piece suspension type process needs further optimization, and it needs guidelines for the selection of industrial equipment. The increase in efficiency could lay in improved additional steps like sweating (a particle melting), recrystallization and washing within the single apparatus. The sweating process, a partial melting, seems to be a promising post treatment of crystals with the aim of a further separation or purification. This is especially of importance if the energy use is monitored. A remelting of the crystals is almost always a necessary step in a process and therefore the sweating can be conducted without additional energy input. The archived purification can in many cases reach the same degree as one crystallization step. Other topics are:

- High recovery of material by means of an improved (better) process integrated (not by means of a separate apparatus) solid-liquid separation within the one apparatus.
- A good control of crystal size distributions and control of the nucleation process which would help a good solid-liquid separation and a good sweating operation.
- Improvement in the design rules and the selection methods for application fields of melt

crystallization processes for the commercial use.
- Improvement in understanding of the heat and mass transfer and the hydrodynamics involved in such a one unit processes.
- Guidelines for the selection of commercial and industrial equipment.

All those topics were raised by the industrial representatives who were involved in the discussions.

<u>**Recommended framework programme**</u>

- **Title**
  Increasing the efficiency of suspension processes in melt crystallization by improving the steps of further purification and separation of organic chemical by means of crystal-melt separation.

- Among the participants five research groups of four countries are interested. These are the groups around:

  <u>**Participants**</u>

Dr Ulrich (Coordinator)	Univ. Bremen, D
Dr Arkenbout	TNO, NL

  <u>**Information by mail**</u>

Prof Benemma	Univ. Nijmegen, NL
Prof Garside	UMIST, GB
Prof Klein	Univ. Lyon, F

- Among the participants or by notice prior to the meeting six companies are so far interested in sponsoring such a project. Not all agreed however that their names could be given here at this point:

  Rhône Poulenc, F
  AMOCO Belgium, B
  Montedipe, I
  BASF, D
  ..., NL
  ..., GB.

The group thinks that such a project should have up to ten contributing companies or research organizations.

WORKING GROUP ON "GLASS MAKING AND CERAMIC FURNACES, CEMENT KILNS AND BAKING OVENS

General conclusions

The Group came to the following general conclusions:

1. The R&D project should derive full benefit from the work carried out in the field of computational fluid dynamics. The codes should be used as powerful tools, but the new project should not propose further developments of general mathematical modelling.

2. The R&D project should be more closely related to industrial experience and derive full benefit from experiments on actual full-scale equipment.

3. The furnace is a part of a whole system, whose parts are intimately interrelated and there is a need for studying all the furnace environment and auxiliary equipment, especially if these equipment have a strong feedback influence on furnace behaviour.

Consequently, in order to propose subtopics, the group decided that the approach should be defined from industrial sectors. These sectors are those characterized by a high energy consumption and an important pollutant rejection.

The following sectors have been selected:

- 1°) the cement industry
- 2°) the glass-making industry
- 3°) ceramics
- 4°) bakery products.

The group also stated that the needs are almost the same whatever particular sector is considered. Indeed, three types of action are proposed in each sector:

a) Modelling of the whole system or of parts of the system which have not been considered yet, but which may have a marked influence on furnace operation. Applications of technologies which received a general interest in the past are to be studied in relation to furnace operation. For instance: new low NOx burner, whose performance may strongly depend on the type of application, implementation of new recuperators and of new heat recovery processes.

b) There is an acute need for validation of existing models by careful measurements on actual processes. This is the only way to have confidence in these models.

c) New control strategies, based on the mathematical models previously developed, are to be settled.

In short, the group selected four sectors and three sorts of actions. It obtained in this way a double-entry table in which specific actions were defined in each box. Numbers appearing in the table refer to the following paragraphs.

Cement industry

In the cement industry, the following potential topics have been defined:

1) Development and validation of mathematical models of the cyclone/preheater system.

2) Burnout and NOx formation when running a precalciner in reducing conditions.

3) Development and validation of mathematical modelling of flames including interaction with the process load.

No current need has been identified for new control strategies since expert systems are already widely used in the cement industry.

Glass-making furnaces

For the glass-making industry, the following topics have been identified:

1) Modelling of the batch melting region.

2) Feasibility study of a fluidized bed regenerator specially designed for the glass making furnace operation.

3) Use of low NOx burners typically designed for glass-making furnaces.

4) Modelling of regenerator operation.

5) Validation of models on actual furnaces.

6) Development of an advanced on-line control strategy using simple models for each part of the system, these models being generated by a 3-D CFD model.

Ceramics

For the ceramic industry, batch and continuous (tunnel) furnaces are to be considered. The following topics have been selected:

1) In tunnel kilns, associated with batch or tunnel dryers, modelling of phenomena such as combustion, radiation and convection in preheating, firing and cooling zones of the kiln, related to aspects such as product quality, productivity, air inleakages and energy consumption. Detailed modelling of flow through the stackings as well as macro-type system modelling should be performed.
Interaction of the furnace and dryers in order to reduce the overall energy consumption.

2) Use of new burner designs, such as regenerative burners, low NOx burners, ...

3) Validation of previously developed models in order to improve temperature uniformity in a cross section (tunnel oven) and thus to decrease the proportion of rejects.

4) Use of on-line control strategies based on an observer, which is a knowledge-based model, sufficiently simplified so as to operate on-line, whose coefficients may be tuned by on-line identification.

Bakery

In the bakery production, the following needs have been detected:

1) Additional modelling of the microstructure of bread formation in order to derive chemical and physical parameters of the bread required for the previously developed models.

2) Additional modelling of the heat exchanging system.

3) Validation of mathematical models by measurements on batch and continuous furnaces in the baking process of bread, biscuits and cakes.

4) Development of advanced control strategies taking into account product quality during the whole baking process.

__Potential savings__

The following potential savings have been evaluated:

- Cement: 5% of energy consumption (which represents 40% of the production cost).
- Glass: 5% of energy consumption (20% of the production cost).
- Ceramics: 20% of energy consumption (as an average: 20% of the production cost).
- Bakery: 30% of energy consumption (low % of the production costs).

Many industries, research centres and universities are ready to cooperate in projects defined above.

__Participants__

Prof Meunier, FP Mons
(Coordinator)
Prof Carvalho, IST Lisbon
Mr Gilbert, British Glass
Mr Jakob, ATZ-EVUS
Prof Henriette, FP Mons
Mr Brichart, INV
Dr Lowes, Blue Circle Ind. PLC
Dr El Khouri, Ecole des Mines de Paris
Ir Devries, TNO

Part-time:
Prof Durst, Univ. Erlangen
Prof Lockwood, Imperial College
Prof Markatos, NTU Athens

WORKING GROUP ON "DRYERS"

Introduction

There is a substantial need of improved energy efficiency in drying processes. Drying accounts for at least 10% of the energy consumption of the chemical industry. Because 90% of current industrial dryers are of the convection type and are using hot air as drying medium, the heat is wasted as a gas stream of about 80°C of temperature. The hot off-gas is the carrier of evaporated liquids. Those might be water vapour or organic solvents which are very often pollutants to the environment and need additional off-gas scrubbing equipment. According to the products which need drying, there is a wide variety of types of drier on the market. In order to improve their energy efficiency or to develop new drying processes several aspects have to be considered: These are economic and environmental aspects as well as the quality of the products which has to be accepted by the market or simply by the next step in the process after the dryer. Significant improvements in energy efficiency of dryers may be realised by the incorporation of appropriate monitoring and control strategies. Such strategies require the on-line measurement of variables, such as material moisture content, for which two possibilities exist: (a) direct measurement using appropriate sensors, and (b) estimation using model based state estimation techniques. Several topics are suggested by the working group:

Types of energy consuming convective drying processes

Convection drying is the most common process. Energy savings are desirable because of the large volume flow of heated gas which is used as a carrier for heat and moisture. The gas is very often released to the environment at elevated temperatures and polluted by solvents and dust which are set free by the drying process itself.

Topics of desired research work are:

- Liquid films or liquid containing suspensions of fine solid particles as well as polymers are used for coatings or in the paper industries and in many large capacity production processes. The geometrical shape of thin liquid layers of fluids with different rheological behaviour on solid surfaces of different materials and shape has to be investigated. In order to minimize the material consumption, the energy flow and the emission of vapour, the liquid layer of undried material has to be as thin and uniform as possible.

- Concentrations of evaporating solvents are normally very low in the off-gas-flow. Research on increased concentrations of the evaporating components in the gaseous phase, up to the saturation point, will reduce energy costs in solvent recovery and solvent recycling. The main emphasis should be concentrated on evaporating of multi-component liquid mixtures used as solvents.

- Research on combinations of different types of applied heat flow to the product surface. The combination of radiation type heat sources with contact or convective drying should be investigated in order to minimize energy consumption. The new concepts should result in more uniform heat flux and temperature fields.

- Many liquid products are sprayed in liquid form in order to increase their surface because of the drying process. Other liquid suspensions are put into their final geometrical shape by spraying and are later solidified by drying. Research on the spray drying process is still desirable in order to gain energy savings by lowering gas outlet temperatures. This is because of better understanding of heat and mass transfer within the drying multiphase system. The application of new optical and modern sensor systems applicable for on-line measurement to production facilities may lead to better physical modelling of the dispersion of droplets encountered in the sprays.

- Solid particles that emerge from some solid-liquid process steps like crystallization or precipitation might be wet. Topic of desired research work for energy reduction is the improved heat transfer to the material surfaces by application of additional dielectric heating. An improved understanding of the superposition process of dielectric, convective and contact heat flux should lead to a reduction in gas flow and outlet temperature of drying processes in the ceramics and building materials industry.

Process integration and computer modelling by numerical methods

Selection, process design, optimization, and control of industrial dryers require the development of reliable sensors and models and robust methodologies. This requirement is particularly important in drying of agricultural products and products of high qualities and quantities, due to the variation of product characteristics and drying conditions. Topics of desired research work are:

- Computer simulation of the special drying processes which are under experimental investigation of this programme. Predictions of the energy consumption of the whole production processes should include waste heat recovery steps. The optimization by the use of energy and process integration techniques should also consider the quality of the product and the impact on environment by reduced pollution and by the reduction of primary energy consumption of the overall production process.

- Research on the development of methods for on-line estimation of the material moisture content in the products using model based state estimation techniques. These activities should support the model development activities of other experimental projects. Research on the development of appropriate control strategies using new sensor systems.

- Develop a computer based system for selection of appropriate dryer types for agricultural products.

Participants

Prof D. Mewes (Coordinator)	University of Hannover, D
J. Adnot	Ecole des Mines de Paris, F
L. Eriksson	Swedish Pulp and Paper, S
A. J. Dalhuijsen	TNO Inst. of applied Physics, NL
P. van Dijck	Monsanto Technical Centre Europe, B
Prof P. Hutchinson	Cranfield Institute of Technology, GB
F. van Overmeire	Centexbel, B
Dr Ch. Papadopoulos	CRES, GR
Dr I. C. Pereira	Inst. Superior Tecnico, P
Dr I. M. Sorensen	Niro Atomizers, DK

WORKING GROUP ON "REFRIGERATION (REPLACEMENT OF CFCs)"

Energy Conservation and Refrigeration

In refrigeration, many possibilities still exist for energy conservation; this applies to both the production of refrigeration (cycle efficiency) and the use of refrigeration.

The workshop mentioned such diverse examples as:

- improved liquid distribution in evaporators;
- advanced defrost;
- enhanced heat transfer in heat exchangers;
- non-azeotropic mixtures;
- inverter driven compressors for local modulation.

The main current issue in refrigeration however concerns the replacement of CFCs by environmentally acceptable refrigerants or refrigeration cycles. Although the CFC issue is essentially environmental, energy use plays a key role in the selection of suitable alternatives.

It was felt therefore that "future R&D" should focus on replacement of CFCs. Nevertheless, it was stressed that energy conservation in refrigeration as such, should receive considerable attention in later phases of the JOULE programme because of the electricity saving consequences and the consequent effect on CO_2 emissions.

Current situation regarding CFC replacement

Apart from NH_3, currently "accepted" refrigerants such as HCFC-22, 123; HFC-134a either still contribute to the destruction of the ozone layer or act as a green-house gas. Additionally, HCFC-22 is under serious threat of regulation because of its Chlorine content and the tightening of Montreal Protocol and EC action.

As more refrigerants become regulated, the refrigeration industry will be left without alternatives with the same safety and reliability characteristics as current CFCs.

This difficulty is compounded by outstanding technical uncertainties about the real long term behaviour of the new refrigerants. It is therefore concluded that, although some alternative refrigerants are now becoming available, there is a strong need to increase the range of alternatives, either as alternative fluids for vapour compression, or for alternative cycles.

R&D needs

Increased range of refrigerants

Several environmentally acceptable fluids are available which show excellent thermodynamic properties but are unfortunately flammable and/or toxic (NH_3, R 152a, DME, propane, butane) Additionally, these is the problem of extending the operating range to higher and lower evaporating temperatures. Worldwide there is an increase interest in investigating the possibilities of using (or extending the use of) these fluids for refrigeration.
Research topics in this area are:

- Safety aspects of flammable refrigerants

    * technology to reduce the refrigerant charge;
    * addition of odour for early leak detection or alarm;
    * use of (non) azeotropic mixtures to reduce the flammability.

- Search for suitable lubricants

    * oil/refrigerant thermodynamics;
    * lubricity.

- Investigation of system performance

    * energy use
    * long term behaviour.

Alternative cycles

Several "old" and "new" alternative (i.e. alternative to vapour compression) refrigeration cycles are currently receiving increasing interest.
Energy use and economics are critical issues but recent studies expect that with the incorporation of modern technology many improvements can be realized. Such factors are particularly important given the fact that refrigeration and air conditioning represent 10% of total world energy demand.

It was felt that at this moment a better understanding is needed of the real advantages and disadvantages of the various cycles. An exception was made for the open air (expansion) cycle; this cycle is expected to have specific advantages for some specific applications such as refrigeration of large cool stores. For this cycle a more detailed study could already be carried out.

R&D needs are thus:

- feasibility assessments of alternative cycles, such as:

    * classical absorption/adsorption
    * advanced (e.g. metal hydride) adsorption
    * expansion cycles ("Brayton", "Joule")
    * compression/absorption.

- detailed technical assessments of open air cycle for specific applications.

Conclusion

In conclusion, it is recommended that research in the refrigeration area be channelled in two main directions.

- increasing the range of available refrigerants to better match operating range and performance specifications including the need to cope with higher and lower evaporating temperatures

- investigation of alternative cycles with the objective of improving performance and the range of applications.

It should be stressed that the interpretations of these definitions should be more general than specific as there is a close interaction between the environmental, application, performance and operating range characteristics which will entail a flexible working approach and cooperation between industry and the research laboratories.

Participants

Ir P. E. J. Vermeulen, TNO Division of Technology for Society
(Coordinator)
K. J. Cornwell, Heriot Watt University
P. Dewin, Ecole des Mines de Paris
P. E. Farrant, National Engineering Laboratory
Prof M. Groll, Universität Stuttgart
Dr Ing U. Hesse, Forschungszentrum für Kältetechnik und Wärmepumpen GmbH
Ir G. Heyen, Institut de Chimie
E. Merlin, AFME
Prof J. T. Mc Mullan, University of Ulster
W.E. Whitman, Leatherhead Food R.A.

WORKING GROUP ON "ENERGY AND THE ENVIRONMENT"

Introduction

The working group discussed the range of activities which could be included in a framework programme to examine the links and trade-offs between energy efficiency and environmental protection. Topics of interest included the energy consequences of higher levels of gaseous and li!quid effluent treatment, the effect on energy efficiency as a result of increased recycling or raw material substitution, and the impact of the choice of fuels. There appeared to be five areas of study:

Methodology

This section would look at the extent to which existing energy and process integration techniques fail when environmental constraints are included within them. Other attempts at producing such methodologies need to be examined, as do methods and techniques for integrating energy efficiency consequences in environmental impact analyses. Efforts need to be made to interface with any other groups who may have broadly similar objectives.

Data and data bases

This involves assembling information to enable engineers to answer specific environmental questions about their processes within the context of their impact on the energy efficiency of the plant. This could provide information on:

- typical energy and environmental consequences of unit operations, e.g. heat usage, waste arising, uncontrolled dispersion of containments, etc.

- the environmental impact of pollutants, and the energy penalties associated with reducing emissions;

- the consequences of fuel switching and energy efficiency on combustion related pollution, such as SO_x, NO_x, CO_2, CO and unburnt fuel;

- the sensitivity of processes to proposed changes in legislation, particularly the introduction of energy penalties such as carbon taxes or pollution credits, which are being considered by some countries.

It was recognised that many such databases exist. The need in this study is to identify the mission pieces of information, and to structure the available data in readily accessible form.

Quantification of environmental consequences

There was considerable discussion of the use of energy as a means of assessing energy and environmental trade-offs. While it was felt that this could shed only a small light on the subject, it seemed to be a useful starting point. This field represented the greatest challenge, and provided the opportunity for original thinkers to develop concepts of environmental thermodynamics or analogies to pinch technology. Such methods should be capable of evaluating not only thermal pollution but also material emissions, such as dusts, acid gases (e.g. Cl_2, SO_3, etc.).

Modelling

There was a need to examine existing optimisation model, particularly multiple criteria optimisation and dynamic simulation techniques, to establish if they could offer anything new in this field. It was felt necessary for the programme to stimulate the assembly and where necessary, the production of models from unit operations used for environmental control. Some which were mentioned included catalytic oxidation, gas scrubbing (dust and trace gas removal), all aspects of incineration, anaerobic digestion, and subsequently, by one of the other groups, the interaction between combustion and heat exchanger fouling.

Applications

It would be important to develop such ideas in close co-operation with industry, using real case study data to test and validate methods and tools. Given the fuzziness of the current state of thinking, it was essential and that some expertise should be built up by actually trying to analyse processes in such a way that energy and environmental considerations were simultaneously considered. This learning process would prove very valuable, and would feed into other areas as the case studies progressed. It was felt important to consider at least two case studies in different industrial sectors. Pulp and paper, and chemicals were two obvious areas for study. However, other areas such as petroleum refining, tyre pyrolysis, pharmaceuticals, etc., were also worthy of consideration.

Participants

Dr R. W. K. Allen (Coordinator)	AEA Industrial Technology, UK
Mr F. Maréchal	LASSC, University of Liège, B
Mr A. Kilakos	University of Liège, B
Mr A. Kontopoulos	University of Liège, B
Prof R. Jottrand	Université Libre de Bruxelles, B
Dr W. Lenz	BASF, D
Prof E. Muratore	Centre Technique du Papier, F
Dr D. Marchio	Ecole des Mines, F
Mme N. Besson	ELF Aquitaine, F
Mr I. Boukis	CRES, GR
Mr G. J. Prokopakis	SPEC Process Services SA, GR
Prof W. van Gool	Rijksuniversiteit Utrecht, NL
Dr C. Costa	University of Porto, P
Miss F. Dendy	Institution of Chemical Engineers, UK
Prof P. Hutchinson	Cranfield Institute of Technology, UK
Mr P. M. M. Brown	Linnhoff March Ltd., UK
Dr M. E. Gill	WS Atkins Engineering Sciences Ltd, UK

WORKING GROUP ON "ADVANCED SENSORS FOR PROCESS CONTROL IN THE PROCESS INDUSTRY"

Introduction

The need for sensors in the process industry is self apparent. The information the sensors provide is of relevance to control the process. The target is to optimize energy consumption and reduce environmental problems.

Currently, sensors are available for a number of process industries such as Chemical, Glass, Moulding, Air Conditioning, Food, etc. The principal applications of sensors in the process industries are for process and environment monitoring and control.

However, new measuring sensors are needed not only to take into account high pressure, explosive or agressive environments due to particular chemical components, but also to take into account some special requirements put forward by the process industries such as moisture content of products, high temperature in harsh environments, mass flow rates of gas-solid and other multiphase flows.

Sensors are usually developed by electrical engineers or by physicists who often, do not take into account the above mentioned requirements. The working group felt that this shortcoming of existing sensors should be removed by a special development programme within JOULE.

There are similar needs in the other working groups and the project on advanced sensors will try to address some of these needs.

Taking all this into account, the working group proposes the following areas of activity:

Applications of sensors to process control

It is recommended that R&D be carried out in order to demonstrate how sensors could be used for control purposes in fields such as:

- Mulltiphase reactors
- Two phase separators
- NOx controlled combustion
- Drying
- Multiphase heat exchangers
- Extrusion and coating.

The emphasis on sensor development in this work programme should be on direct energy reduction rather than the control of product properties.

New Sensors

The working group felt that particular emphasis should be given to sensor developments for mass and flow rate measurements.

In addition, property measurement should be improved and appropriate sensors developed. For example, humidity measurements in harsh environments or of the paper when it enters the drying process.

Humidity in any exhaust gas is again a problem that deters any sensor developer.

The people from industry expressed an interest, in advanced sensor development because of the specific requirements for sensors.

Properties that should get attention of the developers are on line measurements of viscosity for strongly non-Newtonian fluids. Selective measurements of concentrations of chemical species are also needed. The route to multiple sensor detection systems for chemical species should be explored, in order to avoid non coherent information as provided by individual sensors.

Moreover people in the process industry need to be confident in the measurements. This brings in the concept of intelligent sensors which would be able to perform function and accuracy checks of the measurement provided.

The working group also felt that the sensor development project should help to meet needs in industry, so close collaboration with industry is essential.

<u>Participants</u>

J.M. Ferreira de Jesus (Coordinator)	INTERG
F. Durst	LS TM-Erlangen
J. P. Martin	CRN-Chatenay
G. Palazzi	ENEA
G. Casamatta	ENSIGAC-LAC-CNRS-TOULOUSE

WORKING GROUP ON "CATALYTIC COMBUSTION"

Introduction

Catalytic combustion has two main advantages over conventional flames:

1. It makes a better controlled reaction possible and
2. it greatly reduces polluting emissions.

A better controlled reaction makes it possible to

a. intensify a complete process so that energy, which is lost in going to the next process unit, can be conserved,
b. integrate several reactors in one so that it is possible to substantially reduce construction costs,
c. optimize process conditions with respect to energy conservation.

The know-how of catalytic combustion is not generally available due to the high costs of catalysts. This knowledge is well protected by the large companies who put a lot of effort and money into the development. These companies are mainly American and Japanese. It was generally agreed that Europe is behind these countries in the catalytic combustion field.

A major problem for the introduction of catalytic combustion is the necessity for tailored designs of reactors for each application due to the fact that combustion is exothermic and run-aways can easily occur. However, more generic applications in the area of, e.g. methane combustion, exists.

Current situation

In Europe there is relatively little research in the field of catalytic combustion and it is split up in small parts. The main developments remain in the field of the motor-industry and in downstream pollution control in the process industries.

Recommended future R&D

Fundamental research should be done in the following areas:

- Catalysts: oxidation catalysts are mainly based on platinum and rhodium. The utilization of other metals is needed.
- Fouling: Oxidation catalysts are subject to deactivation from polluting fraction in fuels like sulphur. More robustness is needed.
- Undesired side reactions. Undesired products (e.g. Ammonia) occur during reaction. Their formation and prevention should be studied.
- Characterization. The performance of catalysts must be very well determined and understood.

Developments are needed in the following fields.

- Coating of metal surfaces with catalyst for direct contact between catalyst and reactor:
  a. metal - ceramic connection,
  b. metal surface modification (e.g. holes),
- Integration of the catalyst into a reactor for heat removal (exothermic reactions) during combustion.

- Reactor design for catalytic combustors:
    a. fluidized beds,
    b. heat exchangers with catalytic active surfaces,
    c. sinter metal reactors,
    d. honeycomb monoliths,
    e. engines and turbines,
    f. radiation panels,
    g. membrane reactors.
- Process conditions:
    a. hot spots,
    b. fuel slip,
    c. heat transfer:
        - conductance
        - convection
        - radiation
- Modelling to integrate the several aspects of design and process conditions.

Conclusions

- For Europe it is important to put a lot of effort into trying to establish cooperation between the several (small) groups that already work on catalytic combustion and to increase the amount of work.
- There is still a lot of fundamental work to be done before the subject is satisfactorily understood.
- The implementation and introduction of catalytic combustion required the close cooperation of catalyst chemists and process technologists.

Participants

Ir. A. J. M. van Wingerden, VEG-Gasinstituut (NL)
(Coordinator)
Dr W. Glazs, DSM Research, Sections Industrial Catalyst Research (NL)
Dr Jorgensen, AEA Industrial Technology, Harwell (UK)
Mr S. Kolaczkowski, University of Bath (UK)
Mr B. Pitt, Rolls Royce, Industrial and Marine (UK)
Prof D. A. Reay, David Reay & Associates (UK).

WORKING GROUP ON "EFFICIENT USE OF ELECTRICITY"

Energy use patterns in industry in most EC member countries show different trends: whereas fuel and heat consumption stagnated or even fell during the last 15 years, industrial electricity consumption grew by more than 30%. Although there are good reasons for these different trends (e.g. increased application of electricity-using technologies, emission control technologies, further automation), one may question whether the improvement of electricity efficiency has in the past received the same attention as that of fuel efficiency.

The improvement of electricity efficiency is of increasing importance, not only because electricity cost surmounts the fuel cost in industry in most EC member countries since the last few years, but also because electricity use is of great environmental importance given the fact of low transformation efficiency (between 35 and 42%) and of high emissions of NO_x, SO_2 and CO_2 of fossil fuel based power generation.

Some of the end-use sectors where electricity is applied were excluded in the discussion, because they were treated in other working groups or other research programmes of the CEC (e.g. steel production, superconductivity). Given these exclusions, the discussion about future R&D opportunities concentrated on the improvement or substitution of electrothermal processes (see table 1) and of electricity-using components and their process applications.

Table 1: electrothermal processes - major products and technologies

- primary aluminium
- ferro-alloys
- phosphorus, other inorganics
- hardening of metallic surfaces and plastics
- inductive heating
- infrared heating and drying
- dielectric (HF-) heating

Major potentials of efficient electricity use and electricity savings were identified in the fields as follows:

<u>Electrothermal processes</u>

- Primary aluminium: development of permanent anodes, wetted cathodes and better control techniques as improvements of the existing process which could eventually be substituted by carbothermic reduction of ore or alumina in the long term.
- Partial substitution of electrothermal processes by more efficient electrical processes.
- Important improvements of existing processes and components are:
  - improvement of homogeneity in batch processes (ferro-alloys and glass) to improve product quality and reduce heat losses,
  - generator and inductor improvements (use of transistors, MOS and GTO components),
  - process simulation, control and optimisation of
    - infrared drying (paper, textiles, food, or metals)
    - RF moisture profiling and microwave drying, curing and polymerisation.

This subject comes within the broader aim of generic R&D in process simulation and control.

Electricity-using components and their process applications

The possibilities for improving electricity efficiency by improving components and their process applications are multifold and have to be given priority in order to select important R&D projects.

- Electric motors: development of high frequency motors which could lead to important improvements for smaller motors (< 10 kW) in view of today's rather low efficiencies. The same improvement can be expected from small generators (< 10 kW) which may become important in motor based cogeneration modules in the future.
- Improved power electronics; which are important for controlling electric motors and electricity generation by wind turbines or photovoltaïcs in the future. The substitution of mechanical flow control by power electronics control in gaseous media can also contribute to lessening electricity consumption.
- The thermodynamic improvement of pumps, ventilators and compressors, where still exist considerable potentials for improvement but which is not easy to realize given the lack of knowledge of the small and medium-sized manufacturers of these components.
- Surface active substances may reduce the resistance of fluids in pipes (e.g. district heat), or the optimisation of concentrations of transported liquids or gases may decrease power which is needed for transportation.
- Basic research on the physics of the grinding of solid materials (e.g. cement, ceramics and ores) and fibre development for paper production is needed before the electricity efficiency of equipment can be substantially improved or new equipment and systems developed.

Participants of the working group

Dr E. Jochem, FISI
(Coordinator)
D. Bialod, DOPEE
W. C. Dobie, ERDC
L. Eriksson, STFI
Dr J. Ferreiro de Jesus, Instituto Superior Técnico
G. Tomassetti, ENEA.

LIST OF PARTICIPANTS

Belgium

Dr. A. Adjemian
CEC
DG XII
Rue de la Loi 200
B - 1049 Brussels
TEL. (2) 235 74 09
TLX. COMEU B 21877
FAX. 235 80 46

Prof. G. Baron
Vrije Universiteit Brussel
Dienst Chemische Ingenieurs
Techniek en Industriele Scheikunde
Pleinlaan 2
B - 1050 Brussel
TEL. (2) 641 32 50
TLX. 61051 VUBCO B

Prof. Ph. Bourdeau
Director
CEC
DG XII
Rue de la Loi 200
B - 1049 Brussels
TEL. (2) 235 10 70 /235 61 40
TLX. COMEU B 21877
FAX. (2) 236 30 24

Mr. M. Brichard
Institut National du Verre
10 Boulevard Defontaine
B - 6000 Charleroi
TEL. (71) 27 29 11
TLX. 51430 INAVER B
FAX. (71) 33 44 80

Dr. D. Bricknell
R&D Director
Conseil Européen des Fédérations
de l'industrie Chimique - CEFIC
Avenue Louise 250, Bte 71
B - 1050 Bruxelles
TEL. (2) 640 20 95
TLX. 62 444
FAX. (2) 640 19 81

Mr. J.L. Debeys
Hamon-Sobelco
Systèmes Thermiques et Mécaniques
Division Sobelco
Rue Capouillet 50-58
B - 1060 Bruxelles
TEL. (2) 535 13 59
TLX. 21822 B
FAX. (2) 537 00 39

Prof. G. Froment
Rijksuniversiteit Gent
Krijgslaan 281
B - 9000 Gent
TEL. (91) 22 57 15
TLX. 12754 RUGENT
FAX. (91) 21 06 83

Mr. J. Gilbert
C.P.I.V.
Comité Permanent des Industries
du Verre de la CEE
Avenue Louise 89
B - 1050 Bruxelles
TEL. (2) 538 44 46
TLX. 25694 CPIV
FAX. (2) 537 84 69

Mr. Ptacek
CEC
DG XVII
Rue de la Loi 200
B - 1049 Bruxelles
TEL. (2) 235 75 78
TLX. 21877 COMEU B
FAX. (2) 235 01 50

Mr. J. Hanet
Président
Technical Committee CRIET
UCO Bellevue
B - 9218 Gent
TEL. (91) 41 52 35
TLX. 12525 BC. GENT
FAX. (91) 20 50 35

Prof. J.M.E. Henriette
Faculté Polytechnique de Mons
Service de Thermique
Rue de l'Epargne 56
B - 7000 Mons
TEL. (65) 37 44 63
TLX. 57764 UE MONS B
FAX. (65) 37 44 00

Mr. G. Heyen
Université de Liège
Institut de Chimie Appliquée
Sart-Tilman
Bât. 6
B - 4000 Liège
TEL. (41) 56 35 21
TLX. 41397 UNIVLG
FAX. (41) 67 83 56

Mr. G. Hoyaux
CEC
DG XII
Rue de la Loi 200
B - 1049 Brussels
TEL. (2) 235 66 52
TLX. COMEU B 21877
FAX. (2) 236 30 24

Prof. R. Jottrand
Université Libre de Bruxelles
Génie Chimique
Av. Franklin Roosevelt 50
B - 1050 Bruxelles
TEL. (2) 642 29 16
TLX. 23069 UNILIB B
FAX. (2) 642 35 64

Prof. B. Kalitventzeff
Université de Liège
Institut de Chimie Appliquée
Sart-Tilman
Bât. 6
B - 4000 Liège
TEL. (41) 56 35 21
TLX. 41397 UNIVLG
FAX. (41) 56 35 25

Mr. A. Kilakos
Université de Liège
Institut de Chimie Appliquée
Sart-Tilman
Bât. 6
B - 4000 Liège
TEL. (41) 56 35 21
TLX. 41397 UNIVLG
FAX. (41) 67 83 56

Mr. A. Kontopoulos
Université de Liège
Institut de Chimie Appliquée
Sart-Tilman
Bât. 6
B - 4000 Liège
TEL. (41) 56 35 21
TLX. 41397 UNIVLG
FAX. (41) 67 83 56

Dr. J. Kowallik
Director
AKZO België International NV
Marnixlaan 13
B - 1050 Brussels
TEL. (2) 518 04 24
FAX. (2) 518 04 13

Mr. M. Liegeois
Process Engineering Div.
Solvay & Cie
Rue de Ransbeek 310
B - 1120 Bruxelles
TEL. (2) 264 22 54
TLX. 23678
FAX. (2) 264 29 75

Mr. F. Marechal
Université de Liège
Institut de Chimie Appliquée
Sart Tilman B 6
B - 4000 Liège
TEL. (041) 56 35 21
FAX. (041) 56 35 25

Prof. H.L.J. Meunier
Faculté Polytechnique de Mons
Service de Thermique
Rue de l'Epargne 56
B - 7000 Mons
TEL. (65) 37 44 61
TLX. 57764 UE MONS B
FAX. (65) 37 44 00

Dr. P. A. Pilavachi
CEC
DG XII
Rue de la Loi 200
B - 1049 Brussels
TEL. (2) 235 36 67
TLX. COMEU B 21877
FAX. (2) 236 30 24

Ir. P.F.C. Van Dijck
R&D Engineering Services Manager
Monsanto Europe S.A.
Technical Centre Europe
Rue Laid Burniat
B - 1348 Louvain-la-Neuve
TEL. (010) 47 14 32
TLX. 59056
FAX. (010) 45 00 23

Ir. F. Van Overmeire
Centexbel
Grote Steenweg Noord 2
B - 9052 Gent
TEL. (091) 20 41 51
FAX. (091) 20 49 55

Ir. P. Zegers
CEC
DG XII
Rue de la Loi 200
B - 1049 Brussels
TEL. (2) 235 58 45
TLX. COMEU B 21877
FAX. (2) 236 30 24

Germany

Mr. T.U. Bauer
HOECHST AG
Verfahrenstechnik
Postfach 800320
D - 6230 Frankfurt a/Main 80
TEL. (69) 305 42 00
FAX. (69) 30 90 14

Prof. F. Durst
Friedrich-Alexander-Universität
Erlangen-Nürnberg
Lehrstuhl für Strömungsmechanik
Cauerstr. 4
D - 8520 Erlangen
TEL. (9131) 85 95 00/1/2
FAX. (9131) 85 95 03

Prof. M. Groll
Universität Stuttgart
Institut für Kernenergetik & Energiesysteme
IKE
Pfaffenwaldring 31
D - 7000 Stuttgart 80
TEL. (711) 685 24 81 or 24 54
TLX. 7 255 445 univ d
FAX. (711) 685 20 10

Prof. U. Hesse
Universität Hannover
Forschungszentrum für Kältetechnik
und Wärmepumpen
Vahrenwalderstr. 7
D - 3000 Hannover 1
TEL. (511) 35 63 190
FAX. (511) 35 63 100

Mr. G.R. Jakob
ATZ - EVUS
Kropfersrichter Str. 6 - 8
D - 8458 Sulzbach-Rosenberg
TEL. (9661) 60828 or 60687
FAX. (9661) 6889

Dr. E. Jochem
Fraunhofer Institut für Systemtechnik
und Innovationsforschung
Breslauer Straße 48
D - 7500 Karlsruhe 1
TEL. (721) 6809 169
TLX. 7826 308 isi d
FAX. (721) 68 91 52

Dr. W. Lenz
BASF Aktiengesellschaft
Zentralbereich Technische Entwicklung/
Verfahrenstechnik
D - 6700 Ludwigshafen
FAX. (621) 605 65 24

Prof. A. B. Mersmann
Technische Universität München
Lehrstuhl B für Verfahrenstechnik
Postfach 20 24 20
Arcisstraße 21
D - 8000 München 2
TEL. (89) 2105 2070 / 71
TLX. 522 854 tumue d
FAX. (89) 2105 2000

Prof. D. Mewes
Institut für Verfahrenstechnik
Callinstr. 36
D - 3000 Hannover 1
TEL. (511) 762 36 38
TLX. 923868
FAX. (511) 762 30 31

Mr. P. Neumann
Krebsöge Sinterholding GmbH
Postfach 2155
D - 5608 Radevormwald
TEL. (2191) 69 32 38
TLX. 21913831 D
FAX. (2191) 69 32 24

Prof. N. Peters
CEC-Expert
RWTH
Institut für Technische Mechanik
D - 5100 Aachen
TEL. (241) 80 46 16 (home) or 80 46 09
FAX. (241) 20911

Dr. R. Reimert
Lurgi GmbH
Lurgi Allee 5
D - 6000 Frankfurt am Main
TEL. (69) 58 08 32 57
TLX. 41 236-0 lg d
FAX. (69) 58 08 26 28

Mr. S. Rössler
Universität Stuttgart
Inst. für Kernenergetik & Energiesysteme
IKE
Pfaffenwaldring 31
D - 7000 Stuttgart 80
TEL. (711) 685 21 20
TLX. 7 255 445 univ d
FAX. (711) 685 20 10

Mr. M. Sommerfeld
Universität Erlangen-Nürnberg
Lehrstuhl für Strömungsmechanik
Cauerstr. 4
D - 8520 Erlangen
TEL. (9131) 85 95 07
TLX. 629755 TFERL
FAX. (9131) 85 95 03

Dr. J. Ulrich
Universität Bremen
Verfahrenstechnik/FB 4
Postfach 33 04 40
D - 2800 Bremen 33
TEL. (421) 218 26 70
TLX. 242811 uni d
FAX. (421) 218 53 33

Mr. J. Widua
Institut für Verfahrenstechnik
RWTH
Turmstr. 46
D - 5100 Aachen
TEL. (241) 80 54 70
FAX. (241) 40 34 08

Danemark

Dr. J. M. Sørensen
Institut for Kemiteknik
The Technical University of Denmark
DTH 229
DK - 2800 Lyngby
TEL. (42) 88 32 88
FAX. (42) 88 22 58

Spain

Prof. G. Calleja
Complutense University of Madrid
Pabellon de Gobierno
Universidad Complutense
Ciudad Universitaria
E - 28040 Madrid
TEL. (1) 244 57 82
TLX. 22459 E
FAX. (1) 244 57 82

France

Dr. J. Adnot
Ecole des Mines de Paris
Centre d'Energétique
Bld St Michel 60
F - 75272 Paris Cedex 6
TEL. (1) 40 51 91 74
FAX. (1) 43 54 18 98

Mr. A. Bailly
CIAT
Laboratory Manager
Rue J. Falconnier
F - 01350 Culoz
TEL. (79) 42 42 87
TLX. 980 437
FAX. (79) 42 40 13

Mrs. Besson
Elf France
Centre de recherche elf solaize
Chemin du Canal - B.P. 22
F - 69360 Saint Symphorien d'Ozon
TEL. 72 51 81 43
FAX. 72 51 86 51

Mr. Dan Bialod
DOPEE
38, Av. Franklin Roosevelt
F - 77210 Avon
TEL. 607 23404
FAX. 607 23679

Prof. G. Casamatta
E.N.S.I.G.C.
Chemin de la Loge
F - 31078 Toulouse Cedex
TEL. (61) 52 92 41
TLX. 530 171 211
FAX. (61) 55 38 61

Mr. Ph. Dewitte
Ecole des Mines de Paris
60, Boulevard Saint-Michel
F - 75272 Paris Cedex 6
TEL. (1) 40 51 92 49
FAX. (1) 43 54 18 98

Dr. A. Deschamps
Institut Français du pétrole
Head of Separation Dept.
Avenue de Bois-Preau 1-4, BP 311
F - 92506 Rueil Malmaison - Cedex
TEL. (1) 47 52 69 74
TLX. IFP A 20 30 50 F
FAX. (1) 47 52 70 25

Mr. R.C. Dumon
C.E.C.-Expert
28 bis Avenue Mozart
F - 75016 Paris
TEL. (1) 45 27 72 54

Dr. K. El Khoury
Ecole des Mines de Paris
60, Boulevard Saint-Michel
F - 75272 Paris Cedex 6
TEL. (1) 40 51 91 56
FAX. (1) 43 54 18 98

Dr. E. Garcin
Rhône Poulenc Recherches
Centre de Recherches d'Aubervilliers
52, rue de la Haie Coq
F - 93308 Aubervilliers
TEL. (1) 49 37 62 19
TLX. 235 863 F
FAX. (1) 49 37 61 00

Mr. F. Lauro
Chef de Laboratoire
GRETh
CENG 85 X
F - 38041 Grenoble Cedex
TEL. 76 88 35 49
FAX. 76 88 51 61

Prof. P. Le Goff
INPL-CNRS
Institut National Polytechnique de Lorraine
Centre National de la Recherche Scientifique
B.P. 451
F - 54001 Nancy Cedex
TEL. 83 35 21 21
TLX. 960431 F AD NANCY
FAX. 83 32 29 75

Prof. J.P. Martin
Ecole Centrale des Arts et Manufactures
Laboratoire E.M2.C. du CNRS
Grande voie des vignes
F - 92295 Chatenay Malabry Cedex
TEL. (1) 47 02 70 56 / 46 61 33 10
FAX. (1) 47 02 80 35

Mr. C. Marvillet
GRETh
CENG 85 X
F - 38041 Grenoble Cedex
TEL. 76 88 47 88
FAX. 76 88 51 61

Mr. E. Merlin
Agence Française pour la
Maîtrise de l'Energie
27 Rue Louis Vicat
F - 75737 Paris Cedex15
TEL. (1) 47 65 20 71
FAX. (1) 46 45 52 36

Dr. M. J. Messant
Tréfimétaux - TMX
11 bis Rue de l'Hôtel de Ville
F - 92411 Courbevoie Cedex
TEL. (1) 47 89 68 85
TLX. 611005 F TMXCV
FAX. (1) 47 89 69 74

Prof. F. Meunier
Directeur de Recherche
LIMSI - CNRS
B.P. 133
Campus Universitaire
F - 91403 Orsay Cedex
TEL. (1) 69 85 80 56
TLX. 692 166 F
FAX. (1) 69 85 80 88

Mrs. C. Muller
L'Air Liquide
Centre de Recherche Claude Delorme
B. P. 126
F - 78350 Jouy-en-Josas
TEL. (1) 30 67 64 44
FAX. (1) 30 67 64 80

Mr. E. Muratore
Energy Responsible
Centre Technique du Papier
B. P. 7110
F - 38020 Grenoble Cedex
TEL. 76 44 82 36
TLX. 980642 F
FAX. 76 44 71 38

Dr. L.M.L. Pasteur
Business Manager
RHONE POULENC
Avenue d'Alsace 18
F - 92408 Courbevoie
TEL. (1) 47 68 12 07
FAX. (1) 47 68 14 40

Mr. B. Ribier
Agence Française pour la
Maîtrise de l'Energie
27 Rue Louis Vicat
F - 75737 Paris Cedex 15
TEL. (1) 47 65 20 71
FAX. (1) 46 45 52 36

Prof. D. Tondeur
LSGC/CNRS
ENSIC
B.P. 451
1 Rue Grandville 1
F - 54001 Nancy Cedex
TEL. 83 35 21 21
TLX. 960431 F ADNANCY
FAX. 83 32 29 75

Mr. P. Trambouze
Director
Institut Français du Petrole
B.P. 3
F - 69390 Vernaison
TEL. 78 02 20 20
TLX. 350 257
FAX. 78 02 10 51

Mr. R. Vidil
GRETh
CENG 85X
F - 38041 Grenoble Cedex
TEL. (76) 88 33 43
TLX. 320 323
FAX. (76) 88 51 61

Great Britain

Prof. R.W.K. Allen
AEA Industrial Technology
Harwell Laboratory
GB - Oxfordshire OX11 ORA
TEL. (235) 43 28 64
TLX. 83135 ATOMHA G
FAX.(235) 43 25 13

Dr. C.J. Bates
University of Wales
College of Cardiff
School of Engineering
Newport Road
GB - Cardiff CF2 IXH
TEL. (222) 87 42 72
FAX. (222) 87 42 09

Mr. P.M.M. Brown
Linnhoff March Ltd
Tabley Court
Moss Lane
Overtabley
GB - Knutsford WA16 OPL
TEL. (565) 50447
FAX. (565) 50581

Mr. K. Cornwell
Head of Dept Mechanical Eng.
Heriot-Watt University
GB - Edinburgh EH14 4AS
TEL. (31) 449 51 11
TLX. 727 918
FAX. (31) 451 31 29

Dr. B.D. Crittenden
University of Bath
School of Chemical Engineering
Bath
GB - Avon BA2 7AY
TEL. (225) 82 68 26 ext. 5500
TLX. 449097 UOBATH G
FAX. (225) 46 25 08

Ms F.M. Dendy
Technical Director
The Institution of Chemical Engineers
Davis Building
165-171 Railway Terrace
GB - Rugby CV21 3HQ
TEL. (788) 57 82 14
TLX. 311780
FAX. (788) 56 08 33

Mr. W.C. Dobie
ERDC
Electricity Research & Dev. Centre
Capenhurst
GB - Chester CH1 6ES
TEL. (51) 339 4181
TLX. 627124 Reselec G
FAX. (51) 357 1581

Mr. P.E. Farrant
National Engineering Laboratory
East Kilbride
GB - Glasgow G75 OQU
TEL. (3552) 72535
TLX. 777888
FAX. (3552) 63398

Dr. M.E. Gill
W.S. Atkins Engineering Sciences Ltd
Woodcote Grove
Ashley Road
GB - Epsom, Surrey KT18 5BW
TEL. (372) 72 61 40
TLX. 266701 (Atkins G)
FAX. (372) 74 00 55

Dr. L.E. Haseler
HTFS
AEA Technology
Heat Transfer, Fluid Flow Service
B 392.7 Harwell Laboratory
GB - Oxfordshire OX0N ORA
TEL. (235) 82 11 11
FAX. (235) 83 19 81

Dr. J.E. Hesselgreaves
National Engineering Laboratory
East Kilbride
GB - Glasgow G75 OQU
TEL. (3552) 72852
FAX. (3552) 63398

Dr. P.D. Hills
I.C.I. PLC
Brunner House
P.O. Box 7
GB - Winnington, Northwich CW8 4DJ
TEL. (606) 70 48 97
TLX. 629655 ICIMOH G
FAX. (606) 75885

Prof. P. Hutchinson
Cranfield Intitute of Technology
School of Mechanical Engineering
Cranfield Institute of Technology
Cranfield
GB - Bedford MK43 0AL
TEL. (234) 75 27 11
TLX. 825072
FAX. (234) 75 07 28

Dr. J.D. Isdale
National Engineering Laboratory
East Kilbride
GB - Glasgow G75 0QU
TEL. (3552) 20222
TLX. 777888
FAX. (3552) 63398

Dr. N. Jorgensen
AEA Technology
Materials Chemistry Department
B429 Harwell Laboratory
Didcot
GB - Oxfordshire OX11 0RA
TEL. (235) 43 28 96
TLX. 83135 ATOMHA G
FAX. (235) 43 22 78

Mr. P. Kew
Assistant Director
Energy Technology Unit
Dept. of Mechanical Eng.
Heriot-Watt University
GB - Edinburgh EH14 4AS
TEL. (31) 449 51 11
TLX. 727 918
FAX. (31) 451 31 29

Dr. S.T. Kolaczhowski
University of Bath
School of Chemical Engineering
Claverton Down
GB - Bath BA2 7AY
TEL. (225) 82 68 26
TLX. 449097
FAX. (225) 46 25 08 (group 3)

Prof. F.C. Lockwood
Imperial College of Science,
Technology and Medicine
Department of Mechanical Engineering
Exhibition Road
GB - London SW7 2BX
TEL. (71) 589 51 11 ext. 6213/4
TLX. 929484 G
FAX. (71) 823 88 45

Dr. T.M. Lowes
Blue Circle Industries PLC
Technical Services Division
305 London Road
GB - Greenhithe, Kent DA9 9JQ
TEL. (322) 84 22 44
TLX. 27314/896335
FAX. (322) 84 22 66

Dr. E.K. MacDonald
AEA Industrial Technology
Environmental & Process Engineering Dept
B488T6 Harwell Laboratory
GB - Oxfordshire OX11 ORA
TEL. (235) 43 29 17
TLX. 83135 ATOMHA - G
FAX. (235) 43 23 13

Prof. J.T. McMullan
Univeristy of Ulster
Centre for Energy Research
Cromore Road
GB - Corelaine, Co. Londonderry BT52 1SA
TEL. (265) 44141 Ext. 4477
TLX. 32693 UCDEI
FAX. (265) 40900

Mr. A.C. Mercer
ETSU
Energy Technology Support Unit
B156 Harwell Laboratory
GB - Oxfordshire OX11 ORA
TEL. (235) 43 35 68
TLX. 83135 ATOMHA G
FAX. (235) 43 29 23

Dr. M. Patel
Thames Polytechnic
Centre for Numerical Modelling
Wellington Street
GB - Woolwich, London SE18 6PF
TEL. (81) 316 87 32
FAX. (81) 855 40 33

Mr. E.A. Petela
Linnhoff March Ltd
Tabley Court
Moss Lane
Overtabley
GB - Knutsford WA16 OPL
TEL. (565) 50447
FAX. (565) 50581

Mr. B.G. Pitt
Senior Project Planning Engineer
Engineering Planning Dept.
Rolls-Royce Plc
Ansty
GB - Coventry CV7 9JR
TEL. (203) 62 43 29

Dr. A.M. Pritchard
AEA Technology
B 393
GB - Oxfordshire OX11 ORA
TEL. (235) 43 42 43 / 43 28 41
TLX. 83135 ATOMHA G
FAX. (235) 43 26 20

Dr. C. Ramshaw
ICI PLC
Research and Technology Department
Process Technology Group
P.O. Box 8, The Heath
GB - Runcorn Cheshire WA7 4QE
TEL. (928) 51 13 63/ 51 15 24
TLX. 629655 ICIMOH G
FAX. (928) 58 11 78

Prof. D.A. Reay
C.E.C.-Expert
David Reay & Associates
PO Box 25 - Whitley Bay
GB - Tyne and Wear NE26 1QT
TEL. (91) 251 29 85
FAX. (91) 252 22 29

Dr. M.J. Tierney
CFDS, AEA Technology
Harwell Laboratory
GB - Didcot, Oxfordshire OX11 0RA
TEL. (235) 43 28 22
FAX. (235) 43 29 89

Mr. W.E. Whitman
Leatherhead Food RA
Randalls Road
GB - Leatherhead Syrrey KT22 7RY
TEL. (372) 37 67 61
TLX. 929846
FAX. (372) 38 62 28

Greece

Mr. I. Boukis
CRES
Centre for Renewable Energy Sources
Rue Frati, 6 - Fousa
GR - 19400 Koropi Attikis
TEL. 30 1 - 662 64 60/2
FAX. 30 1 - 662 64 62

Prof. A.J. Karabelas
Chemical Process Engineering
Research Institute and Dept of
Chemical Engineering
14 Paraskevopoulou Street - P.O. Box 1517
GR - 540 06 Thessaloniki
TEL. (31) 99 15 43
TLX. 410545
FAX. (31) 85 61 21

Dr. M. Karagiorgas
Interklima Hellas SA
Manufacturers & Distributors
of HVAC Equipment
17°km Av. Spaton
GR - 190 04 Spata
TEL. (01) 66 12 767
TLX. 223120 VEC GR
FAX. (01) 663 41 21

Prof. N.C. Markatos
Head of Dept of Chemical Engineering
National Technical University of Athens
Zografou University Campus
Heroon Polytechniou Street 9
GR - 15773 Athens
TEL. (1) 772 43 23 / 770 98 61
FAX. (1) 770 09 89

Dr. Ch. Papadopoulos
CRES
Centre for Renewable Energy Sources
Frati, 6 - Fousia
GR - 194 00 Koropi Attikis
TEL. (1) 662 64 60 / 61
FAX. (1) 662 64 62

Dr. G. J. Prokopakis
President & Technical Director
SPEC
75 Patission Street
GR - 10434 Athens
TEL. (1) 882 26 81 / 882 29 69
FAX. (1) 822 40 45

Mr. J.D. Tsilikis
Technical Manager
EKO
Hellenic Fuels & Lubricants Co.
P.O. Box 10044
GR - 54110 Thessaloniki
TEL. .. 76 04 12 / 76 04 13
FAX. .. 76 98 97

Dr. P. Valachis
Centre for Renewable Energy Sources
C.R.E.S.
6 Frati Street, Fousa
GR - 194 00 Koropi Attikis
TEL. (1) 662 64 60 / 662 64 61
FAX. (1) 662 64 62

Prof. C.G. Vayenas
University of Patras
Institute of Chemical Engineering
& High Temperature Chemical Processes
P.O. Box 1239
GR - 261 10 Patras
TEL. (61) 99 15 58
TLX. 312239 EFAP GR
FAX. (61) 99 32 55

Prof. S. Yanniotis
Hellas Energy
Kipseli
Saint George Square 10
GR - 11257 Athens
TEL. (1) 822 25 19
TLX. 221292 Mosc
FAX. (1) 823 83 14

Italy

Prof. G. Di Giacomo
Università di L'Aquila
Dipartimento di Chimica
Ingegneria Chimica e Materiali
Monteluco di Roio
I - 67040 L'Aquila
TEL. (862) 43 26 15
TLX. 601156 Aquing I
FAX. (862) 43 26 03

Prof. E. Macchi
Politecnico di Milano
Department of Energetics
Piazza Leonardo da Vinci, 32
I - 20133 Milano
TEL. (2) 23 99 39 07
TLX. 333467 POLIMI I
FAX. (2) 23 99 38 38

Ir. R. Nijsing
Director
CCR-Ispra
Process Engineering Division
Bldg 69
I - 21020 Ispra (VA)
TEL. (332) 78 93 06
TLX. 380042 / 380058 EUR I
FAX. (332) 78 96 48

Mr. G.F. Oliveri del Castillo
Process Eng. Dpt Manager
Montedipe
Via Taramelli 15/17
I - 20124 Milano
TEL. (2) 62 70 75 47
TLX. 310679 MONTED I
FAX. (2) 63 33 92 55

Dr. G. Palazzi
ENEA
Energy Dept.
Experimental Div.
Via Anguillarese 301
I - 00060 S. Maria di Galeria (Roma)
TEL. (6) 30 48 30 39
TLX. 613296 Eneaca I
Fax. (6) 30 48 48 11

Prof. G. Tomassetti
Dept. of Energy Systems
Research Center of Casaccia
P.O. Box 2400
I - 00198 Roma
TEL. (6) 30 48 39 81
FAX. (6) 30 48 63 15

Dr. G. Vergerio
Enimont Anic/Seraus
Piazza Boldrini 1
I - 20097 S. Donato (Mi)
TEL. (2) 520 220 71?? = 520 20 71?
FAX. (2) 520 62 10

Netherlands

Dr. G.J. Arkenbout
TNO - MT
P.O. Box 342
Laan van Westenenk 501
NL - 7300 AH Apeldoorn
TEL. (55) 49 39 48
TLX. 36395 tnoap nl
FAX. (55) 41 98 37

Ir. A.J.P. Bongers
Senior Consultant Process Technology
DSM Research BV
P.O. Box 18
NL - 6160 MD GELEEN
TEL. (4490) 67015
FAX. (4490) 67244

Mr. A.J. Dalhuizen
TNO
Institute of Applied Physics
Stieltjesweg 1
NL - 2600 AD Delft
TEL. (15) 69 20 00
FAX. (15) 78 28 11

Ir. U.A. De Vries
TNO
Institute for Cereals, Flour & Bread
P.O. Box 15
Lawickse Allee 15
NL - 6701 AN Wageningen
TEL. (8370) 99 227
TLX. 45149 igmb nl
FAX. (8370) 21 221

Mr. E. Everts
Novem
Industrial Department
P.O. Box 8242
NL - 3503 RE Utrecht
TEL. (30) 36 34 55
FAX. (30) 31 64 91

Drs. W.Ch. Glasz
Research Chemist Industrial Catalysis
DSM Research BV
P.O. Box 18
NL - 6160 MD GELEEN
TEL. (4490) 61544
FAX. (4490) 67244

Dr. G. Heijkoop
VEG-Gasinstituut
P.O. Box 137
NL - 7300 AC Apeldoorn
TEL. (55) 49 45 20
TLX. 49456
FAX. (55) 41 89 63

Mr. J. Jochems
DSM NV
Coordinator European R&D-Project
Corporate Planning & Development
Postbus 6500
NL - Heerlen
TEL. (45) 78 23 89
TLX. 56018
FAX. (45) 74 04 32

Ir. L.W. Koot
TNO - MT
Dept. of Heat and Refrigeration
Technology
P.O. Box 342
NL - 7300 AH Apeldoorn
TEL. (55) 49 34 93
TLX. 36395 TNO NL
FAX. (55) 41 98 37

Mr. B.P. Ter Meulen
TNO
Dept. of Chemical Engineering
P.O. Box 342
NL - 7300 AH Apeldoorn
TEL. (55) 49 34 93
TLX. 36395 tnoap nl
FAX. (55) 41 98 37

Prof. L.L. van Dierendonck
DSM Research B.V.
Postbus 18
NL - Geleen
TEL. (4490) 61969
TLX. 36777
FAX. (4490) 67244

Ir. A.J.M. van Wingerden
VEG-Gasinstituut
Postbus 137
NL - 7300 AC Apeldoorn
TEL. (55) 49 45 13
TLX. 49456
FAX. (55) 41 89 63

Prof. W. Van Gool
Rijksuniversiteit
Analytisch Chemisch Laboratorium
Croezestraat 77 A
NL - 3522 AD Utrecht
TEL. (30) 89 08 19
FAX. (30) 88 14 72

Mr. J.H.F.M. Vencken
Novem
Industrial Department
P.O. Box 8242
NL - 3503 RE Utrecht
TEL. (30) 36 34 25
FAX. (30) 31 64 91

Ir. P.E.J. Vermeulen
MT - TNO
Heat & Refrigeration Technology Dept.
P.O. Box 342
Laan van Westenenk 501
NL - 7300 AH Apeldoorn
TEL. (55) 49 34 93
TLX. 36395 TNOAP NL
FAX. (55) 41 98 37

Portugal

Prof. M.G. Carvalho
Instituto Superior Técnico
Mechanical Engineering Department
Av. Rovisco Pais
P - 1096 Lisbon Codex
TEL. (1) 89 10 73
TLX. 63423 Istutl P
FAX. (1) 89 92 42

Mr. C. Costa
University of Porto
Faculty of Engineering
Department of Chemical Engineering
Rua dos Bragas
P - 4099 Porto Codex
TEL. (2) 27437
TLX. 27323 FEUP-P
FAX. (2) 31 92 80

Prof. M.V. Heitor
Instituto Superior Tecnico
Mechanical Engineering Department
Av. Rovisco Pais
P - 1096 Lisbon CODEX
TEL. (1) 80 11 81
TLX. 63423 ISTUTL P
FAX. (1) 89 92 42

Prof. J.M. Ferreira de Jesus
INTERG
Av. Rovisco Pais
P - 1096 Lisboa Codex
TEL. (1) 80 82 57
TLX. 63423 INSTUTL P
FAX. (1) 89 92 42

Prof. J.C.F. Pereira
Instituto Superior Técnico
Mechanical Engineering Department
Av. Rovisco Pais
P - 1096 Lisbon Codex
TEL. (1) 89 10 73
TLX. 63423 ISTUTL P
FAX. (1) 89 92 42/ 726 26 33

Prof. A. Reis
CENERTEC
Centro de Energia e Tecnologia
Pr. Dr. P. Teotonio Pereira 125 - 3° Dto
P - 4300 Porto
TEL. (2) 56 11 59
TLX. 26261 ENTEC P
FAX. (2) 56 39 68

Prof. A.E. Rodrigues
Universidade do Porto
Faculdade Engenheria
Department of Chemical Engineering
Rua dos Bragas
P - 4099 Porto Codex
TEL. (2) 27437
TLX. 27323 FEUP P
FAX. (2) 31 92 80

Sweden

Mr. L. Eriksson
Vice President
STFI
Box 5604
Drottning Kristinas Väg 61
S - 114 86 Stockholm
TEL. (8) 22 43 40
TLX. 10880 Woodres S
FAX. (8) 11 55 18

European Communities — Commission

EUR 13541 — Improved energy efficiency in the process industries — Proceedings of a European Seminar, Brussels, 23 and 24 October 1990

P.A. Pilavachi

Luxembourg: Office for Official Publications of the European Communities

1991 — VIII, 312 pp. — 21.0 × 29.7 cm

Energy series

ISBN 92-826-2550-8

Catalogue number: CD-NA-13541-2A-C

Price (excluding VAT) in Luxembourg: ECU 25

A European Seminar on 'Improved energy efficiency in the process industries', held in Brussels on 23 and 24 October 1990, presented preliminary results from current projects carried out within the Joule programme: Rational use of energy in industry. This also comprised a workshop.

Topics covered, relating to present R&D activities within Joule, included the following:

Heat exchangers: enhanced evaporation, shell and tube heat exchangers including distribution of fluids, and fouling.

Low energy separation processes: adsorption, melt-crystallization and supercritical extraction.

Chemical reactors: methanol synthesis and reactors with integral heat exchangers.

Other unit operations: evaporators, glass-melting furnaces, cement kilns and baking ovens, dryers and packed columns and replacements for R12 in refrigeration.

Energy and system process models: batch processes, simulation and control of transients and energy synthesis.

Development of advanced sensors.

The workshop was made up of 13 working groups, formed to discuss future R&D needs. This identified sectors of great significance, both in terms of potential energy savings and, increasingly important, with regard to their prospects for reducing the detrimental impact of the process industries on the environment. The following were covered:

Chemical reactors, heat exchanger intensification, process plant intensification, heat exchanger fouling, gas adsorption, melt crystallization, glass-making and ceramic furnaces, cement kilns and baking ovens, dryers, refrigeration (replacement of CFCs), energy and environmental process integration, advanced sensors for process control, catalytic combustion, efficient use of electricity.

The working groups came up with a number of recommendations for future R&D, many of which were detailed in terms of the content and the impact which such R&D might have on energy use and the environment.